Introduction to Matrices and Linear Transformations

BY

DANIEL T. FINKBEINER, II

Kenyon College

Drawings by Evan Gillespie

 W. H. FREEMAN AND COMPANY
San Francisco and London

(C3)

PREFACE

Matrix theory, or more generally linear algebra, is a relatively recent mathematical development. Its roots extend back 100 years to the work of Hamilton, Cayley, and Sylvester, but it has attracted widespread interest only in the past two or three decades. Today matrices are effective tools in quantum theory as well as classical mechanics; in aeronautical, mechanical, and electrical engineering; in statistics and linear programming and therefore in all the social sciences which these theories serve.

Even a cursory glance at current mathematical literature reveals that matrix theory is in a stage of active growth. It is rather surprising therefore that the mathematical background required for an understanding of matrix theory is sufficiently modest that a substantial first course can be mastered by undergraduates. The major prerequisite is not a specific list of courses in mathematics, but rather the ability to reason abstractly, to proceed logically from hypothesis to conclusion. Anyone who possesses this quality, even latently, is capable of understanding the material presented here, whether he be an economist, psychologist, engineer, chemist, physicist, or mathematician. The necessary mathematical background is normally acquired in one or two years of college mathematics.

Courses in matrix theory are currently presented in several ways. A computational course can be offered in which the calculations themselves are emphasized more than their meaning. Alternately, the study of matrices can be motivated from the familiar problem of solving systems of linear equations, the important connection between matrices and linear transformations being deferred until the end of the course. A third procedure, and the one chosen here, systematically employs the elegant techniques of abstract algebra to develop simultaneously the algebra of matrices and the geometry of linear transformations.

Although an axiomatic approach places a greater burden at the outset of the course on both the instructor and the student, the ultimate gain in understanding linear algebra, and indeed modern mathematics as a whole, amply justifies this extra effort. Undeniably, the understanding of abstract concepts is aided by frequent illustrations from familiar contexts, and a serious attempt has been made here to retain firm contact with concrete ideas while steadily developing a higher degree of generality.

The obvious purpose of this book is to present a lucid and unified introduction to linear algebra at a level which can be understood by undergraduates who possess reasonable mathematical aptitude, and thus to lay a solid foundation from which each student can apply these notions and techniques to the field of his interest. A more subtle but equally serious objective is to prepare the student for advanced scientific work by developing his powers of abstract reasoning. Linear algebra is admirably suited to this purpose.

The present text is a revised form of mimeographed lecture notes written in 1951 for the second semester of a survey course in abstract algebra at Kenyon College. Because linear algebra is a cohesive body of knowledge which blends a variety of algebraic and geometric concepts, I believe that it provides a more natural introduction to abstract algebra than does the usual survey course. The first chapter, supplemented by Appendix A, presents the algebraic notions needed for this study; thus the text can be used by students who have no previous experience with modern algebraic techniques.

The remaining material has been selected and arranged to proceed directly to the problem of equivalence relations and canonical forms. The duality of geometry and algebra is emphasized, but computational aspects are not ignored. Metric notions are deferred until Chapter 9, principally because they are not essential for the major part of this work. Depending upon the ability of the class, there is adequate material for a course of 60 class hours. Chapter 10, and to a lesser extent Chapter 9, may be omitted without interfering seriously with the major aims of this presentation.

Since some results of general interest are stated as exercises, each student is urged to make a practice of reading all exercises and learning the facts stated therein, even though he might choose not to prove all of them.

Revision of the original notes was performed during my tenure as a Science Faculty Fellow of the National Science Foundation. I am greatly indebted to the Foundation for its support, to Princeton University for the use of its facilities during this period, and to Kenyon College for assistance with the original version. Personal gratitude is expressed to J. G. Wendel for mathematical discussions extending over a decade, to A. W. Tucker for making available his recent work on combinatorial equivalence, to W. D. Lindstrom for reading critically selected parts of the manuscript, and to the editors and advisers of the publisher for many helpful suggestions. Appreciation is expressed also to Mrs. Richard Anderson and Mrs. Charles Helsley for their help in preparing the original and revised manuscripts.

February, 1960   D. T. FINKBEINER

CONTENTS

CHAPTER 1

Abstract Systems

§1.1. *Introduction*

When a student begins the study of matrices he soon discovers properties which seem to have no counterpart in his previous mathematical experience. This is as unavoidable as it is exciting. The concepts which he considers and the methods he employs are markedly different from those he has encountered in mathematics through school and into college.

Elementary school mathematics is concerned primarily with the arithmetic of number systems, beginning with the positive integers and developing gradually to include all of the integers and the rational numbers. The later use of letters to represent numbers is a real stride toward abstraction, and the corresponding study is called algebra instead of arithmetic. The algebraic problem of solving quadratic equations reveals the need for still more comprehensive number systems, which leads to the study of real and complex numbers.

An exception to the emphasis on numbers occurs in plane geometry, where the elements studied are called points and lines rather than numbers and equations, and where the relations between geometric figures are no longer numerical equality or inequality but congruence, similarity, parallelism, or perpendicularity. Geometry normally is the student's first excursion from the world of numbers to a realm of deductive thought which is essentially non-numerical.

Trigonometry and analytic geometry provide a bridge between numerical and geometric concepts by using numbers and equations to describe geometric figures. The objects studied are geometric, but the methods used in investigating their properties are numerical. This gradual transition from the study of numbers to the study of non-numerical elements is continued in calculus, where functions and operations on functions are described numerically but have significant geometric interpretations.

Likewise, matrices are described numerically and have important geometric interpretations. Matrices form a type of number system, and in this study we shall be concerned with developing the algebraic properties of this system. However, since matrices are intrinsically related to geometry, while their relation to arithmetic is comparatively superficial, a geometric interpretation of matrix theory is both natural and efficient. After this introductory chapter we turn immediately to a description of the geometric setting for our later work, *finite-dimensional vector spaces*. In Chapter 3 we study *linear transformations* of such spaces, and not until Chapter 4 do we study *matrices* themselves.

It is evident from the Table of Contents that various mathematical systems are discussed in this book, many of which may now be unfamiliar to you. Therefore, we shall begin by describing mathematical systems generally. In order to suggest that our present interest lies primarily in the internal structure of the system, rather than in its relation to the physical world, we speak of an *abstract system*. You are asked not to interpret the word "abstract" as meaning that familiar systems will not arise as particular examples of abstract systems. As we shall see, an abstract system is often defined as a synthesis of some concrete system.

This introductory chapter, which discusses abstract systems from the point of view of modern algebra, has three objectives: to introduce the basic notation used in this book, to extend and modernize the student's mathematical vocabulary, and to capture some of the spirit of abstract mathematics.

To most mathematicians the esthetic appeal of an abstract system is sufficient justification for its study. From a more practical standpoint, the investigation of abstract systems has greatly clarified and unified the fundamental concepts of mathematics, and has provided a description of such important notions as relations, functions, and operations in terms of the simple and intuitive notion of *set*. Such a description is given in Appendix A. If you have a flair for abstraction or a desire for more precision than is afforded in this introductory chapter, you may wish to study Appendix A immediately. Or you may prefer to proceed more gradually, deferring a general study of basic concepts until you have acquired some experience with these ideas in the specific systems considered in this book. In either event, you should not expect to attain immediate and comfortable familiarity with all of the ideas presented here. You should study the text material carefully and work through the examples and exercises in detail, steadily increasing your facility for abstract thought and enhancing your insight into the nature of mathematics.

Exercises

1. Assume that a club of students is organized into committees in such a way that each of the following statements (postulates) is true.

(a) There are at least two students in the club.

(b) Every committee is a collection of one or more students.

(c) For each pair of students there is exactly one committee on which both serve.

(d) No single committee is composed of all the students in the club.

(e) Given any committee and any student not on that committee, there exists exactly one committee on which that student serves which has no students of the first committee in its membership.

Prove each of the statements (theorems) in the following sequence, justifying each step of your proof by appealing to one of the five postulates or to an earlier theorem of the sequence. (Although this system may appear more concrete than abstract, its general nature is indicated by Exercise 2 of this section and Exercise 2 of § 1.2.)

(i) Every student serves on at least two committees.

(ii) Every committee has at least two members.

(iii) There are at least four students in the club.

(iv) There are at least six committees in the club.

2. (i) Translate the description of the system of the previous exercise into geometric language by calling the club a "geometry," a student a "point," and a committee a "line," and by making other changes as needed to carry out the geometric flavor without changing the inherent meaning of the statements.

(ii) Translate the four theorems into geometric language, and similarly translate your proof of the first theorem.

(iii) Find the geometric system with the smallest number of points which satisfies the five postulates. (Such a system is called a finite geometry; other theorems about the system can be discovered and proved.)

§1.2. *Sets*

Before we attempt to describe abstract systems we should first recognize that it is quite hopeless for two individuals to try to carry on an intelligent conversation unless they share some basic knowledge. We now state two general assumptions about the basic knowledge which is used as a foundation for our later discussion:

There is a common understanding of the basic language which we shall use to define other terms.

There is a common understanding of the system of logical reasoning with which we proceed from hypothesis to conclusion.

These assumptions are so general that they now appear to be quite elusive; presently we shall be more specific.   In effect, the first assumption recognizes the futility of trying to define all terms which will be needed, and thereby establishes the need for *undefined terms*.   The second assumption is a declaration that no formal treatment of the rules of deduction will appear in this book.

More specifically, as part of our basic language we assume an intuitive understanding of the notion of a *set*.   The word *set* is used to denote a *collection, class, family,* or *aggregate* of objects which are called *elements* or *members* of the set.   It is evident that this explanation does not define a set or the concept of membership in a set.   These concepts are part of the undefined language which is assumed for this book.

It is customary to denote a set by a capital letter and the elements of a set by small letters.   To denote that an element b *is a member of* a set S, we write

$$b \in S,$$

which can also be read as "b belongs to S."   To denote that b does *not* belong to S we write

$$b \notin S.$$

There are two common ways of specifying a set:

by listing all its elements within braces,

by stating a characteristic property by which we can determine whether or not a given object is an element of that set.

The notation which we adopt for the second method comprises two parts, separated by a vertical line, within braces.   The first part tells us what type of elements are being considered, and the second part specifies the characteristic property.   For example, let I denote the set of all integers, and let S denote the set of all integers whose square is less than seven.   The two methods of writing S are

$$S = \{-2, -1, 0, 1, 2\},$$

where we attach no importance to the order in which the elements are listed, and

$$S = \{x \in I \mid x^2 < 7\},$$

which is read, "S is the set of all integers x such that x^2 is less than 7."

We use the symbol Φ to denote the *void set*, which contains no elements at

all.   While the void set may seem at first to be an artificial notion, its accept-
ance as a bona fide set is convenient.

Sets S and T are said to be *equal* if and only if they contain exactly the
same elements.   In terms of the membership relation, this is expressed as:

$$T = S \text{ means } "x \in T \text{ if and only if } x \in S."$$

The next concept is that of a *subset*.   If S and T are sets, T is said to be a
subset of S, written $T \subseteq S$, if and only if every element of T is an element of
S; that is,

$$T \subseteq S \text{ means } "if x \in T, \text{ then } x \in S."$$

The subset notation $T \subseteq S$ can also be written $S \supseteq T$.   This notation is
analogous to the notation for inequality of numbers: $a \leq b$ means the same
as $b \geq a$.   It is readily verified that equality of sets can be expressed in
terms of the subset notation as:

$$T = S \text{ means } "T \subseteq S \text{ and } S \subseteq T."$$

It is clear from the definition of subset that any set is a subset of itself.
Also, since the void set has no elements the statement "If $x \in \Phi$, then
$x \in S$" is logically valid for any set S.   Thus we have

$$\Phi \subseteq S \text{ and } S \subseteq S \text{ for every set } S.$$

T is said to be a *proper subset* of S if and only if every element of T is an element of S, but not every element of S is an element of T.   This is written:

$$T \subset S \text{ if and only if } T \subseteq S \text{ and } T \neq S.$$

In practice it is sometimes useful to adopt geometric language for sets,
calling an element a point even though the element may have no obvious
geometric character.   When we adopt such descriptive language we must
bear in mind that this is done only for convenience, and we must carefully refrain from assuming any properties
which may be suggested by our language
but which are not otherwise legitimately
established.

A geometric interpretation of sets suggests
the use of sketches, called *Venn diagrams*, to
represent sets and relations between sets.
Thus the subset relation $T \subseteq S$ can be shown

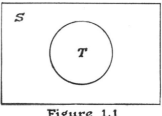

Figure 1.1

graphically as in Figure 1.1.   Such diagrams provide insight concerning sets,
and often they suggest methods by which statements about sets can be
proved or disproved.   However, diagrams are not valid substitutes for
formal proofs.

We now turn our attention to several ways in which sets can be combined
to produce other sets.   Let S be any set, and let K denote the collection of

all subsets of S.   (The elements of K are the subsets of S.)   We shall define three operations on sets, called *union, intersection,* and *complementation:*

Union:	$A \cup B = \{x \in S \mid x \in A \text{ or } x \in B\},$
Intersection:	$A \cap B = \{x \in S \mid x \in A \text{ and } x \in B\},$
Complementation:	$A' = \{x \in S \mid x \notin A\}.$

Thus if A and B are any elements of K, the set "A union B" consists of all elements of S which belong to A, or to B, or to both.   The set "A intersection B" consists of all elements of S which belong to both A and B.   The "complement of A in S" consists of all elements of S which do not belong to A.   If $A \cap B = \Phi$ (the void set), we say that A and B are *disjoint.*   Venn diagrams which illustrate these operations are shown in Figure 1.2.   More

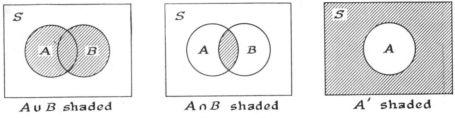

$A \cup B$ shaded $A \cap B$ shaded A' shaded

Figure 1.2

generally, the union and intersection of any family F of subsets of S are defined in an analogous way:

$$\bigcup_{A \in F} A = \{x \in S \mid x \in A \text{ for some } A \in F\},$$

$$\bigcap_{A \in F} A = \{x \in S \mid x \in A \text{ for all } A \in F\}.$$

Based on these definitions, the collection K of all subsets of S forms an algebraic system, about which we can prove the following theorems.

    1.1. $A \subseteq A$ for all $A \in K$.

    1.2.   If $A \subseteq B$ and $B \subseteq A$, then $A = B$.

    1.3.   If $A \subseteq B$ and $B \subseteq C$, then $A \subseteq C$.

    1.4. $A \cup B = B \cup A$ for all $A, B \in K$.

    1.4*. $A \cap B = B \cap A$ for all $A, B \in K$.

    1.5. $A \cup (B \cup C) = (A \cup B) \cup C$ for all $A, B, C \in K$.

    1.5*. $A \cap (B \cap C) = (A \cap B) \cap C$ for all $A, B, C \in K$.

    1.6. $A \cup (B \cap C) = (A \cup B) \cap (A \cup C)$ for all $A, B, C \in K$.

    1.6*. $A \cap (B \cup C) = (A \cap B) \cup (A \cap C)$ for all $A, B, C \in K$.

    1.7. $A \subseteq A \cup B$ for all $A, B \in K$.

    1.7*. $A \cap B \subseteq A$ for all $A, B \in K$.

1.8. $A = A \cup A$ for all $A \in K$.

1.8*. $A = A \cap A$ for all $A \in K$.

1.9. $A \subseteq B$ if and only if $A \cup B = B$.

1.9*. $B \subseteq A$ if and only if $A \cap B = B$.

1.10. $(A')' = A$ for all $A \in K$.

1.11.   If $A \subseteq B$, then $B' \subseteq A'$.

1.12. $(A \cup B)' = A' \cap B'$ for all $A, B \in K$.

1.12*. $(A \cap B)' = A' \cup B'$ for all $A, B \in K$.

1.13. $A \cup \Phi = A$ for all $A \in K$.

1.13*. $A \cap S = A$ for all $A \in K$.

1.14. $A \cup A' = S$ for all $A \in K$.

1.14*. $A \cap A' = \Phi$ for all $A \in K$.

Several observations should be made concerning this list of theorems. First, each theorem marked with an asterisk is a restatement of the theorem having the same number, obtained by interchanging $\cup$ and $\cap$, interchanging Φ and S, and replacing $\subseteq$ by $\supseteq$. In this sense, set union and intersection are dual operations. Next, we notice that Theorems 1.1–1.3 concern the subset relation, Theorems 1.4–1.9* concern union and intersection, Theorems 1.10–1.12* concern complementation, and Theorems 1.13–1.14* assert properties of the special elements Φ and S. Finally, we observe that several statements express properties which are reminiscent of properties of addition and multiplication of numbers. Special names are assigned to these properties because they recur in many different mathematical systems. Expressed in arithmetical notation, these statements are as follows:

Commutativity: **1.4.**		$a + b = b + a,$
1.4*.		$ab = ba;$
Associativity: **1.5.**		$a + (b + c) = (a + b) + c,$
1.5*.		$a(bc) = (ab)c;$
Distributivity: **1.6*.**		$a(b + c) = ab + ac;$
Identity elements: **1.13.**		$a + 0 = a = 0 + a,$
1.13*.		$a(1) = a = (1)a.$

In § 1.4 we shall discuss these terms in a more general context.

To illustrate methods of proving theorems about sets, we now prove three of the listed theorems.

Theorem 1.7. $A \subseteq A \cup B$ for all $A, B \in K$.

PROOF: This is clear from Figure 1.2, but we use Venn diagrams for insight rather than for proof. Formally, we wish to prove that every element of A is an element of $A \cup B$. If $x \in A$, then by the definition of set union, $x \in A \cup B$. By the definition of subset, $A \subseteq A \cup B$.

Theorem 1.4. $A \cup B = B \cup A$ for all $A, B \in K$.

PROOF: Let $x \in A \cup B$. By definition of set union, either $x \in A$ or $x \in B$. Hence either $x \in B$ or $x \in A$. This implies $A \cup B \subseteq B \cup A$. If $x \in B \cup A$, the same argument shows that $B \cup A \subseteq A \cup B$. Hence $A \cup B = B \cup A$.

Theorem 1.11. If $A \subseteq B$, then $B' \subseteq A'$.

PROOF: By hypothesis, $A \subseteq B$. Let $x \in B'$. By definition, $x \notin B$. If $x \in A$, we could deduce $x \in B$, since $A \subseteq B$. This would be a contradiction, so $x \notin A$. Thus $x \in A'$, and $B' \subseteq A'$.

Notice that the proof of Theorem 1.4 rests ultimately upon the meaning of the word "or" in the sentence which defines union, while the proof of Theorem 1.11 rests upon the meaning of the word "not" in the definition of complementation. As an exercise you may develop similar proofs for some of the remaining theorems.

We now introduce a different way of combining sets to form other sets. Let S and T be any sets. The *cartesian product* of S and T is denoted $S \times T$, and is defined to be the set of all pairs of the form (s, t), where $s \in S$ and $t \in T$:

$$S \times T = \{(s, t) \mid s \in S \text{ and } t \in T\}.$$

An element of $S \times T$ is called an *ordered pair;* the first component is an element of S, and the second is an element of T. Two ordered pairs are equal if and only if their first components are the same and their second components are the same.

EXAMPLES

(a) If $S = \{0, 1\}$ and $T = \{2, -2, 0\}$, then

$$S \times T = \{(0, 2), (0, -2), (0, 0), (1, 2), (1, -2), (1, 0)\},$$

and

$$T \times S = \{(2, 0), (2, 1), (-2, 0), (-2, 1), (0, 0), (0, 1)\}.$$

Observe that $S \times T$ and $T \times S$ are different sets.

(b) If R is the set of all real numbers, representing the points on a real coordinate axis, then $R \times R$ is the set of all ordered pairs of real numbers, representing the points on a real coordinate plane.

Exercises

1. (i) List all the subsets of $S = \{a, b, c, d\}$.

(ii) If S is a finite set having m elements, how many subsets does S have? Prove your answer. m^2

2. Referring to Exercise 1, § 1.1, translate the description of the system into the abstract language and notation of sets. Also translate the four theorems but you need not prove them again.

3. Prove the following theorems concerning sets. You may use Theorems 1.1, 1.2, and 1.3 and any theorems previously proved.

> (i) Theorems 1.9 and 1.8.
> (ii) Theorems 1.5* and 1.6*.
> (iii) Theorems 1.10 and 1.12.

4. Show that set union can be expressed in terms of intersection and complementation.

5. Let I denote the set of all integers, and let R denote the set of all real numbers. Describe by means of a graph each of the following sets:

> (i) $I \times I$,
> (ii) $R \times R$,
> (iii) $I \times R$,
> (iv) $R \times I$.

6. Let S and T be arbitrary sets.

> (i) Prove that $S \times T$ and $T \times S$ have an element in common if and only if S and T have an element in common.
> (ii) If S and T have m elements in common, how many elements do $S \times T$ and $T \times S$ have in common?
> (iii) If $T \subseteq S$, show that $T \times T = (T \times S) \cap (S \times T)$.

7. Show that if S has more than three elements, then $S \times S$ has more than 60,000 subsets.

8. The *difference* of two subsets of S is defined by

$$A - B = \{x \in A \mid x \notin B\}.$$

> (i) Find and prove an equation which expresses $A - B$ in terms of the basic set operations ($\cup$, $\cap$, and $'$). Draw an illustrative Venn diagram.
> (ii) Prove: $(A - B)' = A' \cup B$.
> (iii) Is set difference a commutative operation? Prove your answer.

9. The *symmetric difference* $A \ominus B$ of two subsets of S is the set of all elements which belong either to A or to B, but not to both A and B.

$(A \ominus B) \cap A = B - A$

> (i) Find and prove an expression for $A \ominus B$ in terms of the basic set operations ($\cup$, $\cap$, and $'$). Draw an illustrative Venn diagram.
> (ii) Prove that $(A \ominus B)' = (A' \cup B) \cap (A \cup B')$.
> (iii) Is symmetric difference a commutative operation? Prove your answer.
> (iv) Discover a simple description of the set $(A \ominus B) \ominus C$.

$A \ominus B = (A \cap B)'$

(v) Is symmetric difference an associative operation? Prove your answer.

10. Considering only finite sets, let $n(S)$ denote the number of elements in S.

   (i) Prove $n(A \cup B) = n(A) + n(B) - n(A \cap B)$.
   (ii) Discover and prove a similar result for $n(A \cup B \cup C)$.

§1.3. *Functions and Mappings*

It is assumed that you are familiar with numerical functions from your previous mathematical experience; our purpose here is to describe functions in a more general setting. Recall that each numerical function f has a *domain* of definition (a set D of numbers), and that to each $x \in D$ the function f assigns a unique number $f(x)$, which is called the *value* of f at x. As x varies over D, the numbers $f(x)$ form a set R which is called the *range* of f.

A generalization from numerical functions to arbitrary functions is made very easily—we simply drop the requirement that D and R be sets of numbers, and consider them to be abstract sets.

A *function F from a set A into a set B* consists of

1. a non-void subset $D \subseteq A$, called the *domain* of F,
2. a correspondence such that to each $a \in D$ there is associated one and only one $b \in B$.

The element $b \in B$ which is associated with $a \in D$ by the function F is often denoted $F(a)$. The *range* of F is the subset $R \subseteq B$, defined by

$$R = \{b \in B \mid b = F(a) \text{ for some } a \in D\}.$$

If $R = B$, we say that F is a function from A *onto* B.

Here again a translation to geometric language is useful. The domain D and range R are sets of points, and the function F associates with each point of D exactly one point of R.

A reasonable geometric synonym of function is *mapping*, a terminology suggested by Figure 1.3. Likewise, the point $F(x)$ is called the *image of x*

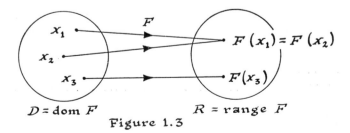

$$D = \text{dom } F \qquad\qquad R = \text{range } F$$

Figure 1.3

under the mapping F. For functions of abstract sets this geometric terminology is more descriptive than that used for numerical functions. There is also a useful notational change which we shall adopt—instead of denoting the image of x under F by the functional notation $F(x)$, we shall omit the parentheses and show $\mathbf{F}$ in boldface type to the right of x. In this new notation a function will be indicated thus:

$$\mathbf{F}: x \longrightarrow x\mathbf{F}, \text{ for all } x \in \text{dom } \mathbf{F}.$$

The omission of parentheses is a simplification, of course; but our decision to write $\mathbf{F}$ to the right of x is motivated by the notation which we shall use later for linear transformations and matrices. Whatever our reason, the symbol $x\mathbf{F}$ denotes the image of $x \in \text{dom } \mathbf{F}$ under the mapping $\mathbf{F}$.

It is important to observe that although a mapping $\mathbf{F}$ assigns a unique image $x\mathbf{F}$ to each $x \in \text{dom } \mathbf{F}$, it is quite possible that a point of range $\mathbf{F}$ is the image of *more than one* point of dom $\mathbf{F}$; i.e., from the equation $x_1\mathbf{F} = x_2\mathbf{F}$ we cannot deduce that $x_1 = x_2$. Therefore, mappings in general are *many-to-one*, in the sense that many distinct points of the domain may be mapped into the same point of the range. Just as with numerical functions, if it happens that each point of range $\mathbf{F}$ is the image of *exactly* one point of dom $\mathbf{F}$, then an *inverse mapping* $\mathbf{F}^*$ can be defined from range $\mathbf{F}$ onto dom $\mathbf{F}$, such that if $y = x\mathbf{F} \in \text{range } \mathbf{F}$, then

$$y\mathbf{F}^* = (x\mathbf{F})\mathbf{F}^* = x, \text{ for every } x \in \text{dom } \mathbf{F}.$$

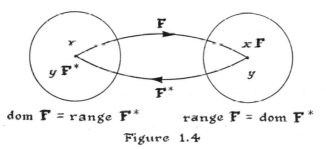

dom $\mathbf{F}$ = range $\mathbf{F}^*$ range $\mathbf{F}$ = dom $\mathbf{F}^*$

Figure 1.4

In summary, we say that a mapping $\mathbf{F}$ is *one-to-one* (or *reversible*) if and only if $x_1\mathbf{F} = x_2\mathbf{F}$ implies $x_1 = x_2$. If $\mathbf{F}$ is one-to-one, then an inverse function $\mathbf{F}^*$ can be defined from range $\mathbf{F}$ to dom $\mathbf{F}$ such that for each $x \in \text{dom } \mathbf{F}$, $(x\mathbf{F})\mathbf{F}^* = x$.

The equation $(x\mathbf{F})\mathbf{F}^* = x$ states that if x is mapped first by $\mathbf{F}$ and if the image $x\mathbf{F}$ is then mapped by $\mathbf{F}^*$, the resultant image is x itself. This is a special instance of the more general concept of *successive mappings*. Suppose that A, B, and C are sets, that $\mathbf{F}$ is a mapping from A *onto* B, and that $\mathbf{G}$ is a mapping from B *into* C. Then we can define a direct mapping $\mathbf{FG}$ from A into C as follows:

$$\mathbf{FG} : x \longrightarrow x\mathbf{FG} = (x\mathbf{F})\mathbf{G} \text{ for all } x \in \text{dom } \mathbf{F}.$$

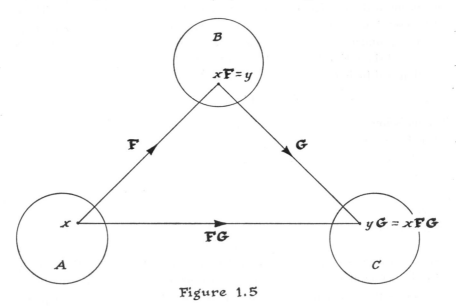

Figure 1.5

The composite mapping **FG** is obtained by the successive application of the mappings **F** and **G**, in that order. In introductory calculus the corresponding numerical function is the familiar "function of a function," which is denoted $G(F)$ in the notation of numerical functions. This concept is very important in matrix theory because matrix multiplication can be interpreted in terms of successive mappings of vector spaces.

Exercises

1. Let S, T, U, and V be sets, and let **F**, **G**, and **H** be mappings, respectively, of S onto T, T onto U, and U onto V.

(i) Describe the domain and range of **FG** and **GH**.

(ii) Show that $\mathbf{F(GH)} = \mathbf{(FG)H}$.

(iii) Suppose that **F** and **G** are both reversible (one-to-one). Show that $\mathbf{(FG)^*} = \mathbf{G^*F^*}$, and that $\mathbf{(F^*)^*} = \mathbf{F}$.

(iv) Suppose $U = S$. Describe the domain and range of **FG** and **GF**. Are these two functions equal? Explain.

(v) Suppose $U = T = S$. Are **FG** and **GF** equal functions? Explain.

2. Let **F** and **G** both be mappings from the real numbers to the real num-

bers. Since multiplication of real numbers is defined, a *product* $\mathbf{F} \odot \mathbf{G}$ of mappings can be defined by

$$x(\mathbf{F} \odot \mathbf{G}) = (x\mathbf{F})(x\mathbf{G}).$$

(The symbol $\odot$ is used to prevent confusion with the successive application of mappings, $\mathbf{FG}$, as in Exercise 1.)   Prove $\mathbf{F} \odot \mathbf{G} = \mathbf{G} \odot \mathbf{F}$.

3. The zero mapping $\mathbf{O}$ is defined by $x\mathbf{O} = 0$ for all real x.   Let

$$x\mathbf{F} = |x| + x,$$
$$x\mathbf{G} = |x| - x.$$

Prove $\mathbf{F} \neq \mathbf{O}$, $\mathbf{G} \neq \mathbf{O}$, but $\mathbf{F} \odot \mathbf{G} = \mathbf{O}$, where $\odot$ is defined as in Exercise 2.

§1.4. *Abstract Systems*

We are now ready to describe the nature of an abstract system.   First a system must have a non-void set of *elements*, the building blocks of the system.   These elements are regarded as having no properties other than those which are prescribed by the system, even though we might use geometric terms or other descriptive names for them.

EXAMPLE

To illustrate this discussion we shall use the specific example of the collection K of all subsets of a given set S.   The system which we describe in this example has K as its set of elements.   Thus an element of the system is a *subset* of S, not an element of S.

Next we need a set of *relations* between elements.   One of the relations must be a definition of equality, which provides a criterion for distinguishing one element from another.   Generalized forms of equality, called *equivalence relations*, play a vital role in matrix theory.   (See § 6.1 and Appendix A.)

EXAMPLE

Equality of two elements of K means that they are the same subset of S. Furthermore, a second relation, denoted $\subseteq$, is defined between various elements of K.

A system will also include a set of *operations*, ways of combining elements to produce other elements of the system.   Since we are working entirely within a given system, we require that the result of an operation on any elements of the system be an element of that system.   Such an operation is called a *closed operation*, and we consider only operations with this property. An operation which combines any *two* elements of a system to produce a single element of the system is called a *binary* operation. Similarly, a *unary* operation maps each *single* element of the system into a corresponding element of the system.

EXAMPLE

For the elements of K we list three operations: union, intersection, and complementation. Union and intersection combine two elements of K to produce an element of K, and therefore can be regarded as mappings of $K \times K$ into K. Complementation operates on any element of K to produce another element of K, and thus can be considered as a mapping of K into K.

To endow the elements, relations, and operations of a system with desired properties, a set of *postulates* is prescribed. These are statements or axioms which are assumed to be valid for the system. Indeed, the postulates are initially the only description of the system.

From the postulates certain deductions can be made by means of the rules of logic which are part of the basic knowledge underlying the system. These deductions are *theorems* of the system, and once proved, they possess the same validity in the system as do the original postulates.

Another important feature of a system is its set of *definitions*, which are agreements concerning terminology for concepts constructed from the skeleton of the system. By means of definitions new relations and operations can be introduced, or elements with special properties can be given distinctive names. As theorems are proved and the known facts of the system grow in number and complexity, a proper use of definitions helps to classify the information of the system and to simplify its internal language.

In summary, an abstract system $\mathcal{S}$ consists of

> a set E of elements,
> a set R of relations,
> a set O of operations,
> a set of postulates,
> a set of theorems,
> a set of definitions.

Of course, the heart of the system is the set of postulates, and all else is derived from the postulates. For notational purposes, however, it is convenient to emphasize the elements, relations, and operations by writing

$$\mathcal{S} = \{E; R; O\}$$

to denote the system. Here E denotes a set of elements, R a set of relations, and O a set of operations.

By way of illustration, let us return to the system of all subsets of a given set, which can be denoted

$$S = \{K; \subseteq; \cup, \cap, '\}.$$

Underlying our introductory discussion of sets was an implicit assumption of the meaning of the words "set" and "membership." Our definitions of the subset relation and the set operations were phrased in terms of the concept of membership, and proofs were constructed on the same basis. In effect, our only postulate for the system S was that we understood the notion of membership. Therefore, our approach was intuitive rather than formal. We now show how we can construct an abstract model of the system of all subsets of a given set.

Let E be an arbitrary set whose elements are denoted $x, y, \ldots$; let $\cup$ and $\cap$ be operations, each of which maps $E \times E$ onto E; let $'$ be an operation which maps E onto E. As postulates we assume only the following:

B1. The operations $\cup$ and $\cap$ are commutative: for all $x, y \in E$,

$$x \cup y = y \cup x \text{ and } x \cap y = y \cap x.$$

B2. Each of the operations $\cup$ and $\cap$ is distributive over the other: for all $w, x, y \in E$,

$$w \cup (x \cap y) = (w \cup x) \cap (w \cup y),$$
$$w \cap (x \cup y) = (w \cap x) \cup (w \cap y).$$

B3. In E there exist distinct elements z and u which are identity elements for $\cup$ and $\cap$, respectively: for all $x \in E$,

$$x \cup z = z \cup x = x \text{ and } x \cap u = u \cap x = x.$$

B4. The operation $'$ satisfies $x \cap x' = z$ and $x \cup x' = u$ for all $x \in E$. The resulting system,

$$\mathcal{B} = \{E; \cup, \cap, '\},$$

is called a *Boolean algebra*.

Notice that postulate B1 has precisely the same form as Theorems 1.4 and 1.4* of § 1.2. Likewise, B2 corresponds to Theorems 1.6 and 1.6*. With z and u replacing Φ and S, respectively, B3 corresponds to Theorems 1.13 and 1.13*, and B4 corresponds to Theorems 1.14 and 1.14*. Therefore, the system S of all subsets of a given set satisfies postulates B1–B4 and is a particular example of a Boolean algebra.

It is worth remarking that the postulates for $\mathcal{B}$ do not mention any relations on E, whereas our development of S made frequent use of the subset relation. This apparent difference can be removed by defining a relation $\subseteq$ on E in terms of the operation $\cup$ as follows: for all $x, y \in E$,

$$x \subseteq y \text{ if and only if } x \cup y = y.$$

Observe that this definition in $\mathcal{B}$ has precisely the same form as Theorem 1.9 in S. Using this definition and B1–B4 we can prove that all of the theorems listed in § 1.2 are valid in any Boolean algebra.

We now return to the consideration of systems in general. Most of the systems which we shall study are defined by postulates which describe the elements and the operations. A few of the postulates occur in so many different systems that it is convenient to assign special terminology to them. To do so, we suppose that S is an abstract system whose set of elements is denoted by E. For the sake of clarity you might wish to interpret the following discussion in terms of a familiar example, such as the system of integers with addition and multiplication as operations, or the system of subsets of a set with union and intersection as operations.

First we consider three properties of binary operations:

Associativity. The operation $*$ is *associative* if and only if for all $a, b, c \in E$,

$$a * (b * c) = (a * b) * c.$$

Commutativity. The operation $*$ is *commutative* if and only if for all $a, b \in E$,

$$a * b = b * a.$$

Distributivity. The operation $\odot$ is *distributive* over the operation $*$ if and only if for all $a, b, c \in E$,

$$a \odot (b * c) = (a \odot b) * (a \odot c).$$

Observe that for integers, both addition and multiplication are associative and commutative, and multiplication is distributive over addition. For subsets, both union and intersection are associative and commutative, and each operation is distributive over the other.

Postulates about elements most often assert the *existence* of elements with unusual properties. We give three examples of such elements.

Identity element. An element $i \in E$ is called an *identity* relative to the operation $*$ if and only if for every $x \in E$,

$$i * x = x = x * i.$$

Inverse element. Given an identity relative to $*$ and an arbitrary element $x \in E$, an element x' is called an *inverse* of x relative to $*$ if and only if

$$x * x' = i = x' * x.$$

Idempotent element. An element $x \in E$ is said to be *idempotent* relative to $*$ if and only if

$$x * x = x.$$

In the system of integers, 0 is an identity of addition, and 1 is an identity of multiplication. Both are idempotent relative to multiplication, but 0 is the only integer which is idempotent relative to addition. Each integer x has an additive inverse, $-x$, but 1 and -1 are the only integers which have a multiplicative inverse which is an integer.

Exercises

1. Prove the following about an abstract system $S = \{E; *, \odot\}$, assuming no properties of the system other than those stated for each case.   see notes 9-23-63

    (i) Each operation can have at most one identity element.

    (ii) If $*$ is associative and has an identity $i \in E$, then each $x \in E$ can have at most one inverse element relative to $*$.

    (iii) If an identity element of an operation exists, it is idempotent relative to that operation.

    (iv) If $\odot$ is distributive over $*$, if i is an identity of $\odot$, and if e is an identity of $*$, then e is idempotent relative to both $\odot$ and $*$.   Is i idempotent relative to $*$?

Interpret these results for the special case of addition and multiplication of real numbers.

2. In each case below determine whether or not the given function describes a closed operation on the given set.

    (i) Multiplication of even integers.   *Yes*

    (ii) Multiplication of odd integers.   *yes*

    (iii) Addition of odd integers.   *yes*

    (iv) Addition of even integers.   *yes*

    (v) Multiplication of real functions which are differentiable.   *yes*

    (vi) Differentiation of real functions which are differentiable.   *yes*

    (vii) Differentiation of polynomials.   *yes*

3. In § 1.2 it was shown that the set operations of union and intersection are associative and commutative, that each is distributive over the other, and that every set is idempotent relative to both operations.   Discuss the existence of identity and inverse elements.

4. Let P be the set of points of the plane.   For $p, q \in P$ define $p * q$ to be the midpoint of the segment from p to q.

    (i) Is $*$ a closed operation on P?   *Yes*

    (ii) Is $*$ commutative?   *Yes*

    (iii) Is $*$ associative?   *Yes*

Substantiate your answers.

5. Let a mapping $\mathbf{T}_1$ of the points of the real coordinate axis into itself be defined by

$$x\mathbf{T}_1 = a_1 + b_1 x,$$

where a_1 and b_1 are fixed real numbers with $b_1 \neq 0$.   Another mapping $\mathbf{T}_2$ of this form would be defined by

$$x\mathbf{T}_2 = a_2 + b_2 x, \; b_2 \neq 0.$$

We define the "product" $T_1 * T_2$ of such mappings by

$$x(T_1 * T_2) = (xT_1)T_2.$$

Prove that

(i) $*$ is associative,
(ii) an identity of $*$ exists,
(iii) each T has an inverse,
(iv) $*$ is not commutative.

Interpret each such mapping geometrically as a change of coordinates on the real line, after considering the two special cases

$$a \text{ arbitrary}, b = 1;$$

$$a = 0, b \text{ arbitrary}.$$

§1.5. *Groups and Fields*

To illustrate the discussion of § 1.4 we now consider two abstract systems which occur frequently in mathematics—*groups* and *fields;* our number systems afford many examples of each.

First consider the set R of all real numbers, together with the operation of addition. Since the sum of any two real numbers is a real number, addition is a closed operation on R. The system $\{R; +\}$ has many properties, three of which are listed below.

1. $+$ is associative; that is, for all $a, b, c \in R$,

$$a + (b + c) = (a + b) + c,$$

2. 0 is an identity element relative to $+$; that is, for all $a \in R$,

$$0 + a = a = a + 0,$$

3. $-a$ is an inverse of a relative to $+$; that is,

$$a + (-a) = 0 = (-a) + a.$$

These three properties, when stated in general form, are precisely the postulates which define an abstract group.

A *group* $\mathcal{G}$ is defined to be a system $\mathcal{G} = \{G; *\}$ having one closed operation and satisfying the following postulates:

G1. $*$ is associative.
G2. An identity element i exists in G.
G3. Each $g \in G$ has an inverse $g' \in G$.

It follows from Exercise 1, § 1.4, that the identity element of any group is unique; likewise, each $g \in G$ has a unique inverse.

Strictly speaking, when we use the term "group" we refer to the system $\mathcal{G}$, rather than the set G of elements of the system.   The elements are members of G, not members of $\mathcal{G}$.   However, this distinction is usually ignored in mathematical literature, so we shall adopt the conventional, although incorrect, terminology.   Thus for any abstract system $\mathcal{S} = \{E; R; O\}$, when we speak of an element of $\mathcal{S}$, we really refer to an element of E.

If we consider the set R of real numbers, together with multiplication as operation, the system $\{R; \cdot\}$ fails to be a group only because $0 \in R$ has no multiplicative inverse.   However, if we let R_0 denote the set of all non-zero real numbers, it is clear that the system $\{R_0; \cdot\}$ satisfies the three group postulates, since 1 is the identity element, and $1/x$ is the inverse of x for each $x \in R_0$.

EXAMPLES OF GROUPS

(a) The rational numbers (or the complex numbers) with addition as the operation.

(b) The non-zero rational numbers (or the non-zero complex numbers) with multiplication as the operation.

(c) The integers with addition as the operation.

(d) The n complex n^{th} roots of unity with multiplication as the operation (see Exercise 1 below).

(e) The mappings of Exercise 5, § 1.4.

It so happens that in all except the last of these examples the group operation is commutative.   A group $\mathcal{G}$ is said to be *commutative* if and only if its operation is commutative.

Now we turn to a second example of an abstract system—a *field*—again using the real number system as an illustration.   We have already observed that $\{R; +\}$ and $\{R_0; \cdot\}$ are both commutative groups.   Furthermore, the two operations are related by the distributive law,

$$a \cdot (b + c) = a \cdot b + a \cdot c.$$

Stated in abstract terms, this is simply the description of a field.

A *field* $\mathfrak{F}$ is defined to be a system $\mathfrak{F} = \{F; \oplus, \odot\}$ having two closed operations and satisfying the following postulates:

F1. The system $\{F; \oplus\}$ is a commutative group whose identity will be denoted by o.

F2. The system $\{F_o; \odot\}$ is a commutative group whose identity will be denoted by i, where $F_o = \{x \in F \mid x \neq o\}$.

F3. The operation $\odot$ is distributive over $\oplus$.

In order to distinguish the two inverses of an element $a \neq o$ relative to the two operations, we denote by $(-a)$ the inverse of a relative to $\oplus$, and by

a^{-1} the inverse of a relative to $\odot$. The distributive law forms a connection between the two operations; for example, the theorem $a \odot o = o$ is valid for any field. Similarly, we can prove for arbitrary fields such well known properties of numbers as

$$(-a) \odot b = -(a \odot b) = a \odot (-b),$$
$$(a \odot b^{-1}) \oplus (c \odot d^{-1}) = [(a \odot d) \oplus (b \odot c)] \odot (b \odot d)^{-1},$$

and many others. You should read these theorems carefully, making sure that you understand the meaning of each term in the abstract sense rather than only for a numerical interpretation.

The familiarity of properties of fields is due to our experience with number systems. The rational numbers, real numbers, and complex numbers all form fields relative to the operations of addition and multiplication.

From the field postulates it is evident that any field must contain at least two elements, o and i, which are distinct since $i \in F_o$ but $o \notin F_o$. Hence the smallest possible field contains two elements; it is easily verified that the field postulates are satisfied for the two-element system whose operations are defined by the tables below. In the $\oplus$-table, the element $x \oplus y$ appears in the row which is labeled x at the left and in the column which is labeled y at the top; the $\odot$-table is read similarly.

$\oplus$	o	i		$\odot$	o	i
o	o	i		o	o	o
i	i	o		i	o	i

This is an example of a finite field.

In the study of vector spaces and matrices we constantly make use of elements of a field. Although most of the results are valid regardless of the choice of the field, we occasionally need to require that the field have special algebraic properties. For example, we sometimes stipulate that the field satisfy the condition $i \oplus i \neq o$, which excludes the two-element field described above. See § 4.2

Exercises

1. The n complex n^{th} roots of unity are the numbers

$$e_k = \cos \frac{2k\pi}{n} + i \sin \frac{2k\pi}{n}, \ k = 0, 1, \ldots, (n-1),$$

where $i^2 = -1$.

(i) Prove that for $n = 3$ the three cube roots of unity, together with multiplication of complex numbers, form a group.

(ii) Prove the corresponding result for any n.

2. For any group $\mathcal{G}$ prove that

    (i) there is only one identity element,

    (ii) each element has only one inverse,

    (iii) $(x')' = x$,

    (iv) $(x * y)' = y' * x'$, where $*$ denotes the group operation.

3. Let $\mathcal{G} = \{G; *\}$ be any group, and let g be a fixed element of G.

    (i) Show that the mapping

$$\mathbf{R}_g : x \longrightarrow x * g$$

is a one-to-one mapping of G onto G.

    (ii) Show that the successive mapping $\mathbf{R}_g \mathbf{R}_h$ is the same mapping as $\mathbf{R}_{g*h}$.

4. Let $\{S; *\}$ be a system for which

    $*$ is associative,

    there exists $e \in S$ such that $x * e = x$ for all $x \in S$,

    for each $x \in S$ there exists $\bar{x} \in S$ such that $x * \bar{x} = e$.

Prove that $\{S; *\}$ is a group. (e is called a *right* identity and $\bar{x}$ is called a *right* inverse.)

5. Consider the real coordinate plane, and let $\mathbf{R}_A$ denote the rotation of the points of the plane through the angle A around the origin, counterclockwise if $A > 0$ and clockwise if $A < 0$. The "product" $\mathbf{R}_A * \mathbf{R}_B$ is defined to be the transformation which results when $\mathbf{R}_A$ is followed by $\mathbf{R}_B$.

    (i) Find a simple expression for $\mathbf{R}_A * \mathbf{R}_B$.

    (ii) Prove that the system $\mathcal{R} = \{R; *\}$ is a commutative group, where R is the set of all rotations of the plane around the origin.

6. In three-dimensional space let $\mathbf{X}_A$, $\mathbf{Y}_A$, and $\mathbf{Z}_A$ denote rotations of the points of space about the x, y, and z axes, respectively, through the angle A, where the positive direction of rotation is chosen to be counterclockwise as viewed toward the origin from the positive side of the axis of rotation. As in Exercise 5, the product of two rotations is defined to be the transformation which results when the first rotation is followed by the second. Show that this product is not commutative.

7. Prove that the following theorems are valid in any field:

    (i) $a \odot o = o$.

    (ii) $(-a) \odot b = -(a \odot b)$.

    (iii) $-(b^{-1}) = (-b)^{-1}$, if $b \neq o$.

8. Prove that the set of all numbers of the form $a + b\sqrt{3}$, where a and b are rational numbers, together with numerical addition and multiplication, form a field.

9. Let $C = R \times R$, where R is the set of real numbers. We define equality, addition, and multiplication in C as follows:

$(a, b) = (c, d)$ if and only if $a = c$ and $b = d$ in R,

$(a, b) + (c, d) = (a + c, b + d)$,

$(a, b) \bullet (c, d) = (ac - bd, ad + bc)$.

Prove that the system $\{C; =; +, \bullet\}$ is a field.

CHAPTER 2

Vector Spaces

§2.1. *Introduction*

The purpose of this chapter is to develop a geometric system, called a *vector space*, upon which most of our study of matrices will be based. Before proceeding to a general definition, however, we shall consider two familiar examples of vector spaces which in all essential respects provide an accurate model of the general system.

First consider the cartesian plane, in which each point is represented uniquely by an ordered pair of real numbers (relative to a chosen rectangular coordinate system). To represent a physical quantity which has both magnitude and direction, such as force, we sometimes think of a vector as an arrow starting at the origin and proceeding to some point, say (a_1, a_2). These coordinates are called the *components* of the vector. The direction of the arrow is chosen as the direction of the force, and the length of the arrow as

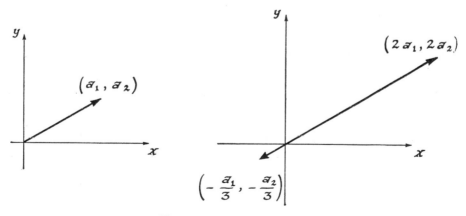

Figure   2.1

the magnitude of the force. If this force is multiplied by a factor k, the resulting vector is described as (ka_1, ka_2); each of its components is multiplied by k.

If a second force is represented by the vector (b_1, b_2), the resultant physical effect of (a_1, a_2) and (b_1, b_2) acting simultaneously on a point (the origin) is described by the parallelogram principle: the resultant vector is the diagonal (from the origin) of the parallelogram having the two given vectors as adjacent sides. An easy application of analytic geometry shows that the resultant vector is described as $(a_1 + b_1, a_2 + b_2)$.

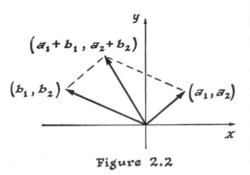

Figure 2.2

Now we observe that neither the magnitude nor the direction of the vector appears in this description of a vector, although each can be calculated from the components of the description. Likewise, the effect of multiplying a vector by a constant and the effect of combining two vectors into their resultant, both can be described very simply directly from the components. As we shall see in the material to follow, a surprising amount of geometry can be developed for vector spaces without any reference to the basically geometric concepts of length and angle; indeed, such metrical considerations are deferred until Chapter 9.

But, we may ask, if length, distance, and angle do not form the basis of this geometry, what concepts are used? The answer has already been given in the first example: multiplication of a vector by a constant, and resultant addition of two vectors.

The second example is even more realistically allied to physical considerations, since we are inclined to believe that we live in three-dimensional space. A vector from the origin to a point in space is represented by the three coordinates (relative to a rectangular coordinate system) of the terminal point, (a_1, a_2, a_3). As in the plane, multiplying (a_1, a_2, a_3) by a constant k yields a vector whose coordinates are (ka_1, ka_2, ka_3); the resultant of (a_1, a_2, a_3) and (b_1, b_2, b_3) is $(a_1 + b_1, a_2 + b_2, a_3 + b_3)$, again by the parallelogram principle. This consistency of form of the representation of vectors enables us to consider vector spaces of higher dimensions where geometric intuition is likely to fail and where physical experiments are not readily conceived. In particular, we note that in each of these examples the vectors form a commutative group relative to the "resultant" operation, which is called vector addition. Concerning the multiplication of a vector by constants, we observe that

1. $[k_1 + k_2](a_1, a_2) = k_1(a_1, a_2) + k_2(a_1, a_2),$
2. $k[(a_1, a_2) + (b_1, b_2)] = k(a_1, a_2) + k(b_1, b_2),$
3. $[k_1 k_2](a_1, a_2) = k_1[k_2(a_1, a_2)],$
4. $1(a_1, a_2) = (a_1, a_2),$

and similarly for vectors in three-dimensional space. This particular selection of observations may seem arbitrary, especially number 4, which appears almost too obvious to record. However, it is important to notice that a strong connection exists between the addition of vectors and the multiplication of vectors by constants. In that sense, numbers 1 and 2 resemble distributivity, number 3 resembles associativity, and number 4 is not unlike an identity.

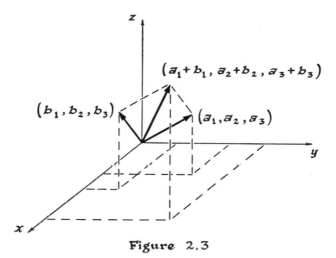

Figure 2.3

Exercises

1. Let (a_1, a_2) and (b_1, b_2) be two points of the plane which form a triangle with $(0, 0)$. For each of the conditions specified below, describe geometrically the set of points $\{k_1(a_1, a_2) + k_2(b_1, b_2)\}$.

(i) $k_1 = 1, k_2 = 1.$
(ii) $k_1 = 1, k_2 = -1.$
(iii) $0 \leq k_1 \leq 1, k_2 = 0.$ line $[(0,0), (a_1, a_2)]$
(iv) $0 \leq k_1 \leq 1, k_2 = 1.$ all 4s
(v) All $k_1, k_2 = 0.$ pt $(0, 0)$
(vi) $0 \leq k_1 \leq 1, 0 \leq k_2 \leq 1.$
(vii) $0 \leq k_1 \leq 1, 0 \leq k_2 \leq 1, k_1 + k_2 = 1.$
(viii) $0 \leq k_1, 0 \leq k_2 \leq 1.$
(ix) All $k_1, 0 \leq k_2.$
(x) All k_1, all $k_2.$

2. Which of the sets in Exercise 1 form an additive group?

3. (i) Consider the collection of all polynomials with real coefficients and of degree not exceeding 2:

$$a(x) = a_1 x^2 + a_2 x + a_3.$$

The sum of two such polynomials and the product of a polynomial by a real number are defined in the usual way, thus forming an abstract system with two operations. In what way does this system resemble the system of points in three-dimensional space as described in this section?

(ii) How might we define "the angle between two polynomials of degree not exceeding 2"?

§2.2. *Vector Spaces over a Field*

The examples just considered reveal that a vector space is somewhat more complicated than the abstract systems in the first chapter, principally because there are two sets of elements involved. One set V consists of abstract elements called *vectors* and denoted by small Greek letters; the other set F is a field whose elements are called *scalars* and are denoted by small Latin letters. In addition to the two field operations, $+$ and $\cdot$, two operations involving vectors are postulated: the "addition" of vectors, denoted $\alpha \oplus \beta$, and the "multiplication" of a scalar and a vector, denoted $a \odot \alpha$. The postulates for an abstract vector space are selected from the examples of § 2.1.

Definition 2.1. A system $\mathcal{V} = \{V, F; +, \cdot, \oplus, \odot\}$ is called a *vector space over the field* $\mathfrak{F}$ if and only if

(a) $\{F; +, \cdot\}$ is a field $\mathfrak{F}$ whose identity elements are denoted by 0 and 1,

(b) $\{V; \oplus\}$ is a commutative group whose identity element is denoted θ,

(c) for all $a, b \in F$ and all $\alpha, \beta \in V$, $a \odot \alpha \in V$ and

    (i) $(a + b) \odot \alpha = (a \odot \alpha) \oplus (b \odot \alpha)$,

    (ii) $a \odot (\alpha \oplus \beta) = (a \odot \alpha) \oplus (a \odot \beta)$,

    (iii) $(ab) \odot \alpha = a \odot (b \odot \alpha)$,

    (iv) $1 \odot \alpha = \alpha$.

Fortunately, the notation used above can be simplified. From the type of letters involved it is always clear whether we are adding two scalars or two vectors, or multiplying two scalars or a scalar and a vector; therefore, we can use $+$ to indicate both types of addition and juxtaposition to indicate both types of multiplication. Thus $(c + a)(\beta + d\alpha)$ denotes

$$(c + a) \odot [\beta \oplus (d \odot \alpha)].$$

Some of the theory of vector spaces is valid even if the scalars form only a *division ring* (a system which satisfies all field postulates except the commutative law of multiplication). For an introduction to vector spaces, however, such generality can be dispensed with. In fact, the field $\mathfrak{F}$ plays a subordinate role in our consideration most of the time. Except for a few places later on, where the nature of $\mathfrak{F}$ is clearly specified, the reader may think of $\mathfrak{F}$ as the field of real numbers without any curtailment of general understanding. Our first theorem concerns multiplication of special scalars and special vectors.

Theorem 2.1. Let θ denote the zero vector, and let $-\alpha$ denote the group inverse of α. Then for all $\alpha \in V$, $a \in F$,

(a) $0\alpha = \theta$,

(b) $(-1)\alpha = -\alpha$,

(c) $a\theta = \theta$.

P R O O F: (a) $\alpha = 1\alpha = (1 + 0)\alpha = 1\alpha + 0\alpha = \alpha + 0\alpha$ by (iv) and (i) of Definition 2.1. Adding $-\alpha$ to both sides, we have $\theta = 0\alpha$.

(b) $\alpha + (-1)\alpha = 1\alpha + (-1)\alpha = (1 - 1)\alpha = \theta$. Hence $(-1)\alpha$ is an inverse of α, and (b) follows from the uniqueness of the group inverse.

(c) $a\theta = a[\alpha + (-\alpha)] = a\alpha + a(-\alpha) = a\alpha + (-a\alpha) = \theta$.

A geometric interpretation of this theorem is instructive, even though the results are not at all surprising. The reader is encouraged to make such interpretations of algebraic statements, and dually, to recognize algebraic statements of geometric results.

EXAMPLES OF VECTOR SPACES OVER
THE FIELD OF REAL NUMBERS

(a) For a fixed positive integer n, the set of all n-tuples of real numbers forms a vector space if addition of vectors and multiplication of a scalar and a vector are defined by

$$(x_1, \ldots, x_n) + (y_1, \ldots, y_n) = (x_1 + y_1, \ldots, x_n + y_n)$$

and

$$a(x_1, \ldots, x_n) = (ax_1, \ldots, ax_n).$$

For $n = 2, 3$ these are the two examples of § 2.1.

(b) A completely trivial example is that in which the zero n-tuple $(0, 0, \ldots, 0)$ is the only vector and the scalar field is the field of real numbers.

(c) Another trivial example is provided by considering the real numbers themselves as vectors and also as scalars. This space is represented geometrically by a line.   More generally, if the elements of any field are considered both as vectors and scalars, and if the vector operations are defined to be the corresponding field operations, the resulting system is a vector space.

(d) For fixed n let V be the set of all polynomials in x with real coefficients and of degree not exceeding n together with the zero polynomial.   Vector sum and scalar multiples are defined as the usual polynomial sum and product by real numbers.

(e) Let V be the set of all real valued functions which are continuous on the interval $0 \le x \le 1$, with operations defined by

$$(f + g)(x) = f(x) + g(x),$$
$$(af)(x) = af(x).$$

Exercises

1. Verify that each of the preceding five examples satisfies the postulates of a vector space.

2. How are the vector spaces of Examples (a) and (d) related?   (See Exercise 3, § 2.1.)

3. Let V be the set of all polynomials (of all degrees) with real coefficients, with the sum of polynomials and the product of a polynomial by a real number defined in the usual way.   Prove that this system is a vector space.

4. Let V be the set of all real valued functions which attain a relative maximum or relative minimum value at $x = 0$, with the sum of two functions and the product of a function by a real number defined in the usual way.   Is this system a vector space?

5. Consider the set of all triples of real numbers (a_1, a_2, a_3) subject to the conditions stated below.   In each case determine whether the system forms a vector space relative to addition of triples and multiplication of a triple by a real number.

    (i) $a_1 = 0$; a_2 and a_3 arbitrary,
    (ii) $a_1 = -a_3$; a_2 arbitrary,
    (iii) a_1, a_2 arbitrary, $a_3 = 1 + a_1 - a_2$,
    (iv) a_1, a_2 arbitrary, $a_3 = 3a_1 - 4a_2$,
    (v) $a_1 a_2 \ge 0$, a_3 arbitrary.

6. Consider the set S of all solutions of a homogeneous differential equation of order n:

$$y^{(n)} + a_1(x)y^{(n-1)} + \ldots + a_{n-2}(x)y'' + a_{n-1}(x)y' + a_n(x)y = 0.$$

Prove that S forms a vector space relative to addition and scalar multiples of functions.

§2.3. *Subspaces*

In the study of any abstract system we are usually interested not only in the full system but also in various subsystems. When considering three-dimensional space our interest is in lines and planes, particularly in those lines and planes which pass through the origin and thereby constitute vector spaces in themselves. A general description of subspaces is given as follows.

> **Definition 2.2.** Given a vector space $\mathcal{U}$ over $\mathcal{F}$. A subset S of vectors is said to form a *subspace* $\mathcal{S}$ of $\mathcal{U}$ if and only if the subsystem $\mathcal{S} = \{S, F; +, \cdot, \oplus, \odot\}$ is a vector space.

Again we are made conscious of the fact that our language and notation can be simplified by ignoring the distinction between a system $\mathcal{S}$ and the set S of elements of the system. Henceforth we shall use $\mathcal{U}$ to denote both a vector space and the set of vectors of a vector space. With this simplification, a subspace $\mathcal{S}$ is a subset of $\mathcal{U}$ which, within itself, forms a vector space; it is understood that the field and the operations for $\mathcal{S}$ are the same as for $\mathcal{U}$.

The postulate that the vectors of a vector space form a group relative to vector addition implies that the zero vector θ is in every subspace. Trivially, the vector space which consists of θ alone is a subspace of every $\mathcal{U}$; likewise, $\mathcal{U}$ is a subspace of $\mathcal{U}$. In three-dimensional space, the non-trivial subspaces are simply all those lines and planes which pass through the origin.

We now seek a simple way of determining whether a given subset $S \subseteq \mathcal{U}$ is a subspace, because it is needlessly tedious to verify that each of the postulates of a vector space is satisfied for S; the next theorem provides an easily applied criterion.

> **Theorem 2.2.** A non-void subset S of $\mathcal{U}$ is a subspace if and only if S is closed under the two operations of vector sum and multiplication of vectors by scalars, as defined for $\mathcal{U}$; that is, for every $\alpha, \beta \in S$ and every $c \in \mathcal{F}$, $\alpha + \beta \in S$ and $c\alpha \in S$.
>
> P R O O F: The condition is clearly necessary. Conversely, assume that S is closed under the operations. Then $(-1)\alpha = -\alpha \in S$ for every $\alpha \in S$, and $\alpha + (-\alpha) = \theta \in S$. Vector addition in S is the same as in $\mathcal{U}$, so it is associative and commutative, and S forms a commutative group. The other postulates are satisfied in S because those properties are inherited from $\mathcal{U}$.

EXAMPLES OF SUBSPACES

(a) In Example (a) of § 2.2, let S be the set of all n-tuples with $x_1 = 0$.

(b) In Example (a) of § 2.2, let S be the set of all n-tuples with $x_1 = kx_2$ for a fixed scalar k.

(c) In Example (e) of § 2.2, let S be the set of all constant functions on the interval $0 \leq x \leq 1$.

A general means of generating subspaces is provided by the following definition.

Definition 2.3.   Given a vector space $\mathcal{V}$, let A be a set of vectors. The set $[A]$ of all *linear combinations* of vectors of A is the collection of all finite sums of the form

$$a_1\alpha_1 + a_2\alpha_2 + \ldots + a_m\alpha_m,$$

where $a_i \in \mathcal{F}$, $\alpha_i \in A$, and $m = 1, 2, 3, \ldots$.

Linear combinations of vectors are so vital in the study of vector spaces that the term *linear space* is used as a synonym for vector space, and the study of certain mappings of such spaces is called *linear algebra*. In the following theorem, which may be proved as an exercise, we have an example of the importance of linear combinations of vectors.

Theorem 2.3.   The set of all linear combinations of any non-void set of vectors of $\mathcal{V}$ is a subspace of $\mathcal{V}$.

Definition 2.4.   The set of all linear combinations of a set A of vectors is called the *subspace spanned by* A and is denoted $[A]$.

The concept of subspaces of $\mathcal{V}$ is roughly analogous to that of subsets of a set, but important distinctions exist. An arbitrary subset of vectors is not a subspace, nor is the void set a subspace. We recall that subsets can be combined by the set operations of union and intersection to produce other subsets. A similar combination is possible for subspaces, but again the analogy is not perfect since the set union of two subspaces is not necessarily a subspace.

Definition 2.5.   Let $\mathcal{S}$ and $\mathcal{T}$ be subspaces of $\mathcal{V}$. The *sum* of $\mathcal{S}$ and $\mathcal{T}$, denoted $\mathcal{S} + \mathcal{T}$, is the set of all vectors $\sigma + \tau$, where $\sigma \in \mathcal{S}$ and $\tau \in \mathcal{T}$.

Definition 2.6.   The *intersection* of $\mathcal{S}$ and $\mathcal{T}$, denoted $\mathcal{S} \cap \mathcal{T}$, is the set of all vectors common to $\mathcal{S}$ and $\mathcal{T}$.

Theorem 2.4. If S and $\mathfrak{I}$ are subspaces of $\mathcal{V}$, then $S + \mathfrak{I}$ and $S \cap \mathfrak{I}$ are subspaces of $\mathcal{V}$.

PROOF: $S + \mathfrak{I}$ is a subspace by Theorem 2.3, since any linear combination of vectors from S and $\mathfrak{I}$ can be written as the sum of a vector from S and a vector from $\mathfrak{I}$ because S and $\mathfrak{I}$ are subspaces. Indeed, $S + \mathfrak{I}$ is simply the subspace generated by the set union of S and $\mathfrak{I}$. Now let $\alpha,\ \beta \in S \cap \mathfrak{I}$, and let $c \in \mathfrak{F}$. Then $\alpha + \beta \in S$, $\alpha + \beta \in \mathfrak{I}$, $c\alpha \in S$, and $c\alpha \in \mathfrak{I}$, since S and $\mathfrak{I}$ are subspaces. Thus $\alpha + \beta \in S \cap \mathfrak{I}$ and $c\alpha \in S \cap \mathfrak{I}$. The operations in $S \cap \mathfrak{I}$ are therefore closed, and $S \cap \mathfrak{I}$ is a subspace by Theorem 2.2.

This theorem justifies the terminology given in Definitions 2.5 and 2.6. The set intersection of two subspaces turns out to be a subspace. However, the set union of two subspaces is not a subspace; the smallest subspace which contains this union is simply the set $[S \cup \mathfrak{I}]$ of all linear combinations of vectors chosen from $S \cup \mathfrak{I}$. Since any such vector is of the form $\sigma + \tau$, where $\sigma \in S$ and $\tau \in \mathfrak{I}$, we write $S + \mathfrak{I}$ to remind us of this fact. We recognize that further ambiguity is introduced in this use of the sign $+$, but once we are aware of the fact the ambiguity is of no consequence.

Exercises

1. If $\mathcal{V}$ is the space of all real valued functions which are continuous on $-1 \leq x \leq 1$, which of the following subsets are subspaces of $\mathcal{V}$?

   (i) All differentiable functions.
   (ii) All polynomials of degree two.
   (iii) All polynomials of degree less than five.
   (iv) All polynomials of degree greater than three.
   (v) All odd functions $(f(-x) = -f(x))$.
   (vi) All even functions $(f(-x) = f(x))$.
   (vii) All functions for which $f(0) = 0$.
   (viii) All non-negative functions.
   (ix) All constant functions.
   (x) All functions for which $f^2(x) \leq 0$.

2. Consider the collection of all subspaces S of a vector space $\mathcal{V}$, together with the operation $+$, sum of subspaces.

   (i) Show that $+$ is associative and commutative.
   (ii) Show that an identity subspace exists relative to $+$.
   (iii) Is this system a commutative group?

3. In the cartesian space of three dimensions, suppose that $\alpha = (2, 1, 0)$, $\beta = (1, 0, -1)$, $\gamma = (-1, 1, 1)$, $\delta = (0, -1, 1)$.   Let $\mathcal{S} = [\alpha, \beta]$, $\mathcal{I} = [\gamma, \delta]$. Describe $\mathcal{S} \cap \mathcal{I}$ and $\mathcal{S} + \mathcal{I}$.

4. Let $\xi \in \mathcal{S} + \mathcal{I}$.   Then ξ can be represented as $\xi = \sigma + \tau$ for some $\sigma \in \mathcal{S}$ and $\tau \in \mathcal{I}$.   Prove that σ and τ are uniquely determined by ξ if and only if $\mathcal{S} \cap \mathcal{I} = [\theta]$.

5. Prove Theorem 2.3.

6. Show that $(\mathcal{R} + \mathcal{S}) \cap \mathcal{I} \supseteq (\mathcal{R} \cap \mathcal{I}) + (\mathcal{S} \cap \mathcal{I})$.   Show by an example in the plane that equality need not hold.

7. Prove that if $\mathcal{R} \subseteq \mathcal{I}$, $(\mathcal{R} + \mathcal{S}) \cap \mathcal{I} = \mathcal{R} + (\mathcal{S} \cap \mathcal{I})$.

§2.4. *Linear Independence*

We now come to one of the most useful concepts in the theory of vector spaces, that of linear independence.

> **Definition 2.7.**   A set $\{\alpha_1, \ldots, \alpha_k\}$ of vectors is said to be *linearly independent* if and only if the equation
>
> $$a_1\alpha_1 + a_2\alpha_2 + \ldots + a_k\alpha_k = \theta$$
>
> implies that $a_1 = a_2 = \ldots = a_k = 0$.

The definition states that the zero vector can be obtained as a linear combination of independent vectors *only* in the trivial way, in which every scalar of the linear combination is zero.   On the other hand if the zero vector is a non-trivial linear combination of vectors γ_i, we have

$$c_1\gamma_1 + c_2\gamma_2 + \ldots + c_m\gamma_m = \theta$$

where not all scalars c_i are zero.   Let c_j be the first non-zero scalar.   We obtain

$$\gamma_j = -\frac{1}{c_j}(c_{j+1}\gamma_{j+1} + \ldots + c_m\gamma_m).$$

In this case the vector γ_j *depends* linearly on the other vectors in the sense that γ_j is a linear combination of the others.   Such a set $\{\gamma_1, \ldots, \gamma_m\}$ is called *linearly dependent*.   Clearly any finite set of vectors is either linearly independent or linearly dependent, any set which contains the zero vector is dependent, and any set which consists of a single non-zero vector is independent.

> **Theorem 2.5.**   Any subset of an independent set is independent, and any set containing a dependent subset is dependent.
>
> P R O O F :   Exercise.

On many occasions we shall need to construct linearly independent sets of vectors. We can begin by choosing any non-zero vector, but how should the next choice be made? The following theorem provides an answer.

Theorem 2.6. Let $\{\alpha_1, \ldots, \alpha_k\}$ be linearly independent, and let $\mathfrak{I} = [\alpha_1, \ldots, \alpha_k]$. Then for any vector ξ, $\{\alpha_1, \ldots, \alpha_k, \xi\}$ is linearly independent if and only if $\xi \notin \mathfrak{I}$.

P R O O F : Suppose scalars $a_1, \ldots, a_{k+1}$ exist such that

$$a_1\alpha_1 + \ldots + a_k\alpha_k + a_{k+1}\xi = \theta.$$

If $a_{k+1} = 0$, then $a_i = 0$ for $i = 1, \ldots, k$ since $\{\alpha_1, \ldots, \alpha_k\}$ is linearly independent. Hence either all the scalars are zero, in which case $\{\alpha_1, \ldots, \alpha_k, \xi\}$ is linearly independent and $\xi \notin \mathfrak{I}$, or else $a_{k+1} \neq 0$, in which case $\{\alpha_1, \ldots, \alpha_k, \xi\}$ is linearly dependent; but then we have

$$\xi = -a_{k+1}^{-1}(a_1\alpha_1 + a_2\alpha_2 + \ldots + a_k\alpha_k) \in \mathfrak{I}.$$

Thus a linearly independent set S of vectors may be extended to a larger linearly independent set by adjoining any vector which does not lie in the space spanned by S; of course it is possible that no such vector exists, since S might span $\mathfrak{V}$. The next two theorems concern the selection of a linearly independent subset of a dependent set of vectors.

Theorem 2.7. Let $S = \{\alpha_1, \ldots, \alpha_k\}$ be a set of non-zero vectors. Then S is dependent if and only if

$$\alpha_m \in [\alpha_1, \ldots, \alpha_{m-1}]$$

for some $m \leq k$.

P R O O F : If for some m, $\alpha_m \in [\alpha_1, \ldots, \alpha_{m-1}]$, then $\{\alpha_1, \ldots, \alpha_m\}$ is dependent and so is S (Theorem 2.5). Conversely, suppose S is dependent and let m be the least integer such that $\{\alpha_1, \ldots, \alpha_m\}$ is dependent. Then for suitable scalars $c_1, \ldots, c_m$, not all zero,

$$\sum_{i=1}^{m} c_i\alpha_i = \theta.$$

If $c_m = 0$, then $\{\alpha_1, \ldots, \alpha_{m-1}\}$ is dependent, contradicting the definition of m. Hence

$$\alpha_m = -c_m^{-1}(c_1\alpha_1 + \ldots + c_{m-1}\alpha_{m-1}) \in [\alpha_1, \ldots, \alpha_{m-1}].$$

Theorem 2.8. If $\mathfrak{I} \neq [\theta]$ is spanned by the set $S = \{\alpha_1, \ldots, \alpha_k\}$, there exists a linearly independent subset of S which also spans $\mathfrak{I}$.

F I R S T P R O O F : If S is independent, there is nothing to prove. Otherwise by Theorem 2.7 there is a least integer i such that $\alpha_i \in [\alpha_1, \ldots, \alpha_{i-1}]$. Let $S_1 = S - \alpha_i$. Clearly $\mathfrak{I} = [S_1]$, and the argument can be repeated on S_1. Either S_1 is independent, in which case the proof is complete, or for some j, $S_2 = S_1 - \alpha_j$ spans $\mathfrak{I}$. The theorem follows by repeating the argument a finite number of times.

S E C O N D P R O O F: Let $\alpha_{r_1} \neq \theta$ and let $\mathfrak{I}_1 = [\alpha_{r_1}]$. Then $\mathfrak{I}_1 \subseteq \mathfrak{I}$, and equality holds if $\alpha_i \in \mathfrak{I}_1$ for $i = 1, \ldots, k$, in which case the proof is complete. Otherwise by Theorem 2.6 $\{\alpha_{r_1}, \alpha_{r_2}\}$ is linearly independent for some α_{r_2}. Let $\mathfrak{I}_2 = [\alpha_{r_1}, \alpha_{r_2}]$. Clearly $\mathfrak{I}_2 \subseteq \mathfrak{I}$, and the argument can be repeated to construct a linearly independent subset of S which spans $\mathfrak{I}$.

In each of these proofs we constructed an independent subset S' of S such that $[S'] = [S]$. Thus for every $\xi \in \mathfrak{I}$, $\{S', \xi\}$ is dependent, and if S'' is any set of vectors of $\mathfrak{I}$ which contains S' as a subset, either $S'' = S'$ or S'' is dependent. An independent set which has the property that it cannot be extended in $\mathfrak{I}$ to a larger independent set is called a *maximal independent subset* of $\mathfrak{I}$. This concept is used in the next section.

Corollary. Any finite set of non-zero vectors contains a maximal independent subset.

This corollary may be strengthened by dropping the word "finite," but we have no need here for the stronger result, and shall pursue the idea no further.

Exercises

1. (i) Referring to the vectors of Exercise 3, § 2.3, select an independent subset of $\{\alpha, \beta, \gamma, \delta\}$, containing three vectors.

(ii) Prove that the vectors of your answer to (i) form a maximal independent subset of $\mathfrak{V}$.

(iii) Still referring to Exercise 3, § 2.3, choose any non-zero vector $\xi_1 \in \mathfrak{S} \cap \mathfrak{I}$. Find vectors ξ_2 and ξ_3 such that $\mathfrak{S} = [\xi_1, \xi_2]$ and $\mathfrak{I} = [\xi_1, \xi_3]$. Prove that $[\xi_1, \xi_2, \xi_3] = \mathfrak{S} + \mathfrak{I}$.

2. Select a maximal linearly independent subset of each of the following sets of vectors.

(i) $(1, 0, 1, 0)$, $(0, 1, 0, 1)$, $(1, 1, 1, 1)$, $(-1, 0, 2, 0)$.

(ii) $(0, 1, 2, 3)$, $(3, 0, 1, 2)$, $(2, 3, 0, 1)$, $(1, 2, 3, 0)$.

(iii) $(1, -1, 1, -1)$, $(-1, 1, -1, -1)$, $(1, -1, 1, -2)$, $(0, 0, 0, 1)$.

3. For each example of the preceding exercise in which the largest independent subset contains fewer than four vectors, adjoin vectors (a_1, a_2, a_3, a_4) to obtain a linearly independent set of four vectors.

4. Prove Theorem 2.5.

5. In the space of real n-tuples prove that the vectors

$$\alpha_1 = (1, 1, 1, \ldots, 1, 1)$$
$$\alpha_2 = (0, 1, 1, \ldots, 1, 1)$$
$$\alpha_3 = (0, 0, 1, \ldots, 1, 1)$$
$$\vdots$$
$$\alpha_n = (0, 0, 0, \ldots, 0, 1)$$

are linearly independent.

§2.5. *Basis*

At the beginning of the chapter, when we first discussed the physical concept of a vector in three-dimensional space, our description was made in terms of that ordered triple of numbers which specified the coordinates of the end point of the "arrow," relative to a rectangular coordinate system. We shall now examine this idea more carefully. First we observe that

$$(a_1, a_2, a_3) = a_1(1, 0, 0) + a_2(0, 1, 0) + a_3(0, 0, 1)$$
$$= a_1\epsilon_1 + a_2\epsilon_2 + a_3\epsilon_3,$$

where ϵ_i, $i = 1, 2, 3$, represents the triple whose ith component is 1 and whose other components are zero. Clearly, $\{\epsilon_1, \epsilon_2, \epsilon_3\}$ spans the space and is linearly independent. Therefore, this set is a maximal linearly independent subset of the space. These three vectors are unit vectors along three coordinate axes, and every point in the space acquires a unique system of coordinates relative to these vectors, the coordinates being the three scalars used to represent a given vector as a linear combination of the ϵ_i.

From the proofs of Theorem 2.8 it is clear that there is nothing unique about the way we might choose a maximal independent subset of a space. Many such subsets exist for three-dimensional space, and indeed for any space $\mathcal{V} \neq [\theta]$. For example, a second maximal linearly independent set in three-dimensional space is

$$\beta_1 = (0, 1, 1)$$
$$\beta_2 = (1, 0, 1)$$
$$\beta_3 = (1, 1, 0),$$

and if we let $s = \frac{1}{2}(a_1 + a_2 + a_3)$ we have the linear representation

$$(a_1, a_2, a_3) = (s - a_1)\beta_1 + (s - a_2)\beta_2 + (s - a_3)\beta_3.$$

The scalars of this representation are uniquely determined, but they are different from the scalars which represent the same point relative to the ϵ_i vectors. We now turn to a general consideration of these observations.

Definition 2.8. A maximal linearly independent subset of a vector space υ is called a *basis* of υ. If υ contains a finite basis, υ is said to be *finite-dimensional;* otherwise υ is *infinite-dimensional.*

In this book we shall content ourselves with a study of finite-dimensional spaces.

Since a basis for υ spans υ, every vector $\xi \in \upsilon$ is a linear combination of basis vectors,

$$\xi = c_1\alpha_1 + \ldots + c_k\alpha_k.$$

The scalars in this representation are unique; for suppose

$$\xi = b_1\alpha_1 + \ldots + b_k\alpha_k.$$

Then $\theta = \xi - \xi = (c_1 - b_1)\alpha_1 + \ldots + (c_k - b_k)\alpha_k$, and since the α_i are linearly independent, $c_i - b_i = 0$ for every $i = 1, \ldots, k$. We have proved the following theorem.

Theorem 2.9. Every vector of υ has a unique representation as a linear combination of the vectors of a fixed basis of υ.

This theorem reveals a significant interpretation of bases. Given a basis $\{\alpha_1, \ldots, \alpha_n\}$, each vector ξ can be represented in one and only one way as a linear combination of basis vectors,

$$\xi = c_1\alpha_1 + \ldots + c_n\alpha_n.$$

Thus ξ determines uniquely an n-tuple of scalars, $(c_1, \ldots, c_n)$ which can be regarded as the coordinates of ξ relative to the α-basis. Hence each basis of υ determines a system of coordinates for υ. This suggests than any n-dimensional vector space is not unlike the space of all n-tuples of scalars, a fact which we later prove. We shall make repeated use of this interpretation of a basis as a coordinate system for υ.

EXAMPLES OF BASES

(a) Consider the space of ordered pairs of real numbers, represented geometrically by the cartesian plane. The unit vectors (vectors of unit length along the chosen x and y axes) are $\epsilon_1 = (1, 0)$ and $\epsilon_2 = (0, 1)$, respectively. These two vectors form a basis since they are independent, and $(x, y) = x\epsilon_1 + y\epsilon_2$, so that ϵ_1 and ϵ_2 span the space. But also $\alpha_1 = (a, 0)$ and $\alpha_2 = (0, b)$ form a basis for any a and b different from zero. Furthermore, $\beta_1 = (1, 1)$

and $\beta_2 = (-2, 1)$ form a basis.   As shown in Figure 2.4, any pair of vectors which do not lie on the same line forms a basis for the plane.

(b) More generally for the space of all real n-tuples, let ϵ_i be the n-tuple whose i^{th} component is 1, the other components being zero, $i = 1, 2, \ldots, n$. The ϵ_i are linearly independent, and $(a_1, \ldots, a_n) = a_1\epsilon_1 + \ldots + a_n\epsilon_n$, so the ϵ_i form a basis.   Throughout this book we shall reserve the symbols ϵ_i to represent the vectors of this particular basis, and reserve the symbol $\mathcal{E}_n$ to represent the space of real n-tuples with this choice of basis.

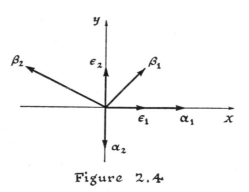

Figure 2.4

(c) Consider the space of all real polynomials of degree not exceeding a fixed natural number n.   Then $x^0 = 1, x^1, \ldots, x^n$ form a basis.

(d) An example of an infinite-dimensional space is the space of all real polynomials.   Each polynomial is of finite degree but we include *all* finite degrees.   The polynomials x^k, $k = 0, 1, 2, \ldots$, form a basis.

We have seen that any vector space has many bases; however, every basis has the important property stated in the following theorem.

Theorem 2.10.   Every basis for a finite-dimensional vector space $\mathcal{V}$ has the same number of elements

PROOF: Let $A = \{\alpha_1, \ldots, \alpha_k\}$ and $B = \{\beta_1, \ldots, \beta_m\}$ be bases for $\mathcal{V}$. Each set is a maximal independent set, so $B_1 = \{\alpha_1, \beta_1, \beta_2, \ldots, \beta_m\}$ is dependent.   By Theorem 2.7 some β_i is a linear combination of the vectors which precede it, and there exists a subset B_1' of B_1 which contains α_1 as the first vector and which is a basis for $\mathcal{V}$.   Then $B_2 = \{\alpha_2, B_1'\}$ is dependent, and some vector is a linear combination of the ones which precede it.   This vector cannot be α_1 or α_2 since A is linearly independent.   Hence there exists a subset B_2' of B_2 which contains α_2 and α_1 as the first and second vectors and which is a basis for $\mathcal{V}$.   Let $B_3 = \{\alpha_3, B_2'\}$ and repeat the argument.   If all the β_i are removed in this way before k steps, we obtain the basis $B_j = \{\alpha_j, \alpha_{j-1}, \ldots, \alpha_1\}$ for $j < k$, which contradicts the independence of A since $\alpha_k \in [B_j]$.   Hence at least k steps are required to remove all the β_i.   Hence $k \leq m$.   Reversing the roles of A and B in the replacement process, we obtain $m \leq k$, so the proof is complete.

Exercises

1. Verify that the several sets described in Examples (a)–(d) of this section are bases.

2. Let $\{\alpha_1, \ldots, \alpha_n\}$ be a basis for $\mathcal{V}$, and let c_i be arbitrary non-zero scalars, $i = 1, 2, \ldots, n$. Prove that $\{c_1\alpha_1, c_2\alpha_2, \ldots, c_n\alpha_n\}$ is a basis for $\mathcal{V}$. Interpret geometrically for $n = 3$.

3. Show that any three points which do not lie in a plane through the origin determine a basis for three-dimensional space.

4. Beginning with $\alpha_1 = (-1, 1, 2)$, construct two bases for the space of all real triples in such a way that if $\{\alpha_1, \alpha_2, \alpha_3\}$ and $\{\alpha_1, \alpha_2', \alpha_3',\}$ are the two bases then also $\{\alpha_2, \alpha_3, \alpha_3'\}$ is a basis.

5. Given the basis $\alpha_1 = (1, 1, 1, 1)$, $\alpha_2 = (0, 1, 1, 1)$, $\alpha_3 = (0, 0, 1, 1)$, $\alpha_4 = (0, 0, 0, 1)$, express each vector ϵ_i, $i = 1, 2, 3, 4$, as a linear combination of the α's. Likewise express each α_i as a linear combination of the ϵ's.

6. Let $\{\alpha_1, \ldots, \alpha_n\}$ and $\{\beta_1, \ldots, \beta_n\}$ be two bases for the space of all real n-tuples. Define the mapping $\mathbf{T}$ of the space into itself by the statement,

$$\text{if } \xi = \sum_{i=1}^{n} c_i\alpha_i, \text{ then } \xi\mathbf{T} = \sum_{i=1}^{n} c_i\beta_i.$$

Verify that

  (i) $\mathbf{T}$ maps α_i onto β_i, $i = 1, \ldots, n,$
  (ii) $\mathbf{T}$ is a one-to-one mapping,
  (iii) $(\xi + \eta)\mathbf{T} = \xi\mathbf{T} + \eta\mathbf{T},$
  (iv) $(k\xi)\mathbf{T} = k(\xi\mathbf{T}).$

§2.6. *Dimension*

Now that the number of elements in any basis for $\mathcal{V}$ has been shown to be unique, we use this number as a definition of the dimension of a vector space.

Definition 2.9. The *dimension* of a finite-dimensional vector space is the number of vectors in any basis. The dimension of $\mathcal{V}$ is denoted $d(\mathcal{V})$.

By definition, a set of vectors is a basis of $\mathcal{V}$ if and only if two conditions are satisfied:

the set must be linearly independent, *and*
the set must span $\mathcal{V}$.

However, for an n-dimensional space and a set of n vectors, these two conditions turn out to be equivalent. This result (Theorem 2.12) simplifies the

task of verifying that a given set is a basis.   We first prove another useful
theorem.

Theorem 2.11.   Any linearly independent set of vectors in an n-dimen-
sional space $\mathcal{V}$ can be extended to a basis.

P R O O F :   Let $\{\alpha_1, \ldots, \alpha_k\}$ be linearly independent, and let $\{\beta_1, \ldots, \beta_n\}$
be   a   basis.   Let $\mathfrak{I}_k = [\alpha_1, \ldots, \alpha_k]$.   If $\beta_i \in \mathfrak{I}_k$ for $i = 1, \ldots, n$,
then $\mathfrak{I}_k = \mathcal{V}$.   Otherwise   for   some j, $\beta_j \not\subset \mathfrak{I}_k$ so   by   Theorem   2.6
$\{\alpha_1, \ldots, \alpha_k, \beta_j\}$ is independent.   Thus the original set has been ex-
tended to a larger independent set, and the theorem follows by repeating
the argument until the enlarged set spans $\mathcal{V}$.

Theorem 2.12.   Let $A = \{\alpha_1, \ldots, \alpha_n\}$ be an arbitrary set of n vectors
of an n-dimensional space $\mathcal{V}$.
(a) A is a basis for $\mathcal{V}$ if and only if A is linearly independent.
(b) A is a basis for $\mathcal{V}$ if and only if $[A] = \mathcal{V}$.

P R O O F :   If A is linearly independent, A may be extended to a basis by
Theorem 2.11.   But a basis contains only n vectors, so A is a basis.   To
prove the second statement, suppose $\mathcal{V} = [A]$.   By Theorem 2.8 a
linearly independent subset of A also spans $\mathcal{V}$ and hence is a basis.   But
any basis contains n vectors, so A itself must be that subset.   The
"only if" statements of (a) and (b) are valid by the definition of a basis.

If $\mathcal{S}$ and $\mathfrak{I}$ are subspaces of $\mathcal{V}$, what can be said about the dimensions of
the spaces $\mathcal{S} + \mathfrak{I}$ and $\mathcal{S} \cap \mathfrak{I}$ (§ 2.3)?   A partial answer is available.

Theorem 2.13. $d(\mathcal{S} + \mathfrak{I}) + d(\mathcal{S} \cap \mathfrak{I}) = d(\mathcal{S}) + d(\mathfrak{I})$.
P R O O F :   Of the four subspaces involved in this theorem, $\mathcal{S} \cap \mathfrak{I}$ is a
subspace of each of the others, and both $\mathcal{S}$ and $\mathfrak{I}$ are subspaces of $\mathcal{S} + \mathfrak{I}$.
Our proof begins with the choice of a basis $\{\alpha_1, \ldots, \alpha_k\}$ for $\mathcal{S} \cap \mathfrak{I}$, where
$k = d(\mathcal{S} \cap \mathfrak{I})$.   Then $d(\mathcal{S}) = k + i$ and $d(\mathfrak{I}) = k + j$ for some non-
negative i and j.   The basis for $\mathcal{S} \cap \mathfrak{I}$ can be extended to a basis
$\{\alpha_1, \ldots, \alpha_k, \beta_{k+1}, \ldots, \beta_{k+i}\}$ for $\mathcal{S}$.   A different extension similarly produces a basis $\{\alpha_1, \ldots, \alpha_k, \gamma_{k+1}, \ldots, \gamma_{k+j}\}$ for $\mathfrak{I}$.   Combining these two
bases gives a set $\{\alpha_1, \ldots, \alpha_k, \beta_{k+1}, \ldots, \beta_{k+i}, \gamma_{k+1}, \ldots, \gamma_{k+j}\}$ of $k + i + j$
vectors.   The theorem follows immediately when it is proved that this
set is a basis for $\mathcal{S} + \mathfrak{I}$, which is left as an exercise.   (Remember that
since the dimension of $\mathcal{S} + \mathfrak{I}$ is not yet known to be $k + i + j$, it must
be shown that this set is linearly independent *and* spans $\mathcal{S} + \mathfrak{I}$.)

It should be noticed that Theorem 2.13 is similar in form to Exercise 10 of
§ 1.2, concerning the number of elements in the union and intersection of

finite sets. In geometric terms, Theorem 2.13 proves, for example, that in three-dimensional space any two distinct planes through the origin intersect in a line through the origin.

Exercises

1. Prove Theorem 2.13 in detail.

2. Determine the dimension of each of the five spaces given as examples in § 2.2.

3. Show that if subspaces $\Re$ and $\S$ have the same dimension and if $\Re \subseteq \S$, then $\Re = \S$.

4. Let $\S$ be a k-dimensional proper subspace of the n-dimensional space $\mathcal{V}$.

(i) Show that an $(n - k)$-dimensional subspace $\mathfrak{I}$ exists such that $\S \cap \mathfrak{I} = [\theta]$.

(ii) Deduce that $\S + \mathfrak{I} = \mathcal{V}$ and that every $\xi \in \mathcal{V}$ has a *unique* representation $\xi = \sigma + \tau$, where $\sigma \in \S$ and $\tau \in \mathfrak{I}$.

(iii) Show that $\mathfrak{I}$ is *not* uniquely determined by $\S$ and $\mathcal{V}$.

5. (i) Referring to Exercise 6, § 2.3, if necessary, prove that for subspaces $\Re$, $\S$, $\mathfrak{I}$ of $\mathcal{V}$ $d(\Re + \S + \mathfrak{I}) \leq d(\Re) + d(\S) + d(\mathfrak{I}) - d(\Re \cap \S) - d(\Re \cap \mathfrak{I}) - d(\S \cap \mathfrak{I}) + d(\Re \cap \S \cap \mathfrak{I})$.

(ii) Compare (i) with the corresponding formula for the number of elements in finite subsets (Exercise 10(ii), § 1.2).

(iii) Show that the result of (i) cannot be strengthened to equality in all cases (Exercise 6, § 2.3).

§2.7. *Isomorphism of Vector Spaces*

We now turn our attention to a problem which has been constantly in the background of our development of vector spaces. We began by making an informal description of the spaces $\mathcal{E}_2$ and $\mathcal{E}_3$, which were familiar from our knowledge of analytic geometry, and then generalized the form of our observations in order to define an abstract vector space. Abstract vector spaces are of two types—finite-dimensional or infinite-dimensional—and we agreed that we shall study only finite-dimensional spaces in this book. But in considering bases we began to suspect that any n-dimensional space over a field is essentially the same as the space of n-tuples of field elements; with a special choice of basis we called this space $\mathcal{E}_n$.

In order to formulate our suspicions more precisely, we must first agree upon a meaning of the phrase "essentially the same." This is a problem of importance for all abstract systems, but we confine our attention here to vector spaces; a more general discussion is given in Appendix A, § A.6.

Consider two vector spaces,

$$\mathcal{V} = \{V, F; +, \cdot, \oplus, \odot\}$$

and

$$\mathcal{W} = \{W, F; +, \cdot, +, \bullet\},$$

over the same field $\mathcal{F}$. The vectors of the two systems might have different mathematical names, as suggested by the various examples of vector spaces given in § 2.2, and the vector operations of the two systems might be defined in different ways. However, suppose we can rename the vectors of the first system, assigning to each vector of the first system the name of a vector of the second system, with different names being given to distinct vectors. Suppose further that the new names are assigned in such a way that the vector operations of the renamed first system coincide exactly with the corresponding operations of the second system. Then we would agree that the two systems are identical twins which are distinguishable by name only, and not by behavior. This is what we mean by "essentially the same"; the mathematical term for this concept is *isomorphism*. We first define the more general notion of *homomorphism*.

Definition 2.10. Let

$$\mathcal{V} = \{V, F; +, \cdot, \oplus, \odot\}$$

and

$$\mathcal{W} = \{W, F; +, \cdot, +, \bullet\}$$

be vector spaces over a field $\mathcal{F}$. A mapping $\mathbf{H}$ of $\mathcal{V}$ into $\mathcal{W}$ is called a *homomorphism*, provided that for all $\alpha, \beta \in \mathcal{V}$ and all $a \in \mathcal{J}$,

$$(\alpha \oplus \beta)\mathbf{H} = \alpha\mathbf{H} + \beta\mathbf{H},$$

and

$$(a \odot \alpha)\mathbf{H} = a \bullet \alpha\mathbf{H}.$$

If every vector of $\mathcal{W}$ is in the range of $\mathbf{H}$, $\mathbf{H}$ is said to be a *homomorphism* of $\mathcal{V}$ *onto* $\mathcal{W}$.

Definition 2.11. A *one-to-one* homomorphism $\mathbf{J}$ of $\mathcal{V}$ onto $\mathcal{W}$ is called an *isomorphism*. If such a mapping exists, $\mathcal{V}$ and $\mathcal{W}$ are said to be *isomorphic*.

Thus to establish that two vector spaces $\mathcal{V}$ and $\mathcal{W}$ over the same field $\mathcal{F}$ are isomorphic, we need to exhibit a one-to-one mapping of $\mathcal{V}$ onto $\mathcal{W}$ which preserves the two operations of vector sum and multiplication of a vector by a scalar. We are now ready to prove the following theorem.

Theorem 2.14.   Any n-dimensional vector space $\mathcal{V}$ over $\mathcal{F}$ is isomorphic to the space $\mathcal{E}_n$ of all n-tuples of elements of $\mathcal{F}$.

P R O O F :   Let $\{\alpha_1, \ldots, \alpha_n\}$ be a basis for $\mathcal{V}$. By Theorem 2.9 every $\xi \in \mathcal{V}$ has a unique representation as a linear combination of the α_i,

$$\xi = c_1\alpha_1 + \ldots + c_n\alpha_n.$$

To each $\xi \in \mathcal{V}$ we associate the corresponding n-tuple $(c_1, \ldots, c_n) \in \mathcal{E}_n$. This is a mapping of $\mathcal{V}$ onto $\mathcal{E}_n$, and distinct vectors of $\mathcal{V}$ map into distinct vectors of $\mathcal{E}_n$. Furthermore, let $\xi = \sum_{i=1}^{n} c_i\alpha_i$ and $\eta = \sum_{i=1}^{n} b_i\alpha_i$. Then

$$\xi + \eta = \sum_{i=1}^{n} (c_i + b_i)\alpha_i \longrightarrow (c_1 + b_1, \ldots, c_n + b_n)$$

$$= (c_1, \ldots, c_n) + (b_1, \ldots, b_n),$$

and

$$k\xi = \sum_{i=1}^{n} (kc_i)\alpha_i \longrightarrow (kc_1, \ldots, kc_n) = k(c_1, \ldots, c_n).$$

Hence vector sum and scalar multiplication are preserved by the mapping, and the systems are isomorphic.

This result tells us that any two vector spaces of the same finite dimension n are isomorphic, since each is isomorphic to $\mathcal{E}_n$. (See Exercise 4, below.) It allows us to think of any such abstract space in terms of the more familiar space of n-tuples. The preferred basis $\{\epsilon_1, \ldots, \epsilon_n\}$ of $\mathcal{E}_n$ plays no role at all in this isomorphism; therefore we shall denote by $\mathcal{V}_n$ a vector space of dimension n with an arbitrary basis.

The isomorphism theorem suggests that for finite-dimensional spaces our attempt to obtain generality by giving an abstract definition of vector spaces was not wholly successful. Any n-dimensional space over $\mathcal{F}$ is isomorphic to the space of n-tuples of elements of $\mathcal{F}$; in particular, $\mathcal{E}_n$ is a prototype of all spaces of dimension n. However, it is usually quite inconvenient to work with a prescribed basis, and many of our later results will be concerned with geometric properties which are valid in any coordinate system. Also, the n-tuple notation is often unnecessarily cumbersome. Hence we prefer to use the general notation for vectors, remembering that we can represent vectors as n-tuples of field elements, without loss of generality, whenever that particular representation proves to be convenient.

Exercises

1. Establish an isomorphism between the space of all polynomials of degree not exceeding n and the space $\mathcal{E}_{n+1}$. What are the images of the basis vectors under the isomorphism?

2. Let $\mathbf{J}$ be an isomorphism of the spaces $\mathcal{V}_n$ and $\mathcal{W}_n$. Let $\{\alpha_1, \ldots, \alpha_k\}$ be a linearly independent set of vectors in $\mathcal{V}_n$, $k \leq n$. Prove that $\{\alpha_1\mathbf{J}, \ldots, \alpha_k\mathbf{J}\}$ is linearly independent in $\mathcal{W}_n$.   Deduce that the isomorphic image of a basis is a basis.

3. Let $\mathbf{H}$ be a homomorphism of $\mathcal{V}_n$ into $\mathcal{W}_n$.   Prove that $\mathbf{H}$ is an isomorphism if and only if, for every $\xi \neq \theta$ in $\mathcal{V}_n$, $\xi\mathbf{H} \neq \theta$ in $\mathcal{W}_n$.

4. Suppose that vector spaces $\mathcal{V}$ and $\mathcal{W}$ are both isomorphic to the same space $\mathcal{U}$.   Show how these two isomorphisms can be combined to yield an isomorphism of $\mathcal{V}$ onto $\mathcal{W}$.

CHAPTER 3

Linear Transformations

§3.1. *Homomorphisms of Vector Spaces*

A study of vector spaces can be extended beyond the preliminary investigations of the preceding chapter, and we shall develop further theory as it is needed. For the present, however, we turn our attention from the spaces themselves to the subject of homomorphisms of vector spaces. In this chapter and the next we shall see that such homomorphisms are intimately related to matrices.

We assume that $\mathcal{V}$ and $\mathcal{W}$ are vector spaces over the same field $\mathcal{F}$. From Definition 2.10, a homomorphism of $\mathcal{V}$ into $\mathcal{W}$ is a mapping $\mathbf{H}$ which preserves the two operations involving vectors; that is, for all $\alpha, \beta \in \mathcal{V}$, $a \in \mathcal{F}$, the following equations hold in $\mathcal{W}$:

1. $(\alpha + \beta)\mathbf{H} = \alpha\mathbf{H} + \beta\mathbf{H}$,
2. $(a\alpha)\mathbf{H} = a(\alpha\mathbf{H})$.

We now show that equations 1 and 2 can be replaced by the single condition

3. $(a\alpha + b\beta)\mathbf{H} = a(\alpha\mathbf{H}) + b(\beta\mathbf{H})$.

Clearly, equation 1 follows from equation 3 by selecting $a = 1 = b$, and equation 2 follows by choosing $b = 0$. Conversely,

$$(a\alpha + b\beta)\mathbf{H} = (a\alpha)\mathbf{H} + (b\beta)\mathbf{H}$$

by equation 1, which then reduces to $a(\alpha\mathbf{H}) + b(\beta\mathbf{H})$ by equation 2.

Condition 3 is the requirement of linearity, and since a homomorphism is a mapping, it is reasonable to use geometric language to describe mappings. Henceforth we shall call such a homomorphism a *linear transformation*.

Definition 3.1. A *linear transformation* $\mathbf{T}$ from a vector space $\mathcal{V}$ to a vector space $\mathcal{W}$, both over the scalar field $\mathcal{F}$, is a mapping of $\mathcal{V}$ into $\mathcal{W}$ such that for all $\alpha, \beta \in \mathcal{V}$ and for all $a, b \in \mathcal{F}$,

$$(a\alpha + b\beta)\mathbf{T} = a(\alpha\mathbf{T}) + b(\beta\mathbf{T}).$$

This definition is stated more elegantly in the form "a linear transformation from $\mathcal{U}$ to $\mathcal{W}$ is a homomorphism of $\mathcal{U}$ into $\mathcal{W}$." We remark that either form of the definition includes the possibility that $\mathcal{W}$ and $\mathcal{U}$ are the same space.

Before proceeding we call attention to our choice of notation for linear transformations, which will have important consequences for the notation which we later adopt for matrices. Since a linear transformation $\mathbf{T}$ is a function from $\mathcal{U}$ to $\mathcal{W}$ we could use standard functional notation in which $\mathbf{T}(\alpha)$ represents the "value" of the function $\mathbf{T}$ at the vector α. But, as we observed in § 1.3, if we wish to emphasize the geometric character of $\mathbf{T}$ as a mapping, and particularly if successive mapping (function of a function) is considered often, the notation $\alpha\mathbf{T}$ is a useful substitute for $\mathbf{T}(\alpha)$. In this respect the notation for linear transformations is not standardized, and you are advised when consulting other books to ascertain whether the author uses $\mathbf{T}(\alpha)$ (left hand notation) or $\alpha\mathbf{T}$ (right hand notation) for linear transformations and matrices. Right hand notation is used in this book.

We shall regard linear transformations as the elements of an abstract system whose nature is to be investigated. First we need to decide upon the relations and operations of the system. Since linear transformations are functions, we accept the notion of equality of functions as a definition of equality of linear transformations.

Definition 3.2. Two linear transformations $\mathbf{T}_1$ and $\mathbf{T}_2$ from $\mathcal{U}$ to $\mathcal{W}$ are said to be *equal* if and only if $\alpha\mathbf{T}_1 = \alpha\mathbf{T}_2$ for all $\alpha \in \mathcal{U}$.

This means that equal transformations determine the same mapping of the vectors of $\mathcal{U}$ into vectors of $\mathcal{W}$, and that a linear transformation is determined by its effect on the vectors of $\mathcal{U}$. We use this method of description to define operations on linear transformations.

Definition 3.3. The *sum* $\mathbf{T}_1 \oplus \mathbf{T}_2$ and *scalar multiple* $c \odot \mathbf{T}_1$ of linear transformations from $\mathcal{U}$ to $\mathcal{W}$ are defined, respectively, by
(a) $\alpha(\mathbf{T}_1 \oplus \mathbf{T}_2) = \alpha\mathbf{T}_1 + \alpha\mathbf{T}_2$, all $\alpha \in \mathcal{U}$,
(b) $\alpha(c \odot \mathbf{T}_1) = c(\alpha\mathbf{T}_1)$, all $\alpha \in \mathcal{U}$, $c \in \mathcal{F}$.
If $\mathbf{T}_1$ is a linear transformation from $\mathcal{U}$ to $\mathcal{W}$ and $\mathbf{T}_2$ is a linear transformation from $\mathcal{W}$ to $\mathcal{Y}$, then the linear transformation $\mathbf{T}_1 \square \mathbf{T}_2$ from $\mathcal{U}$ to $\mathcal{Y}$ is defined by the successive mapping
(c) $\alpha(\mathbf{T}_1 \square \mathbf{T}_2) = (\alpha\mathbf{T}_1)\mathbf{T}_2$, all $\alpha \in \mathcal{U}$.

Therefore, for the set of linear transformations which map $\mathcal{U}$ *into itself* there are three well-defined operations:

Sum:	$\mathbf{T}_1 \oplus \mathbf{T}_2,$
Scalar multiple:	$c \odot \mathbf{T}_1,$
Product:	$\mathbf{T}_1 \boxdot \mathbf{T}_2.$

It may be verified that the set of all linear transformations from $\mathcal{V}$ into $\mathcal{V}$ is closed under these operations; that is, the resulting transformation is *linear* in each case.

Several special linear transformations merit our attention. The *zero* linear transformation $\mathbf{Z}$ is defined by

$$\alpha \mathbf{Z} = \theta \text{ for every } \alpha \in \mathcal{V}.$$

The *identity* linear transformation $\mathbf{I}$ is defined by

$$\alpha \mathbf{I} = \alpha \text{ for every } \alpha \in \mathcal{V}.$$

Corresponding to each linear transformation $\mathbf{T}$ there is the *negative* linear transformation, denoted $-\mathbf{T}$ and defined by

$$\alpha(-\mathbf{T}) = -\alpha \mathbf{T}.$$

You should verify that these names are justified; that is, that

$$\mathbf{T} \oplus \mathbf{Z} = \mathbf{T} \text{ for every } \mathbf{T},$$
$$\mathbf{T} \boxdot \mathbf{I} = \mathbf{I} \boxdot \mathbf{T} = \mathbf{T} \text{ for every } \mathbf{T},$$
$$\mathbf{T} \oplus -\mathbf{T} = \mathbf{Z} \text{ for every } \mathbf{T}.$$

Once again we simplify our notation by using customary symbols for the operations on linear transformations.

EXAMPLES OF LINEAR TRANSFORMATIONS

(a) The space $\mathcal{E}_2$ of pairs of real numbers is represented geometrically by the plane. The transformation defined by $(x, y)\mathbf{T} = (kx, ky)$ for fixed scalar k is a linear transformation which maps each point P into the point Q which is collinear with P and the origin and k times as far from the origin as P is.

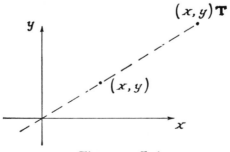

Figure 3.1

(b) Again in $\mathcal{E}_2$, the transformation defined by

$$(x, y)\mathbf{T} = (x \cos \Psi - y \sin \Psi, \, x \sin \Psi + y \cos \Psi)$$

is a linear transformation which rotates each point of the plane about the origin and through the angle Ψ.

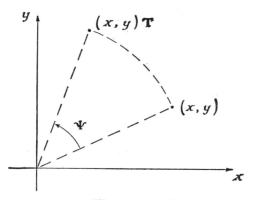

Figure 3.2

(c) In $\mathcal{E}_2$ let $\mathbf{T}_1$, $\mathbf{T}_2$, and $\mathbf{T}_3$ be defined by

$$(x, y)\mathbf{T}_1 = (x, 0),$$
$$(x, y)\mathbf{T}_2 = (0, y),$$
$$(x, y)\mathbf{T}_3 = (y, x).$$

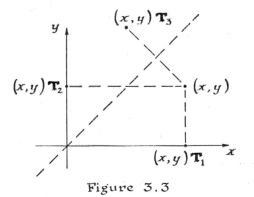

Figure 3.3

All of these transformations are linear. $\mathbf{T}_1$ is a projection of each point of the plane onto the x axis; $\mathbf{T}_2$ is a projection onto the y axis; $\mathbf{T}_3$ is a reflection across the line $y = x$. Observe that $(x, y)\mathbf{T}_1\mathbf{T}_2 = (x, 0)\mathbf{T}_2 = (0, 0)$, so $\mathbf{T}_1\mathbf{T}_2 = \mathbf{Z}$ but $\mathbf{T}_1 \neq \mathbf{Z}$ and $\mathbf{T}_2 \neq \mathbf{Z}$. Hence *a product of non-zero transformations can be the zero transformation.* Also, $(x, y)\mathbf{T}_2\mathbf{T}_3 = (0, y)\mathbf{T}_3 = (y, 0)$; however, $(x, y)\mathbf{T}_3\mathbf{T}_2 = (y, x)\mathbf{T}_2 = (0, x)$. Hence $\mathbf{T}_2\mathbf{T}_3 \neq \mathbf{T}_3\mathbf{T}_2$, so the *multiplication of transformations is not commutative.* Finally, observe that $(x, y)\mathbf{T}_1\mathbf{T}_1 = (x, 0)\mathbf{T}_1 = (x, 0) = (x, y)\mathbf{T}_1$, so that $\mathbf{T}_1{}^2 = \mathbf{T}_1$. Thus *there exist idempotent transformations* other than $\mathbf{I}$ and $\mathbf{Z}$.

(d) In the space of polynomials P_m of degree $m \leq n$, let

$$P_m(x)\mathbf{D} = \frac{d}{dx}P_m(x).$$

Familiar properties of the derivative show that $\mathbf{D}$ is linear. Observe also that $P(x)\mathbf{D}^{n+1} = 0$ for every polynomial in the space, so $\mathbf{D}^{n+1} = \mathbf{Z}$. Thus *there exist non-zero transformations* $\mathbf{T}$ *such that a finite power of* $\mathbf{T}$ *is* $\mathbf{Z}$. A transformation $\mathbf{T}$ is called *nilpotent of index* k if $\mathbf{T}^k = \mathbf{Z}$ but $\mathbf{T}^{k-1} \neq \mathbf{Z}$.

Exercises

1. Prove that the sum, product, and scalar multiple of linear transformations are all linear.

2. Show that the transformations $\mathbf{Z}$, $\mathbf{I}$, and $-\mathbf{T}$ are entitled to the names zero, identity, and negative.

3. Verify that each transformation listed in Examples (a)–(d) is linear.

4. Prove that $\theta\mathbf{T} = \theta$ for any linear transformation $\mathbf{T}$.

5. If we regard the complex numbers as a vector space [Example (c), § 2.2], is the conjugate mapping, $(a + ib)\mathbf{T} = a - ib$, a linear transformation?

6. Let $\mathbf{T}$ be a linear transformation of $\mathcal{U}$ into $\mathcal{W}$.

(i) Show that any subspace of $\mathcal{U}$ is mapped by $\mathbf{T}$ into a subspace of $\mathcal{W}$.

(ii) Conversely, show that if $\mathcal{Y}$ is a subspace of $\mathcal{W}$, the set of all vectors mapped into $\mathcal{Y}$ is a subspace of $\mathcal{U}$.

7. (i) Show that the effect of a linear transformation $\mathbf{T}$ from $\mathcal{U}$ to $\mathcal{W}$ is determined by the effect of $\mathbf{T}$ on any basis of $\mathcal{U}$.

(ii) Conversely, let $\{\alpha_1, \ldots, \alpha_n\}$ be a basis of $\mathcal{U}$ and let $\{\beta_1, \ldots, \beta_n\}$ be any set of n vectors in $\mathcal{W}$. Show how the correspondence $\alpha_i \longrightarrow \beta_i$ can be used to define a linear transformation from all of $\mathcal{U}$ into $\mathcal{W}$.

8. Which of the following transformations on $\mathcal{E}_3$ are linear? Describe the geometric effect of each.

(i) $(a_1, a_2, a_3)\mathbf{T} = (a_1 + 1, a_2 + 1, 0)$,

(ii) $(a_1, a_2, a_3)\mathbf{T} = (a_2, a_1, a_3)$,

(iii) $(a_1, a_2, a_3)\mathbf{T} = (a_1, a_2, 1)$,

(iv) $(a_1, a_2, a_3)\mathbf{T} = (a_1, -a_2, -a_3)$.

9. Consider the system $\mathcal{L} = \{L, F; +, \cdot, \oplus, \odot\}$ where L is the set of all linear transformations from a vector space $\mathcal{U}$ to a space $\mathcal{W}$ and where the special symbols refer to sum and scalar multiple of linear transformations. Verify that $\mathcal{L}$ is a vector space over $\mathcal{F}$.

10. In the space of all polynomials P of all degrees define mappings $\mathbf{M}$ and $\mathbf{D}$ by

$$P(x)\mathbf{D} = \frac{d}{dx}\,P(x),$$

$$P(x)\mathbf{M} = xP(x).$$

(i) Prove that both $\mathbf{D}$ and $\mathbf{M}$ are linear transformations.

(ii) Is $\mathbf{D}$ nilpotent on this space? Compare with $\mathbf{D}$ in Example (d).

(iii) Prove that $\mathbf{MD} - \mathbf{DM} = \mathbf{I}$.

(iv) Deduce that $(\mathbf{DM})^2 = \mathbf{D}^2\mathbf{M}^2 + \mathbf{DM}$.

§3.2. *Linear Algebras*

We now consider the system $\mathcal{L}$ of all linear transformations of a vector space $\mathcal{V}$ into itself. The two operations, sum and scalar multiple, are similar to the vector operations of an abstract vector space, and indeed the system $\mathcal{L} = \{L, F; +, \cdot, \oplus, \odot\}$ is a vector space over $\mathcal{F}$ (Exercise 9, § 3.1). The "vectors" of the space $\mathcal{L}$ are linear mappings of the space $\mathcal{V}$ into itself. But because there is a third operation, the product of mappings, defined for the "vectors" of this space, $\mathcal{L}$ forms a system which is called a *linear algebra*.

Definition 3.4. A *linear algebra* $\mathcal{L}$ over a field $\mathcal{F}$ is a system

$$\mathcal{L} = \{L, F; +, \cdot, \oplus, \odot, \boxdot\}$$

which satisfies the postulates:

(a) the system $\{L, F; +, \cdot, \oplus, \odot\}$ is a vector space over $\mathcal{F}$,

(b) $\boxdot$ is a binary operation on $\mathcal{L}$ which is closed, associative, and bilinear.

This second postulate requires elaboration, but first we agree to dispense with the special notation. Then (b) simply asserts that for all a, $b \in \mathcal{F}$ and all $\mathbf{T}_1$, $\mathbf{T}_2$, $\mathbf{T}_3 \in \mathcal{L}$,

Closed: $\mathbf{T}_1\mathbf{T}_2 \in \mathcal{L}$,

Associative: $\mathbf{T}_1(\mathbf{T}_2\mathbf{T}_3) = (\mathbf{T}_1\mathbf{T}_2)\mathbf{T}_3$,

Bilinear: $\begin{cases} \mathbf{T}_1(a\mathbf{T}_2 + b\mathbf{T}_3) = a\mathbf{T}_1\mathbf{T}_2 + b\mathbf{T}_1\mathbf{T}_3, \\ (a\mathbf{T}_2 + b\mathbf{T}_3)\mathbf{T}_1 = a\mathbf{T}_2\mathbf{T}_1 + b\mathbf{T}_3\mathbf{T}_1. \end{cases}$

The *dimension* of $\mathcal{L}$ is defined to be its dimension as a vector space.

Theorem 3.1. The system $\mathcal{L}$ of all linear transformations on the vector space $\mathcal{V}_n$ over a field $\mathcal{F}$ is a linear algebra over $\mathcal{F}$ of dimension n^2.

P R O O F :   In exercises we have verified that $\mathcal{L}$ is a vector space over $\mathcal{F}$

and that the product of linear transformations is linear, so we need consider only the properties of products of transformations.   Since "product" here means successive mapping,

$$\alpha[\mathbf{T}_1(\mathbf{T}_2\mathbf{T}_3)] = (\alpha\mathbf{T}_1)(\mathbf{T}_2\mathbf{T}_3)$$
$$= (\alpha\mathbf{T}_1\mathbf{T}_2)\mathbf{T}_3$$
$$= [\alpha(\mathbf{T}_1\mathbf{T}_2)\mathbf{T}_3]$$
$$= \alpha[(\mathbf{T}_1\mathbf{T}_2)\mathbf{T}_3].$$

Also,

$$\alpha[\mathbf{T}_1(a\mathbf{T}_2 + b\mathbf{T}_3)] = (\alpha\mathbf{T}_1)(a\mathbf{T}_2 + b\mathbf{T}_3)$$
$$= (\alpha\mathbf{T}_1)(a\mathbf{T}_2) + (\alpha\mathbf{T}_1)(b\mathbf{T}_3)$$
$$= a(\alpha\mathbf{T}_1)\mathbf{T}_2 + b(\alpha\mathbf{T}_1)\mathbf{T}_3$$
$$= a(\alpha\mathbf{T}_1\mathbf{T}_2) + b(\alpha\mathbf{T}_1\mathbf{T}_3)$$
$$= \alpha(a\mathbf{T}_1\mathbf{T}_2) + \alpha(b\mathbf{T}_1\mathbf{T}_3)$$
$$= \alpha(a\mathbf{T}_1\mathbf{T}_2 + b\mathbf{T}_1\mathbf{T}_3).$$

A similar calculation verifies the second condition of bilinearity.   Thus $\mathcal{L}$ is a linear algebra.   To prove that the dimension of $\mathcal{L}$ is n^2 we use Theorem 2.14 to represent $\mathcal{U}_n$ as n-tuples of elements of $\mathcal{F}$, and define the n^2 linear transformations $\mathbf{T}_{ij}$, where $i, j = 1, \ldots, n$, by

$$(x_1, \ldots, x_n)\mathbf{T}_{ij} = (0, \ldots, 0, x_i, 0, \ldots, 0)$$

where the jth component of the image vector is x_i, and all other components are zero.   It can be shown that the $\mathbf{T}_{ij}$ are linearly independent linear transformations which span $\mathcal{L}$.   However this fact is more readily seen in terms of matrices, so the completion of this proof is deferred until § 4.3.

One additional remark is of interest here.   An abstract linear algebra may or may not have an identity of multiplication.   However, it can be shown that *any* linear algebra with an identity and of dimension k is isomorphic to a subalgebra of the algebra of all linear transformations on $\mathcal{U}_k$.   This fact provides a concrete representation of any such abstract linear algebra and a striking illustration of the generality of linear transformations and their importance in linear algebra.

Exercises

1. Let $\mathcal{C}$ be a linear algebra over $\mathcal{F}$ and let $\{\alpha_1, \ldots, \alpha_m\}$ be a basis for $\mathcal{C}$. The product of any two elements of $\mathcal{C}$ is an element of $\mathcal{C}$ and hence is a

linear combination of the α_i. Hence each pair α_i, α_j of basis vectors determines m scalars c_{ijk}, $k = 1, \ldots, m$ such that

$$\alpha_i\alpha_j = \sum_{k=1}^{m} c_{ijk}\alpha_k, \text{ for all } i, j = 1, \ldots, m.$$

(i) Show that the product of any two elements of $\mathfrak{a}$ is determined
by the m^3 scalars c_{ijk}.

(ii) Find a necessary and sufficient condition on the scalars c_{ijk} that
the algebra be commutative ($\xi\eta = \eta\xi$ for all $\xi, \eta \in \mathfrak{a}$).

(iii) Show that any finite-dimensional vector space can be made into a
linear algebra by defining the trivial product in which $c_{ijk} = 0$ for all i, j, k.

2. An important example of a linear algebra of dimension four, given a
century ago by Hamilton, was a forerunner of the study of matrices. The
elements of the algebra are called *quaternions*, and the scalars are the real
numbers. In a notation similar to that of the complex numbers, a quaternion
is an expression of the form

$$a_1 1 + a_2 i + a_3 j + a_4 k.$$

Equality, sum, and scalar multiple are defined componentwise; quaternion
product is defined by bilinearity and the following multiplication table for
the basis elements, wherein the product xy appears in the row labeled x at the
left and in the column labeled y at the top:

	1	i	j	k
1	1	i	j	k
i	i	-1	k	$-j$
j	j	$-k$	-1	i
k	k	j	$-i$	-1 .

(i) Verify that this product is closed. All other postulates of a
linear algebra are also satisfied.

(ii) Show that every quaternion except $0 + 0i + 0j + 0k$ has an
inverse relative to this product; that is,

$$(a_1 + a_2 i + a_3 j + a_4 k)(b_1 + b_2 i + b_3 j + b_4 k) = 1 + 0i + 0j + 0k,$$

for suitable b_1, b_2, b_3, b_4.

(iii) Is the product commutative?

From this we conclude that the quaternions form a non-commutative
"division algebra." An important theorem of Frobenius proves that the
quaternions form the *only* non-commutative division algebra over the real
numbers.

§3.3. *Rank and Nullity of a Linear Transformation*

We recall that a linear transformation $\mathbf{T}$ is, by definition, a homomorphism from a space $\mathcal{U}$ into a space $\mathcal{W}$, where $\mathcal{U}$ and $\mathcal{W}$ may be the same space, but are not necessarily so. The domain of $\mathbf{T}$ is the space $\mathcal{U}$, and the range of $\mathbf{T}$ is a subset $\mathfrak{R}_\mathbf{T}$ of $\mathcal{W}$, the set of all images $\alpha\mathbf{T}$ of the vectors of $\mathcal{U}$:

$$\mathfrak{R}_\mathbf{T} = \{\beta \in \mathcal{W} |\, \beta = \alpha\mathbf{T} \text{ for some } \alpha \in \mathcal{U}\}.$$

It is easily proved that $\mathfrak{R}_\mathbf{T}$ is actually a *subspace* of $\mathcal{W}$, for if $\beta, \gamma \in \mathfrak{R}_\mathbf{T}$, then $\beta = \alpha_1\mathbf{T}$ and $\gamma = \alpha_2\mathbf{T}$. Hence $\beta + \gamma = \alpha_1\mathbf{T} + \alpha_2\mathbf{T} = (\alpha_1 + \alpha_2)\mathbf{T} \in \mathfrak{R}_\mathbf{T}$. Also for $c \in \mathfrak{F}$, $c\beta = c(\alpha_1\mathbf{T}) = (c\alpha_1)\mathbf{T} \in \mathfrak{R}_\mathbf{T}$. By Theorem 2.2, $\mathfrak{R}_\mathbf{T}$ is a subspace of $\mathcal{W}$.

Another important set associated with any vector space homomorphism $\mathbf{T}$ is the *kernel* $\mathfrak{N}_\mathbf{T}$ of the homomorphism, which is defined to be the set of all vectors in $\mathcal{U}$ which are mapped into θ:

$$\mathfrak{N}_\mathbf{T} = \{\alpha \in \mathcal{U} |\, \alpha\mathbf{T} = \theta\}.$$

To see that $\mathfrak{N}_\mathbf{T}$ is a subspace of $\mathcal{U}$, let $\alpha, \beta \in \mathfrak{N}_\mathbf{T}$, $c \in \mathfrak{F}$. Then $(\alpha + \beta)\mathbf{T} = \alpha\mathbf{T} + \beta\mathbf{T} = \theta + \theta = \theta$, so $\alpha + \beta \in \mathfrak{N}_\mathbf{T}$; also $(c\alpha)\mathbf{T} = c(\alpha\mathbf{T}) = c\theta = \theta$, so $c\alpha \in \mathfrak{N}_\mathbf{T}$. Thus $\mathfrak{N}_\mathbf{T}$ is a subspace of $\mathcal{U}$.

These two subspaces, $\mathfrak{R}_\mathbf{T}$ and $\mathfrak{N}_\mathbf{T}$, called, respectively, the *range space* of $\mathbf{T}$ and the *null space* of $\mathbf{T}$, are of major importance in the study of linear algebra, as are their dimensions.

Definition 3.5.
(a) The *range space* $\mathfrak{R}_\mathbf{T}$ of a linear transformation $\mathbf{T}$ is the set of all images $\alpha\mathbf{T} \in \mathcal{W}$ as α ranges over $\mathcal{U}$.
(b) The *rank* $\rho(\mathbf{T})$ of a linear transformation $\mathbf{T}$ is the dimension of its range space.

Definition 3.6.
(a) The *null space* $\mathfrak{N}_\mathbf{T}$ of a linear transformation $\mathbf{T}$ is the set of all vectors $\alpha \in \mathcal{U}$ for which $\alpha\mathbf{T} = \theta \in \mathcal{W}$.
(b) The *nullity* $\nu(\mathbf{T})$ of a linear transformation $\mathbf{T}$ is the dimension of its null space.

Theorem 3.2. If $\mathbf{T}$ is a linear transformation from $\mathcal{U}$ to $\mathcal{W}$ and if $\mathbf{S}$ is a linear transformation from $\mathcal{W}$ to $\mathcal{Y}$, then
(a) $\mathfrak{R}_\mathbf{TS} \subseteq \mathfrak{R}_\mathbf{S}$ and $\rho(\mathbf{TS}) \le \rho(\mathbf{S})$,
(b) $\mathfrak{N}_\mathbf{TS} \supseteq \mathfrak{N}_\mathbf{T}$ and $\nu(\mathbf{TS}) \ge \nu(\mathbf{T})$.
PROOF: Exercise.

Thus we see that each linear transformation $\mathbf{T}$ from $\mathcal{V}$ to $\mathcal{W}$ automatically selects a subspace $\mathfrak{N}_\mathbf{T}$ of $\mathcal{V}$ and a subspace $\mathfrak{R}_\mathbf{T}$ of $\mathcal{W}$. These two subspaces are related in an interesting manner, as indicated by the following theorem and its corollaries.

Theorem 3.3. Let $\{\alpha_1, \ldots, \alpha_{\nu(\mathbf{T})}\}$ be a basis for $\mathfrak{N}_\mathbf{T}$. Extend this basis to any basis $\{\alpha_1, \ldots, \alpha_{\nu(\mathbf{T})}, \alpha_{\nu(\mathbf{T})+1}, \ldots, \alpha_n\}$ for $\mathcal{V}_n$. Then $\{\alpha_{\nu(\mathbf{T})+1}\mathbf{T}, \ldots, \alpha_n\mathbf{T}\}$ is a basis for $\mathfrak{R}_\mathbf{T}$.

P R O O F : Let $\{\alpha_1, \ldots, \alpha_n\}$ be chosen as in the statement of the theorem. Any vector of $\mathfrak{R}_\mathbf{T}$ is of the form $\xi\mathbf{T}$ for some $\xi \in \mathcal{V}_n$. Let $\xi = \sum_{i=1}^n a_i\alpha_i$; then

$$\xi\mathbf{T} = \left(\sum_{i=1}^n a_i\alpha_i\right)\mathbf{T} = \sum_{i=1}^n a_i(\alpha_i\mathbf{T}) = \sum_{i=\nu(\mathbf{T})+1}^n a_i(\alpha_i\mathbf{T}),$$

since $\alpha_i\mathbf{T} = \theta$ for $i = 1, 2, \ldots, \nu(\mathbf{T})$. Hence $\{\alpha_{\nu(\mathbf{T})+1}\mathbf{T}, \ldots, \alpha_n\mathbf{T}\}$ spans $\mathfrak{R}_\mathbf{T}$. Since we do not know the dimension of $\mathfrak{R}_\mathbf{T}$ we must also prove linear independence. Suppose scalars b_i, not all zero, exist such that

$$\theta = \sum_{\nu(\mathbf{T})+1}^n b_i(\alpha_i\mathbf{T}) = \left(\sum_{\nu(\mathbf{T})+1}^n b_i\alpha_i\right)\mathbf{T}.$$

Then $\sum_{\nu(\mathbf{T})+1}^n b_i\alpha_i \in \mathfrak{N}_\mathbf{T}$; but $\{\alpha_1, \ldots, \alpha_{\nu(\mathbf{T})}\}$ spans $\mathfrak{N}_\mathbf{T}$, so for suitable scalars c_i,

$$\sum_{\nu(\mathbf{T})+1}^n b_i\alpha_i = \sum_1^{\nu(\mathbf{T})} c_i\alpha_i.$$

This contradicts the linear independence of $\{\alpha_1, \ldots, \alpha_n\}$, so the vectors $\{\alpha_{\nu(\mathbf{T})+1}\mathbf{T}, \ldots, \alpha_n\mathbf{T}\}$ are linearly independent and therefore form a basis for $\mathfrak{R}_\mathbf{T}$.

Theorem 3.4. If $\mathbf{T}$ is a linear transformation from $\mathcal{V}_n$ to $\mathcal{W}$, then $\rho(\mathbf{T}) + \nu(\mathbf{T}) = n$.

P R O O F : Exercise.

Now if we consider $\mathcal{W}$ and $\mathcal{V}_n$ to be the same space, then $\mathbf{T}, \mathbf{T}^2, \mathbf{T}^3, \ldots$ are all well defined transformations of $\mathcal{V}_n$ into itself. The corresponding range and null spaces form chains as indicated in the following result.

Theorem 3.5. If $\mathbf{T}$ is a linear transformation on $\mathcal{V}_n$, then
(a) $\mathcal{V}_n \supseteq \mathfrak{R}_\mathbf{T} \supseteq \mathfrak{R}_{\mathbf{T}^2} \supseteq \ldots \supseteq \mathfrak{R}_{\mathbf{T}^k} \supseteq \ldots,$
(b) $[\theta] \subseteq \mathfrak{N}_\mathbf{T} \subseteq \mathfrak{N}_{\mathbf{T}^2} \subseteq \ldots \subseteq \mathfrak{N}_{\mathbf{T}^k} \subseteq \ldots.$
Furthermore, if p is a positive integer such that $\mathfrak{R}_{\mathbf{T}^p} = \mathfrak{R}_{\mathbf{T}^{p+1}}$, then for every integer $k \geq 1$ we have $\mathfrak{R}_{\mathbf{T}^p} = \mathfrak{R}_{\mathbf{T}^{p+k}}$ and $\mathfrak{N}_{\mathbf{T}^p} = \mathfrak{N}_{\mathbf{T}^{p+k}}$.

P R O O F : The chains are established by repeated application of

Theorem 3.2. The dimension relation of Theorem 3.4 shows that $\mathcal{R}_{\mathbf{T}^p} = \mathcal{R}_{\mathbf{T}^{p+k}}$ if and only if $\mathcal{N}_{\mathbf{T}^p} = \mathcal{N}_{\mathbf{T}^{p+k}}$. Now assume $\mathcal{N}_{\mathbf{T}^p} = \mathcal{N}_{\mathbf{T}^{p+1}}$, and let $\xi \in \mathcal{N}_{\mathbf{T}^{p+k}}$. Then

$$\theta = \xi \mathbf{T}^{p+k} = (\xi \mathbf{T}^{k-1})\mathbf{T}^{p+1}.$$

Hence $\xi \mathbf{T}^{k-1} \in \mathcal{N}_{\mathbf{T}^{p+1}} = \mathcal{N}_{\mathbf{T}^p}$. If $k > 1$, the argument may be repeated to give $\xi \mathbf{T}^{k-2} \in \mathcal{N}_{\mathbf{T}^p}$, etc., so finally $\xi \in \mathcal{N}_{\mathbf{T}^p}$. Thus $\mathcal{N}_{\mathbf{T}^{p+k}} \subseteq \mathcal{N}_{\mathbf{T}^p}$, and the chain relation gives $\mathcal{N}_{\mathbf{T}^p} \subseteq \mathcal{N}_{\mathbf{T}^{p+k}}$, so equality holds.

This result gives us a fairly clear picture of the range and null spaces of an iterated transformation. As $\mathbf{T}$ is iterated on $\mathcal{V}_n$, the corresponding null spaces form a *strictly increasing* sequence of subspaces up to a certain number $p \leq n$ of iterations, at which point the increase stops. Thereafter, further application of $\mathbf{T}$ maps into θ only those vectors which are mapped into θ by $\mathbf{T}^p$. Likewise, the range spaces form a *strictly decreasing* sequence up to p iterations, and further application of $\mathbf{T}$ maps $\mathcal{R}_{\mathbf{T}^p}$ *onto* itself.

Exercises

1. Prove Theorem 3.2.
2. Prove Theorem 3.4.
3. Prove the following relations for rank and nullity:
   (i) $\rho(\mathbf{T} + \mathbf{S}) \leq \rho(\mathbf{T}) + \rho(\mathbf{S})$,
   (ii) $\nu(\mathbf{T} + \mathbf{S}) \geq \nu(\mathbf{T}) + \nu(\mathbf{S}) - n$,
   (iii) $\nu(\mathbf{T}) + \nu(\mathbf{S}) \geq \nu(\mathbf{TS}) \geq \max \{\nu(\mathbf{T}), \nu(\mathbf{S})\}$,
   (iv) $\rho(\mathbf{T}) + \rho(\mathbf{S}) - n \leq \rho(\mathbf{TS}) \leq \min \{\rho(\mathbf{T}), \rho(\mathbf{S})\}$.

4. Specify the range space and null space of each of the linear transformations given in the examples of § 3.1.

5. Illustrate the statements of Exercise 3 above by using the linear transformations $\mathbf{T}_2$ and $\mathbf{T}_3$ of Example (c), § 3.1.

6. Show that if $\rho(\mathbf{T}) = 1$, then $\mathbf{T}^2 = c\mathbf{T}$ for some scalar c.

7. Let $\mathbf{T}$ be a nilpotent linear transformation on $\mathcal{V}$, so that for every $\eta \in \mathcal{V}$, $\eta \mathbf{T}^p = \theta$ but for some $\xi \in \mathcal{V}$, $\xi \mathbf{T}^{p-1} \neq \theta$.

   (i) Show that $\{\xi, \xi\mathbf{T}, \xi\mathbf{T}^2, \ldots, \xi\mathbf{T}^{p-1}\}$ is linearly independent.

   (ii) If $\mathcal{S}$ is the subspace spanned by the vectors of (i), show that $\sigma\mathbf{T} \in \mathcal{S}$ for every $\sigma \in \mathcal{S}$. (That is, $\mathbf{T}$ maps the space $\mathcal{S}$ into itself. Such a space is said to be *invariant under* $\mathbf{T}$, or $\mathbf{T}$-*invariant*.)

§3.4. *Non-singular Transformations*

The range and null spaces of a linear transformation $\mathbf{T}$ have an intrinsic connection with the important concept of *non-singularity* of $\mathbf{T}$, which is defined below. *A priori*, the definition of a non-singular transformation has nothing to do with the range space or null space of the transformation. The simple relation of these notions is included in Theorem 3.6, which characterizes non-singularity in various ways.

Definition 3.7. A linear transformation $\mathbf{T}$ is said to be *non-singular* if and only if there exists a linear transformation $\mathbf{T}^*$ such that $\mathbf{T}\mathbf{T}^* = \mathbf{I}$. Otherwise $\mathbf{T}$ is said to be *singular*.

Theorem 3.6. Let $\mathbf{T}$ be a linear transformation on $\mathcal{V}_n$ to $\mathcal{W}$; the following statements are equivalent.

(a) $\mathbf{T}$ is non-singular.
(b) If $\alpha \neq \beta$, then $\alpha\mathbf{T} \neq \beta\mathbf{T}$.
(c) $\mathfrak{N}_{\mathbf{T}} = [\theta]$.
(d) $\nu(\mathbf{T}) = 0$.
(e) $\rho(\mathbf{T}) = n$.
(f) If $\{\alpha_1, \ldots, \alpha_n\}$ is a basis for $\mathcal{V}_n$, then $\{\alpha_1\mathbf{T}, \ldots, \alpha_n\mathbf{T}\}$ is a basis for $\mathfrak{R}_{\mathbf{T}}$.

P R O O F : Our proof consists of a cycle of implications.

(a) implies (b). Assume $\mathbf{T}$ is non-singular and that $\alpha'\mathbf{T} = \beta\mathbf{T}$. Then $(\alpha\mathbf{T})\mathbf{T}^* = (\beta\mathbf{T})\mathbf{T}^*$, $\alpha\mathbf{I} = \beta\mathbf{I}$, and $\alpha = \beta$.

(b) implies (c). Let $\xi \neq \theta$; then $\xi\mathbf{T} \neq \theta\mathbf{T} = \theta$, so $\mathfrak{N}_{\mathbf{T}} = [\theta]$.

(c) implies (d). Definition 3.6.

(d) implies (e). Theorem 3.4.

(e) implies (f). Theorem 3.3.

(f) implies (a). Let $\{\alpha_1, \ldots, \alpha_n\}$ be a basis for $\mathcal{V}_n$; then $\{\alpha_1\mathbf{T}, \ldots, \alpha_n\mathbf{T}\}$ is a basis for $\mathfrak{R}_{\mathbf{T}}$. Hence each $\eta \in \mathfrak{R}_{\mathbf{T}}$ has a unique expression of the form $\eta = \sum_{i=1}^{n} b_i(\alpha_i\mathbf{T})$. Let $\mathbf{T}^*$ be the mapping from $\mathfrak{R}_{\mathbf{T}}$ to $\mathcal{V}_n$ defined by $\eta\mathbf{T}^* = \sum_{i=1}^{n} b_i\alpha_i$. We must show that $\mathbf{T}^*$ is linear and that $\mathbf{T}\mathbf{T}^* = \mathbf{I}$ on $\mathcal{V}_n$. For each $\xi \in \mathcal{V}_n$,

$$\xi = \sum_{i=1}^{n} a_i\alpha_i,$$

$$\xi\mathbf{T} = \left(\sum_{i=1}^{n} a_i\alpha_i\right)\mathbf{T} = \sum_{i=1}^{n} a_i(\alpha_i\mathbf{T}) \in \mathfrak{R}_{\mathbf{T}},$$

$$(\xi\mathbf{T})\mathbf{T}^* = \sum_{i=1}^{n} a_i\alpha_i = \xi \text{ by definition of } \mathbf{T}^*.$$

Hence $\mathbf{T}\mathbf{T}^* = \mathbf{I}$ on $\mathcal{V}_n$. Let $\eta = \sum_{i=1}^{n} b_i(\alpha_i\mathbf{T})$ and $\zeta = \sum_{i=1}^{n} c_i(\alpha_i\mathbf{T})$. Then

$$(b\eta + c\zeta)\mathbf{T}^* = \left[b\sum_{i=1}^{n} b_i(\alpha_i\mathbf{T}) + c\sum_{i=1}^{n} c_i(\alpha_i\mathbf{T})\right]\mathbf{T}^*$$

$$(b\eta + c\zeta)\mathbf{T}^* = \left[\sum_{i=1}^{n} (bb_i + cc_i)(\alpha_i\mathbf{T}) \right]\mathbf{T}^*$$

$$= \left[\sum_{i=1}^{n} (bb_i + cc_i)\alpha_i \right]\mathbf{T}\mathbf{T}^*, \text{ since } \mathbf{T} \text{ is linear,}$$

$$= \sum_{i=1}^{n} (bb_i + cc_i)\alpha_i, \text{ since } \mathbf{T}\mathbf{T}^* = \mathbf{I},$$

$$= b \sum_{i=1}^{n} b_i\alpha_i + c \sum_{i-1}^{n} c_i\alpha_i$$

$$= b\eta\mathbf{T}^* + c\zeta\mathbf{T}^*, \text{ by definition of } \mathbf{T}^*.$$

Hence, $\mathbf{T}^*$ is linear, and $\mathbf{T}$ is non-singular.

Since a linear transformation is a homomorphism of $\mathcal{V}$ onto $\mathcal{R}_\mathbf{T}$, a non-singular transformation is simply an isomorphism of $\mathcal{V}$ onto $\mathcal{R}_\mathbf{T}$. This interpretation lends intuitive feeling to the statements of the preceding theorem, since in an isomorphism distinct vectors have distinct images, the kernel is trivial, and it seems entirely reasonable that dimension must be preserved. We remark that if $\mathbf{T}$ maps $\mathcal{V}$ into $\mathcal{V}$, then $\mathbf{T}$ *is non-singular if and only if* $\mathcal{R}_\mathbf{T} = \mathcal{V}$. If we insist on distinguishing $\mathcal{V}$ and $\mathcal{W}$, then it is still true that $\mathcal{R}_\mathbf{T}$ and $\mathcal{V}$ are isomorphic if and only if $\mathbf{T}$ is non-singular.

The significance of Theorem 3.6 (as well as other results we prove about linear transformations) will become more evident when the theory of matrices is developed in subsequent chapters. Indeed, for *every* theorem we prove about linear transformations there is a corresponding theorem about matrices. The next result is surprisingly simple to prove in terms of linear transformations, but a matric proof of the corresponding result is relatively obscure.

Theorem 3.7.   If $\mathbf{T}\mathbf{T}^* = \mathbf{I}$ on $\mathcal{V}_n$, then $\mathbf{T}^*\mathbf{T} = \mathbf{I}$ on $\mathcal{R}_\mathbf{T}$.

P R O O F :   By hypothesis, $\mathbf{T}$ is non-singular, so any $\beta \in \mathcal{R}_\mathbf{T}$ can be represented uniquely as $\beta = \alpha\mathbf{T}$ for some $\alpha \in \mathcal{V}_n$, by Theorem 3.6. Then $\beta(\mathbf{T}^*\mathbf{T}) = (\alpha\mathbf{T})(\mathbf{T}^*\mathbf{T}) = \alpha(\mathbf{T}\mathbf{T}^*)\mathbf{T} = \alpha\mathbf{T} = \beta$. Hence $\mathbf{T}^*\mathbf{T} = \mathbf{I}$.

Now we have earned the right to call $\mathbf{T}^*$ the *inverse* of $\mathbf{T}$, and write $\mathbf{T}^{-1}$ in place of $\mathbf{T}^*$. Thus $\mathbf{T}$ is non-singular if and only if $\mathbf{T}$ has an inverse in the algebra of all linear transformations on $\mathcal{V}_n$. Observe that not every non-zero linear transformation has an inverse; for example, $\mathbf{T}_1$ of Example (c), § 3.1, has a one-dimensional range space and hence is singular but non-zero.

Theorem 3.8.   Let $\mathbf{T}$ and $\mathbf{S}$ be linear transformations of $\mathcal{V}_n$ into $\mathcal{V}_n$. If $\mathbf{T}$ is non-singular, $\rho(\mathbf{TS}) = \rho(\mathbf{S}) = \rho(\mathbf{ST})$.

P R O O F :   By Theorem 3.6, $\mathcal{R}_\mathbf{T} = \mathcal{V}$, so $\mathcal{R}_\mathbf{TS} = \mathcal{R}_\mathbf{S}$, and the first equality is established. By the same theorem, the only vector mapped into θ by

T is θ itself.   Therefore $\mathfrak{N}_{ST} = \mathfrak{N}_S$, and the proof is completed by applying Theorem 3.4.

It should be observed that $\mathfrak{R}_{ST}$ and $\mathfrak{R}_S$ need not be equal, since **T** might map a vector of $\mathfrak{R}_S$ into a vector which is not in $\mathfrak{R}_S$.   All we know is that $\mathfrak{R}_{ST}$ and $\mathfrak{R}_S$ have the same dimension.   As an example, let **T** be the rotation of the plane through an angle of $45°$, and let **S** be the projection of (x, y) onto $(x, 0)$.   Then $\mathfrak{R}_S$ is the line $y = 0$ and $\mathfrak{R}_{ST}$ is the line $y = x$.

Theorem 3.9.   **TS** is non-singular if and only if both **T** and **S** are non-singular; if **TS** is non-singular, then $(TS)^{-1} = S^{-1}T^{-1}$.
P R O O F :   Exercise.

Theorem 3.10.   If **T** is non-singular and $c \neq 0$, then
(a) $(T^{-1})^{-1} = T$,
(b) $(cT)^{-1} = c^{-1}T^{-1}$.
P R O O F :   Exercise.

Exercises

1. Prove Theorem 3.9.
2. Prove Theorem 3.10.
3. Any linear transformation of the plane is determined by its effect on the two vectors $\epsilon_1 = (1, 0)$ and $\epsilon_2 = (0, 1)$.   Suppose $\epsilon_1 T = (a, b)$ and $\epsilon_2 T = (c, d)$.   Express in terms of a, b, c, d a necessary and sufficient condition that **T** be non-singular.   Interpret geometrically.
4. Show that the set of all non-singular linear transformations on $\mathcal{V}_n$ form a group.   This group is called the *full linear group* $\mathcal{L}_n(\mathcal{F})$.
5. Let $\mathcal{V}$ be the infinite-dimensional space of all real polynomials.   For $P \in \mathcal{V}$, let **D** and **J** be the linear transformations defined by

$$P(x)\mathbf{D} = \frac{d}{dx} P(x)$$

$$P(x)\mathbf{J} = \int_0^x P(t)dt.$$

Verify that $\mathbf{JD} = \mathbf{I}$ but $\mathbf{DJ} \neq \mathbf{I}$.   Moreover, prove that **DJ** is singular. What can you conclude about the validity of Theorem 3.7 in infinite-dimensional spaces?   Is Theorem 3.9 valid for infinite-dimensional spaces?

§3.5. *Specific Form of a Linear Transformation*

Finally we approach the bridge which connects linear transformations and matrices.   Suppose that a basis $\{\alpha_1, \ldots, \alpha_n\}$ is chosen for $\mathcal{V}$, and consider the images of the basis vectors under a linear transformation $\mathbf{T}$.   For simplicity we assume that $\mathbf{T}$ maps $\mathcal{V}$ into $\mathcal{V}$.   (See Exercise 4, this section, for the general case.)   For each i, $\alpha_i\mathbf{T}$ is a vector of $\mathcal{V}$, and hence it has a *unique* representation as a linear combination of basis vectors.   That is,

$$\alpha_i\mathbf{T} = a_{i1}\alpha_1 + a_{i2}\alpha_2 + \ldots + a_{in}\alpha_n$$

$$= \sum_{j=1}^{n} a_{ij}\alpha_j, \text{ for each } i = 1, 2, \ldots, n.$$

This is a system of n linear equations, the coefficients a_{ij} of which describe the effect of $\mathbf{T}$ on the chosen basis.   But any vector ξ of $\mathcal{V}$ can be represented uniquely as a linear combination of the basis vectors:

$$\xi = \sum_{i=1}^{n} c_i\alpha_i.$$

Hence

$$\xi\mathbf{T} = \left(\sum_{i=1}^{n} c_i\alpha_i\right)\mathbf{T} = \sum_{i=1}^{n} c_i(\alpha_i\mathbf{T})$$

$$= \sum_{i=1}^{n} c_i\left(\sum_{j=1}^{n} a_{ij}\alpha_j\right) = \sum_{i=1}^{n}\left(\sum_{j=1}^{n} c_i a_{ij}\alpha_j\right)$$

$$= \sum_{j=1}^{n}\left(\sum_{i=1}^{n} c_i a_{ij}\right)\alpha_j.$$

Therefore the effect of $\mathbf{T}$ on any vector ξ is described in terms of the scalars c_i (which represent ξ in terms of the chosen basis) and the scalars a_{ij} (which describe the effect of $\mathbf{T}$ on the chosen basis).

   This representation of $\mathbf{T}$ is so vital in our future work that we repeat, for emphasis, the idea involved.   Given a linear transformation $\mathbf{T}$ on $\mathcal{V}$ we choose a basis for $\mathcal{V}$.   The image of *each* basis vector is described by n scalars which depend on $\mathbf{T}$ *and on the chosen basis*.   Furthermore, these scalars (n^2 in all) describe $\mathbf{T}$ completely since the image of *any* vector can be determined from the n^2 scalars.

   Conversely, any n^2 scalars determine, *with respect to the fixed basis*, a unique linear transformation as follows: given a_{ij}, for $i, j = 1, \ldots, n$, let $\mathbf{T}$ be the linear transformation defined by the equations

$$\alpha_1\mathbf{T} = a_{11}\alpha_1 + a_{12}\alpha_2 + \ldots + a_{1n}\alpha_n,$$
$$\alpha_2\mathbf{T} = a_{21}\alpha_1 + a_{22}\alpha_2 + \ldots + a_{2n}\alpha_n,$$
$$\cdot \qquad \cdot \qquad \cdot \qquad \qquad \cdot$$
$$\cdot \qquad \cdot \qquad \cdot \qquad \qquad \cdot$$
$$\cdot \qquad \cdot \qquad \cdot \qquad \qquad \cdot$$
$$\alpha_n\mathbf{T} = a_{n1}\alpha_1 + a_{n2}\alpha_2 + \ldots + a_{nn}\alpha_n.$$

Since a linear transformation is determined by its effect on any basis (Exercise 7(i), § 3.1), $\xi\mathbf{T}$ is defined for all $\xi \in \mathcal{V}$.   These results are summarized in the following theorem.

Theorem 3.11. With respect to a chosen basis, every linear transformation on $\mathcal{V}_n$ determines n^2 scalars. Conversely, each square array of n^2 scalars determines uniquely (using the convention just described) a linear transformation.

In the next chapter we shall consider square (more generally, rectangular) arrays of scalars, calling each such array a matrix. Theorem 3.11 tells us that every linear transformation determines an array of this type, relative to a fixed basis, and every array determines a linear transformation, again with a fixed basis being used to define the transformation. In order that these arrays be useful in representing facts about linear transformations, we shall define operations on matrices in such a way as to imitate the corresponding operations on linear transformations.

To illustrate, let us consider the representation of the product of two linear transformations $\mathbf{T}$ and $\mathbf{S}$ from $\mathcal{V}$ to $\mathcal{V}$. Let $\{\alpha_1, \ldots, \alpha_n\}$ be a basis for $\mathcal{V}$. Then, using the method just described, we obtain n^2 scalars a_{ik} which represent $\mathbf{T}$ and n^2 scalars b_{kj} which represent $\mathbf{S}$, both in terms of the α-basis:

$$\alpha_i \mathbf{T} = \sum_{k=1}^{n} a_{ik}\alpha_k, \qquad i = 1, \ldots, n,$$

$$\alpha_k \mathbf{S} = \sum_{j=1}^{n} b_{kj}\alpha_j, \qquad k = 1, \ldots, n.$$

To find a representation of $\mathbf{TS}$ we calculate as follows:

$$\alpha_i(\mathbf{TS}) = (\alpha_i \mathbf{T})\mathbf{S} = \left(\sum_{k=1}^{n} a_{ik}\alpha_k\right)\mathbf{S} = \sum_{k=1}^{n} a_{ik}(\alpha_k \mathbf{S})$$

$$= \sum_{k=1}^{n} a_{ik}\left(\sum_{j=1}^{n} b_{kj}\alpha_j\right)$$

$$= \sum_{k=1}^{n} \left(\sum_{j=1}^{n} a_{ik}b_{kj}\alpha_j\right)$$

$$= \sum_{j=1}^{n} \left(\sum_{k=1}^{n} a_{ik}b_{kj}\alpha_j\right)$$

$$= \sum_{j=1}^{n} \left(\sum_{k=1}^{n} a_{ik}b_{kj}\right)\alpha_j.$$

The last form of the equation can be written

$$\alpha_i(\mathbf{TS}) = \left(\sum_{k=1}^{n} a_{ik}b_{k1}\right)\alpha_1 + \left(\sum_{k=1}^{n} a_{ik}b_{k2}\right)\alpha_2 + \ldots + \left(\sum_{k=1}^{n} a_{ik}b_{kn}\right)\alpha_n$$

for $i = 1, \ldots, n$. Hence the n^2 scalars which represent $\mathbf{TS}$ relative to the α-basis are

$$\sum_{k=1}^{n} a_{ik}b_{kj}, \qquad i, j = 1, 2, \ldots, n.$$

This observation is precisely what guides us in the next chapter where the product of matrices is defined formally.

We now return to the simpler case of representing a single transformation relative to a chosen basis. To illustrate how the a_{ij} depend on the chosen basis as well as on $\mathbf{T}$, let us consider the rotation of the plane through an angle of 90°. Referring to the usual coordinates, choose $\epsilon_1 = (1, 0)$ and $\epsilon_2 = (0, 1)$ as a basis. Then

$$\epsilon_1 \mathbf{T} = (1, 0)\mathbf{T} = \quad (0, 1) = \quad 0\epsilon_1 + 1\epsilon_2,$$
$$\epsilon_2 \mathbf{T} = (0, 1)\mathbf{T} = (-1, 0) = -1\epsilon_1 + 0\epsilon_2,$$

and the four scalars which represent $\mathbf{T}$ are

$$a_{11} = 0 \qquad a_{12} = 1$$
$$a_{21} = -1 \qquad a_{22} = 0.$$

Now let us choose a different basis, say $\alpha_1 = (1, 1)$ and $\alpha_2 = (-1, 0)$. Then

$$\alpha_1 \mathbf{T} = \quad (1, 1)\mathbf{T} = (-1, 1) = \quad 1\alpha_1 + \quad 2\,\alpha_2,$$
$$\alpha_2 \mathbf{T} = (-1, 0)\mathbf{T} = (0, -1) = -1\alpha_1 + (-1)\alpha_2,$$

and the four scalars which represent $\mathbf{T}$ with respect to the new basis are

$$b_{11} = 1 \qquad b_{12} = 2$$
$$b_{21} = -1 \qquad b_{22} = -1.$$

In our thinking about linear transformations we have hitherto used the phrase "image of α under $\mathbf{T}$" to describe $\alpha\mathbf{T}$. Using the plane for simplicity, the geometric picture we have of $\mathbf{T}$ is that $\mathbf{T}$ performs a rearrangement of the vectors (points) of the plane. Each point is moved by $\mathbf{T}$ into a new position (which might happen to coincide with the old one). In case $\mathbf{T}$ is non-singular, a second means of interpreting $\mathbf{T}$ is sometimes convenient. If $\mathbf{T}$ is non-singular, the image of a basis is again a basis. But in Chapter 2 we saw that each basis determines a coordinate system, so a change of basis is nothing more than a change of coordinates. Thus we may picture the points of the plane not being moved about by $\mathbf{T}$ but remaining fixed and acquiring a new set of coordinates.

To summarize, a non-singular transformation may be interpreted in two ways:

Dynamic. (Alibi.) $\mathbf{T}$ moves each point P into a point $P\mathbf{T}$ in such a way that if $P \neq Q$ then $P\mathbf{T} \neq Q\mathbf{T}$.

Static. (Alias.) $\mathbf{T}$ assigns new coordinates to each point in such a way that if the old coordinates of P and Q are different, then the new coordinates of P and Q also differ.

Exercises

1. A linear transformation **T** of the plane is known to carry the point $P(1, 1)$ into the point $P'(-2, 0)$ and to carry $Q(0, 1)$ into $Q'(-1, 1)$.

(i) Choose $\{\epsilon_1, \epsilon_2\}$ as a basis, and determine $\epsilon_1\mathbf{T}$ and $\epsilon_2\mathbf{T}$.

(ii) What scalars represent **T** relative to $\{\epsilon_1, \epsilon_2\}$?

(iii) What is the image under **T** of an arbitrary point $R(a, b)$?

(iv) Choose the basis vectors $\{\beta_1, \beta_2\}$ to be the points P and Q. What scalars represent **T** relative to $\{\beta_1, \beta_2\}$?

(v) Show that **T** is non-singular, and find scalars which represent $\mathbf{T}^{-1}$ relative to $\{\epsilon_1, \epsilon_2\}$.

2. Let $\alpha_1 = \epsilon_1 + 2\epsilon_2$, $\alpha_2 = -\epsilon_1 + \epsilon_2$, and let **S** be the linear transformation determined by this change of basis; that is, $\epsilon_1\mathbf{S} = \alpha_1$, $\epsilon_2\mathbf{S} = \alpha_2$.

(i) What scalars represent **S** relative to $\{\epsilon_1, \epsilon_2\}$?

(ii) What scalars represent **S** relative to $\{\alpha_1, \alpha_2\}$?

(iii) What scalars represent $\mathbf{S}^{-1}$ relative to $\{\epsilon_1, \epsilon_2\}$?

(iv) Find the image under **S** of the vector $a\epsilon_1 + b\epsilon_2$.

3. Referring to Exercises 1 and 2 for the definitions of **S** and **T**, consider the product transformations **TS** and **ST**.

(i) What scalars represent **TS** relative to $\{\epsilon_1, \epsilon_2\}$? Answer in two ways: first by determining $\epsilon_1\mathbf{TS}$ and $\epsilon_2\mathbf{TS}$, and second by applying the formula $c_{ij} = \sum_{k=1}^{n} a_{ik}b_{kj}$ of § 3.5.

(ii) Similarly, calculate the scalars which represent **ST** relative to $\{\epsilon_1, \epsilon_2\}$.

(iii) Find the images of the point (a, b) under the transformations **TS** and **ST**.

4. Consider a linear transformation **T** of $\mathcal{V}_m$ onto $\mathcal{W}_n$ and a linear transformation **S** of $\mathcal{W}_n$ onto $\mathcal{Y}_p$. Choose bases $\{\alpha_1, \ldots, \alpha_m\}$ for $\mathcal{V}_m$, $\{\beta_1, \ldots, \beta_n\}$ for $\mathcal{W}_n$, and $\{\gamma_1, \ldots, \gamma_p\}$ for $\mathcal{Y}_p$. Then **T** is represented relative to the α-basis for $\mathcal{V}_m$ and the β-basis for $\mathcal{W}_n$ by the mn scalars a_{ik}, where

$$\alpha_i\mathbf{T} = \sum_{k=1}^{n} a_{ik}\beta_k, \qquad i = 1, \ldots, m.$$

Likewise, **S** is represented relative to the β-basis for $\mathcal{W}_n$ and the γ-basis for $\mathcal{Y}_p$ by the np scalars b_{kj}, where

$$\beta_k\mathbf{S} = \sum_{j=1}^{p} b_{kj}\gamma_j, \qquad k = 1, \ldots, n.$$

The product transformation **TS** of $\mathcal{V}_m$ onto $\mathcal{Y}_p$ is represented relative to the α-basis for $\mathcal{V}_m$ and the γ-basis for $\mathcal{Y}_p$ by mp scalars c_{ij}.

(i) Show that $c_{ij} = \sum_{k=1}^{n} a_{ik} b_{kj}$ for $i = 1, \ldots, m$ and $j = 1, \ldots, p$.

(ii) Indicate how the corresponding discussion of § 3.5 follows as a special case of this result.

5.   (i) Prove that $\mathbf{T}$ is idempotent if and only if $\eta\mathbf{T} = \eta$ for every $\eta \in \mathfrak{R}_\mathbf{T}$.

(ii) Prove that if $\mathbf{T}$ is idempotent, there exists a basis for $\mathfrak{V}$ such that $\alpha_i\mathbf{T} = \alpha_i$ for $1 \le i \le \rho(\mathbf{T})$ and $\alpha_i\mathbf{T} = \theta$ for $\rho(\mathbf{T}) < i \le n$.

(iii) What array of scalars represents an idempotent transformation relative to the basis described in (ii)?

CHAPTER 4

Matrices

§4.1. *Matrices and Matrix Operations*

The considerations of the last section show that if $\mathbf{T}$ is a linear transformation on a vector space $\mathcal{V}$ of dimension n over $\mathcal{F}$, then $\mathbf{T}$ determines n^2 scalars which describe $\mathbf{T}$ completely. The determination of these scalars requires the choice of a basis for $\mathcal{V}$, and various choices of bases lead to different sets of scalars, each set representing $\mathbf{T}$ relative to a suitable basis.

Suppose we fix a basis and refer all our considerations to this basis. Then each $\mathbf{T}$ determines a unique set of scalars which are the coefficients of the images under $\mathbf{T}$ of the basis vectors, expressed in terms of that basis. A fundamental method of matrix theory is to investigate properties of $\mathbf{T}$ by observing properties of the set of scalars which represents $\mathbf{T}$, and vice versa.

Although we shall often be interested in linear transformations from $\mathcal{V}$ to itself, we also consider the more general case of linear transformations from $\mathcal{V}_m$ to $\mathcal{W}_n$, as described in Exercise 4, § 3.5. Let $\mathcal{V}_m$ be a vector space with an arbitrary but fixed basis $\{\alpha_1, \ldots, \alpha_m\}$. Let $\mathbf{T}$ be a linear transformation of $\mathcal{V}_m$ into a vector space $\mathcal{W}_n$, and let $\{\beta_1, \ldots, \beta_n\}$ be any fixed basis for $\mathcal{W}_n$. For each $i = 1, 2, \ldots, m$, $\alpha_i \mathbf{T}$ is a uniquely determined vector of $\mathcal{W}_n$ and hence is uniquely represented as a linear combination of the $\beta_j, j = 1, 2, \ldots, n$:

$$
\begin{aligned}
\alpha_1 \mathbf{T} &= a_{11}\beta_1 + a_{12}\beta_2 + \ldots + a_{1n}\beta_n, \\
\alpha_2 \mathbf{T} &= a_{21}\beta_1 + a_{22}\beta_2 + \ldots + a_{2n}\beta_n, \\
&\qquad\qquad \vdots \\
\alpha_m \mathbf{T} &= a_{m1}\beta_1 + a_{m2}\beta_2 + \ldots + a_{mn}\beta_n.
\end{aligned}
$$

(*4.1*)

Notice the meaning of the subscripts: the first subscript i of a_{ij} means that a_{ij} is one of the coefficients of the representation of the vector $\alpha_i \mathbf{T}$ relative to the β-basis, and the second subscript j of a_{ij} means that a_{ij} is the coefficient of β_j in that representation. Relative to the two bases, $\mathbf{T}$ is completely determined by the mn scalars a_{ij}, together with this interpretation of the meaning of the subscripts. This means not only that we have selected bases for $\mathcal{V}_m$ and $\mathcal{W}_n$, but that we have written the basis vectors in a specific order in each case, and we tacitly agree to observe this order. If we were to interchange the order, say of α_1 and α_2, then we would merely interchange the first two lines of (4.1), whereas an interchange of β_1 and β_2 would interchange the first two columns on the right hand side. The mn scalars representing $\mathbf{T}$ would be the same, but they would be written in a different arrangement from that of (4.1). To avoid ambiguity, therefore, we agree to pay attention to the order of the basis vectors.

With this convention understood, we can dispense with writing the α_i and β_j, and represent $\mathbf{T}$ by the rectangular array of scalars,

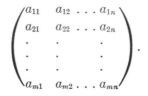

$$\begin{pmatrix} a_{11} & a_{12} & \ldots & a_{1n} \\ a_{21} & a_{22} & \ldots & a_{2n} \\ \cdot & \cdot & & \cdot \\ \cdot & \cdot & & \cdot \\ \cdot & \cdot & & \cdot \\ a_{m1} & a_{m2} & \ldots & a_{mn} \end{pmatrix}.$$

This array of m rows and n columns of field elements is denoted more compactly by (a_{ij}), $i = 1, \ldots, m$ and $j = 1, \ldots, n$. The component a_{ij} is the scalar in the ith row and the jth column, so the first index i is called the *row index*, and the second index j is called the *column index*.

Definition 4.1. A rectangular array containing m rows and n columns of elements of a field $\mathfrak{F}$ is called an $m \times n$ *matrix* over $\mathfrak{F}$.

More completely, a matrix is an element of an abstract system for which several relations and operations are defined, and a study of this system comprises matrix theory. In defining relations and operations for matrices we shall be guided by the principle that if matrices are to be used to represent linear transformations, their algebraic properties must reflect those of linear transformations.

First let us consider equality; two linear transformations are equal if and only if they have exactly the same effect on each vector, and therefore if and only if they have the same effect on each vector of a basis. The latter means that two equal linear transformations have identical matric representations relative to a fixed choice of ordered bases for $\mathcal{V}_m$ and $\mathcal{W}_n$.

Definition 4.2. Two $m \times n$ matrices $A = (a_{ij})$ and $B = (b_{ij})$ are *equal* if and only if $a_{ij} = b_{ij}$ for every $i = 1, 2, \ldots, m$ and every $j = 1, 2, \ldots, n$.

The matric representations of the transformations $\mathbf{T} + \mathbf{S}$ and $c\mathbf{T}$, expressed in terms of the representations of $\mathbf{T}$ and $\mathbf{S}$, provide the motivation for the following two definitions.

Definition 4.3. The *sum* of two $m \times n$ matrices $A = (a_{ij})$ and $B = (b_{ij})$ is the $m \times n$ matrix $C = (c_{ij})$, where

$$c_{ij} = a_{ij} + b_{ij},$$

for every $i = 1, 2, \ldots, m$ and every $j = 1, 2, \ldots, n$.

Definition 4.4. The *scalar multiple* of an $m \times n$ matrix $A = (a_{ij})$ by a scalar c is the $m \times n$ matrix $C = (c_{ij})$, where

$$c_{ij} = ca_{ij},$$

for every $i = 1, 2, \ldots, m$ and every $j = 1, 2, \ldots, n$.

Notice in particular that equality, sum, and scalar multiple are all defined componentwise. Also note that equality and sum are defined only for matrices of the same dimensions. An example for 2×3 matrices will make the definitions clear. Let $A = \begin{pmatrix} 1 & -2 & 0 \\ 0 & 1 & 2 \end{pmatrix}$, $B = \begin{pmatrix} 0 & 2 & 1 \\ 0 & -1 & -1 \end{pmatrix}$; then

$$A + B = \begin{pmatrix} 1+0 & -2+2 & 0+1 \\ 0+0 & 1-1 & 2-1 \end{pmatrix} = \begin{pmatrix} 1 & 0 & 1 \\ 0 & 0 & 1 \end{pmatrix}$$

and

$$3A = \begin{pmatrix} 3 & -6 & 0 \\ 0 & 3 & 6 \end{pmatrix}.$$

Since addition and scalar multiplication of matrices are defined in terms of the field operations, we may expect certain properties of the field operations to be inherited by matrices. For example, matrix addition is associative and commutative, and scalar multiplication is distributive over matrix addition. These properties, and those listed below, may be proved as exercises.

1. $A + B = B + A$.
2. $(A + B) + C = A + (B + C)$.
3. $c(A + B) = cA + cB$.
4. $(c + d)A = cA + dA$.

In particular, the $m \times n$ matrix Z, all of whose components are zero, is the identity of addition for all $m \times n$ matrices.

5. $A + Z = A$.
6. $A + (-1)A = Z$.
7. $0(A) = Z$.

Next consider how matrix multiplication should be defined in order to simulate the product of linear transformations. The product **TS** was defined as a successive mapping, and this is possible only when **T** maps $\mathcal{V}_m$ into $\mathcal{W}_n$ and **S** maps $\mathcal{W}_n$ into $\mathcal{Y}_p$. The corresponding matrix product AB should be defined whenever the number of columns of A equals the number of rows of B, since each represents the dimension of $\mathcal{W}_n$. The exact form of the multiplication is indicated by Exercise 4, § 3.5, which calculates the representation of **TS** in terms of bases for $\mathcal{V}_m$, $\mathcal{W}_n$, and $\mathcal{Y}_p$.

Definition 4.5. If $A = (a_{ik})$ is an $m \times n$ matrix and if $B = (b_{kj})$ is an $n \times p$ matrix, the *product* AB is the $m \times p$ matrix $C = (c_{ij})$, where

$$c_{ij} = \sum_{k=1}^{n} a_{ik}b_{kj}$$

for every $i = 1, 2, \ldots, m$ and every $j = 1, 2, \ldots, p$.

Some of the time we shall be concerned with transformations of a space into itself. The corresponding matrices will be square, n rows and n columns, if n is the dimension of the space. Thus if A and B are square matrices of the same dimension, then AB and BA are both defined, but not necessarily equal.

We refer to Definition 4.5 to learn a technique for matrix multiplication. Each element in the product AB of an $m \times n$ matrix A by an $n \times p$ matrix B is the sum of n products of scalars. To find the element c_{ij} which is in the ith row and jth column of AB we multiply each element in the ith row of A by the corresponding element in the jth column of B, and then add:

$$c_{ij} = a_{i1}b_{1j} + a_{i2}b_{2j} + \ldots + a_{in}b_{nj}:$$

In practice we can perform this computation easily by the technique of using the left index finger to run across the ith row of the left hand matrix and simultaneously using the right index finger to run down the jth column of the right hand matrix, multiplying elements in corresponding positions and adding successively the products obtained. An example may help to clarify the procedure.

$$A = \begin{pmatrix} 1 & 0 & -1 \\ 2 & 4 & 7 \\ 5 & 3 & 0 \end{pmatrix}, \qquad B = \begin{pmatrix} 6 & 1 \\ 0 & 4 \\ -2 & 3 \end{pmatrix};$$

$$AB = \begin{pmatrix} (1)(6) + (0)(0) + (-1)(-2) & (1)(1) + (0)(4) + (-1)(3) \\ (2)(6) + (4)(0) + (7)(-2) & (2)(1) + (4)(4) + (7)(3) \\ (5)(6) + (3)(0) + (0)(-2) & (5)(1) + (3)(4) + (0)(3) \end{pmatrix}$$

$$= \begin{pmatrix} 8 & -2 \\ -2 & 39 \\ 30 & 17 \end{pmatrix}.$$

Exercises

1. Verify properties 1 through 7, page 65, for addition and scalar multiples of matrices. Deduce that the set of all $m \times n$ matrices over a field $\mathfrak{F}$ forms a commutative group relative to addition.

2. Compute AB, AC, B^2, BC, CA, given that

$$A = \begin{pmatrix} 1 & 0 & -1 \\ 0 & 2 & 3 \end{pmatrix}, \qquad B = \begin{pmatrix} 2 & -1 & 4 \\ 1 & 0 & -2 \\ 0 & 3 & 1 \end{pmatrix}, \qquad C = \begin{pmatrix} 0 & 2 \\ -1 & 0 \\ 3 & 1 \end{pmatrix}.$$

Are any other binary products possible for these three matrices?

3. Referring to Example (c) of § 3.1, recall that $\{\epsilon_1, \epsilon_2\}$ is the basis chosen for $\mathcal{E}_2$.

(i) Find the matrices A, B, and C which represent $\mathbf{T}_1$, $\mathbf{T}_2$, and $\mathbf{T}_3$, respectively.

(ii) Calculate AB, BC, CB, and A^2, and from the results deduce statements for matrices which are analogous to the statements observed in the discussion of these linear transformations.

4. (i) Relative to the preferred basis $\{\epsilon_1, \epsilon_2, \ldots, \epsilon_n\}$ for $\mathcal{E}_n$ find the matrix E_{ij} which represents the linear transformation $\mathbf{T}_{ij}$ which was defined in the proof of Theorem 3.1.

(ii) Show that any $n \times n$ matrix is a linear combination of the matrices E_{ij}, for $i, j = 1, \ldots, n$.

(iii) Show that if a linear combination of the matrices E_{ij} equals Z then each coefficient of that linear combination is zero.

5. Show that the system of all 1×1 matrices over a field $\mathfrak{F}$, together with matrix addition and multiplication, is a field which is isomorphic to $\mathfrak{F}$.

6. Prove that the set of all complex 2×2 matrices of the form

$$\begin{pmatrix} a + ib & c + id \\ -c + id & a - ib \end{pmatrix}$$

forms a system which is isomorphic to the algebra of quaternions as described in Exercise 2, § 3.2.

7. Read "What is a Matrix?", by C. C. MacDuffee, *American Mathematical Monthly*, volume 50 (1943), pp. 360–365.

§4.2. *Special Types of Matrices*

Before proceeding with a general study of matrix operations, we shall consider certain classes of matrices which play an important role in matrix theory. The few calculations we have made in the examples and exercises have warned us to expect the unexpected; from Exercise 3, § 4.1, we see that matrix multiplication is not commutative (even when both AB and BA are defined) and also that a product of non-zero matrices can equal the zero matrix.

Identity matrix. We seek a matrix I such that $IX = XI = X$ for every matrix X. But if X is $m \times n$, I must have m columns in order that IX be defined and n rows in order that XI be defined. But then IX is $n \times n$, XI is $m \times m$, and X is $m \times n$. Hence m and n must be equal, so X must be square, say $n \times n$, and I must be likewise. Thus we must speak of the *identity matrix of dimension n*, which is easily seen to be

$$I = (\delta_{ij}) = \begin{pmatrix} 1 & 0 & 0 & . & . & . & 0 \\ 0 & 1 & 0 & . & . & . & 0 \\ 0 & 0 & 1 & . & . & . & 0 \\ . & . & . & & & & . \\ . & . & . & & & & . \\ . & . & . & & & & . \\ 0 & 0 & 0 & . & . & . & 1 \end{pmatrix},$$

where δ_{ij} is called the *Kronecker delta* and is defined by

$$\delta_{ij} = \begin{cases} 1 \text{ if } i = j \\ 0 \text{ if } i \neq j, \text{ for } i, j = 1, 2, \ldots, n. \end{cases}$$

Scalar matrices. Although matrix multiplication is not commutative, the $n \times n$ identity matrix commutes with every $n \times n$ matrix. Are there other square matrices $A = (a_{ij})$ which have the property that $AX = XA$ for every $n \times n$ matrix $X = (x_{ij})$? A straightforward approach would be to determine scalars a_{ij} which satisfy the n^2 equations,

$$\sum_{k=1}^{n} a_{ik}x_{kj} = \sum_{k=1}^{n} x_{ik}a_{kj}, \qquad i, j = 1, 2, \ldots, n.$$

This is a somewhat fearful task. Instead, we argue as follows: let E_{rs} be the $n \times n$ matrix with $e_{rs} = 1$ and $e_{ij} = 0$ if $i \neq r$ or $j \neq s$. If A commutes with all $n \times n$ matrices, then in particular we must have

$$AE_{rs} = \begin{pmatrix} 0 & \dots & a_{1r} & \dots & 0 \\ 0 & \dots & a_{2r} & \dots & 0 \\ & \cdot & \cdot & \cdot & \\ & \cdot & \cdot & \cdot & \\ 0 & \dots & a_{nr} & \dots & 0 \end{pmatrix} = \begin{pmatrix} 0 & 0 & \dots & 0 \\ \cdot & & & \cdot \\ \cdot & & & \cdot \\ a_{s1} & a_{s2} & \dots & a_{sn} \\ \cdot & & & \cdot \\ 0 & 0 & \dots & 0 \end{pmatrix} = E_{rs}A,$$

where every element not in column s of the first matrix is zero, and every element not in row r of the second matrix is zero. Hence we have $a_{rr} = a_{ss}$, $a_{ir} = 0$ if $i \neq r$, and $a_{sj} = 0$ if $j \neq s$. Thus if A commutes with all the E_{rs} matrices, A must have the same element k in every position of the *main diagonal* and zeros elsewhere:

$$a_{ij} = k\delta_{ij}, \qquad i, j = 1, 2, \dots, n,$$

$$A = \begin{pmatrix} k & 0 & \cdot & \cdot & 0 \\ 0 & k & \cdot & \cdot & 0 \\ \cdot & \cdot & & & \cdot \\ \cdot & \cdot & & & \cdot \\ \cdot & \cdot & & & \\ 0 & 0 & \cdot & \cdot & k \end{pmatrix} = kI.$$

Such a matrix is called a *scalar matrix*, being merely a scalar multiple of I. Clearly, a scalar matrix commutes with every matrix, so the question is answered completely.

Diagonal matrices. Scalar matrices form a subclass of the class of *diagonal matrices*, which are defined by the property that $a_{ij} = 0$ if $i \neq j$. Thus zeros appear everywhere except possibly on the main diagonal. Clearly, the sum of diagonal matrices is diagonal; so is the product, for if A and B are diagonal and $AB = C$, then

$$c_{ij} = \sum_{k=1}^{n} a_{ik}b_{kj} = a_{ii}b_{ij} = \begin{cases} a_{ii}b_{ii} & \text{if } j = i \\ 0 & \text{if } j \neq i. \end{cases}$$

$$\begin{pmatrix} a_{11} & 0 & \dots & 0 \\ 0 & a_{22} & \dots & 0 \\ \cdot & \cdot & & \cdot \\ \cdot & \cdot & & \cdot \\ \cdot & \cdot & & \cdot \\ 0 & 0 & \dots & a_{nn} \end{pmatrix} \begin{pmatrix} b_{11} & 0 & \dots & 0 \\ 0 & b_{22} & \dots & 0 \\ \cdot & \cdot & & \cdot \\ \cdot & \cdot & & \cdot \\ \cdot & \cdot & & \cdot \\ 0 & 0 & \dots & b_{nn} \end{pmatrix} = \begin{pmatrix} c_{11} & 0 & \dots & 0 \\ 0 & c_{22} & \dots & 0 \\ \cdot & \cdot & & \cdot \\ \cdot & \cdot & & \cdot \\ \cdot & \cdot & & \cdot \\ 0 & 0 & \dots & c_{nn} \end{pmatrix}.$$

Triangular matrices. A still more inclusive class of square matrices is that for which $a_{ij} = 0$ whenever $i > j$. Such a matrix is called (upper) *triangular* because all the non-zero elements lie on or above the main diagonal:

$$\begin{pmatrix} a_{11} & a_{12} & \cdots & a_{1n} \\ 0 & a_{22} & \cdots & a_{2n} \\ & & \cdot & & \cdot \\ & & \cdot & & \cdot \\ & & \cdot & & \cdot \\ 0 & 0 & \cdots & a_{nn} \end{pmatrix}.$$

A triangular matrix for which $a_{ii} = 0$ for $i = 1, \ldots, n$ is called *strictly triangular*. Clearly, any triangular matrix is the sum of a strictly triangular matrix and a diagonal matrix.

Idempotent matrices. A matrix A is said to be *idempotent* if and only if $A^2 = A$. An example other than Z and I is $\begin{pmatrix} 1 & -1 \\ 0 & 0 \end{pmatrix}$.

Nilpotent matrices. A matrix A is said to be *nilpotent* of index p if $A^p = Z$ but $A^{p-1} \neq Z$. Any strictly triangular matrix is nilpotent. (See Exercise 5.)

Non-singular matrices. This special type of matrix is of great importance.

> **Definition 4.6.** An $n \times n$ matrix A is said to be *non-singular* if and only if a matrix B exists such that
> $$AB = I.$$
> Otherwise A is said to be *singular*.

First we point out the formal similarity of Definition 4.6 to Definition 3.7 which concerned non-singular linear transformations. For transformations we proved in Theorem 3.7 that if $\mathbf{TT}^* = \mathbf{I}$ then $\mathbf{T}^*\mathbf{T} = \mathbf{I}$. Is the corresponding result valid for matrices? We would like to prove that if $AB = I$ then $BA = I$. In terms of matrix multiplication we would have to prove that if

$$\sum_{k=1}^{n} a_{ik}b_{kj} = \delta_{ij}, \qquad i, j = 1, 2, \ldots, n,$$

then

$$\sum_{k=1}^{n} b_{ik}a_{kj} = \delta_{ij}, \qquad i, j = 1, 2, \ldots, n,$$

which is true but by no means obvious. However, after the discussion of the following section we prove this result merely by pointing to Theorem 3.7. Anticipating this proof, we call B the *inverse of A*, denoted A^{-1}. Thus non-singular matrices are those which possess a multiplicative inverse.

For the next two types of matrices considered here, we need the notion of the transpose of A, which is simply the matrix obtained by reflecting A across its main diagonal.

Definition 4.7. Given $A = (a_{,j})$, the *transpose* of A, denoted A', is defined by

$$A' = (b_{ij}),$$

where $b_{ij} = a_{ji}$.

Theorem 4.1.

(a) $(A')' = A$,
(b) $(A + B)' = A' + B'$,
(c) $(AB)' = B'A'$.

PROOF: Exercise.

(handwritten: $(a_{ij} + b_{ij})' = (c_{ij})' = c_{ji} = a_{ji} + b_{ji} = A' + B'$)

(handwritten: $(\sum_{k=1}^{n} a_{ik} b_{kj})' = \sum a_{ki} b_{jk} = \sum b_{jk} a_{ki}$)

Symmetric matrices. An $n \times n$ matrix A is said to be *symmetric* if and only if $A = A'$. Obviously any diagonal matrix is symmetric.

Skew-symmetric matrices. An $n \times n$ matrix A is said to be *skew-symmetric* (or simply *skew*) if and only if $A' = -A$. This implies of course that if $1 + 1 \neq 0$ in the base field, then every diagonal element of a skew matrix is zero. We exclude from our consideration any field in which $1 + 1 = 0$. (See § 1.5.)

(handwritten margin: excludes 2 el. fld, 0, 1)

Now let A be any square matrix. If $1 + 1 \neq 0$ in $\mathfrak{F}$,

$$A = \tfrac{1}{2}(A + A') + \tfrac{1}{2}(A - A').$$

Since $A + A'$ is symmetric and $A - A'$ is skew (see Exercise 8), this expresses A as a sum of two matrices, the first of which is symmetric and the second skew.

Row vectors and column vectors. Relative to a fixed basis, every vector of $\mathcal{V}_n$ has a unique representation as an n-tuple of scalars, $(a_1, \ldots, a_n)$. Except for the presence of commas, this is formally the same as a matrix of one row and n columns. Accordingly, a $1 \times n$ matrix is called a *row vector*. The transpose of a row vector is an $n \times 1$ matrix, n rows and one column, and is called a *column vector*. If A is a row vector, where $A = (a_1 a_2 \ldots a_n)$, and if B' is a column vector, where $B = (b_1 b_2 \ldots b_n)$, then both AB' and $B'A$ are defined:

$$AB' = (a_1 a_2 \ldots a_n) \begin{pmatrix} b_1 \\ b_2 \\ \cdot \\ \cdot \\ \cdot \\ b_n \end{pmatrix} = (a_1 b_1 + a_2 b_2 + \ldots + a_n b_n),$$

which is a 1×1 matrix, or by Exercise 5, § 4.1, a scalar:

$$
B'A = \begin{pmatrix} b_1 \\ b_2 \\ \cdot \\ \cdot \\ \cdot \\ b_n \end{pmatrix} (a_1 \, a_2 \ldots a_n) = \begin{pmatrix} b_1 a_1 & b_1 a_2 & \ldots & b_1 a_n \\ b_2 a_1 & b_2 a_2 & \ldots & b_2 a_n \\ \cdot & \cdot & & \cdot \\ \cdot & \cdot & & \cdot \\ \cdot & \cdot & & \cdot \\ b_n a_1 & b_n a_2 & \ldots & b_n a_n \end{pmatrix},
$$

which is an $n \times n$ matrix.

Exercises

1. Prove that $IA = AI = A$ for every square matrix A.

2. Show that for each n the set of all $n \times n$ scalar matrices over $\mathfrak{F}$ forms a field which is isomorphic to $\mathfrak{F}$.

3. (i) Prove that all $n \times n$ diagonal matrices commute.

(ii) Prove that if A commutes with all $n \times n$ diagonal matrices, then A is diagonal.

4. Prove that the set of all $n \times n$ triangular matrices is closed under matrix sum and product. Deduce that the set of all non-singular $n \times n$ triangular matrices forms a multiplicative group.

5. Show that any 4×4 strictly triangular matrix is nilpotent. How would you generalize your proof for the $n \times n$ case?

6. Prove that if A is idempotent and $A \neq I$, then A is singular.

7. Prove Theorem 4.1.

8. Prove for every square matrix A:

(i) AA' is symmetric,
(ii) $A + A'$ is symmetric,
(iii) $A - A'$ is skew.

9. Prove that A^2 is symmetric if either A is symmetric or A is skew.

10. If A and B are both symmetric, prove that

(i) $A + B$ is symmetric,
(ii) AB is symmetric if and only if A and B commute.

11. If A and B are skew, prove that $A + B$ is skew.

12. Prove $(A')^{-1} = (A^{-1})'$ if A is non-singular.

13. Let $\{\alpha_1, \alpha_2, \alpha_3\}$ be a basis for $\mathcal{V}_3$, and let

$$
\begin{aligned}
\beta_1 &= \alpha_1 - 2\alpha_2, \\
\beta_2 &= \alpha_1 + \alpha_2 + \alpha_3, \\
\beta_3 &= \alpha_2 - \alpha_3.
\end{aligned}
$$

(i) Prove $\{\beta_1, \beta_2, \beta_3\}$ is a basis, and express each α_i as a linear combination of the β_j.

(ii) If $\mathbf{T}$ is defined by $\alpha_i\mathbf{T} = \beta_i$, find the matrix A which represents $\mathbf{T}$ relative to the α-basis.

(iii) If $\mathbf{S}$ is defined by $\beta_i\mathbf{S} = \alpha_i$, find the matrix B which represents $\mathbf{S}$ relative to the β-basis.

(iv) Prove by matrix calculations that $AB = I$.

§4.3. *Fundamental Isomorphism Theorem*

We might expect that the next step in our development of the theory of matrices would be to establish various properties of matrix operations. This is correct, but instead of verifying such properties directly we prove a theorem which clarifies the connection between matrices and linear transformations. This connection is an isomorphism, and therefore we can obtain properties of matrices from theorems already proved about linear transformations. Not only does this method avoid duplication of effort, but it substitutes geometric insight for involved arithmetic calculations.

From Theorem 3.1 we know that the set of all linear transformations on an n-dimensional vector space over $\mathfrak{F}$ forms a linear algebra

$$\mathfrak{L} = \{L, F; +, \cdot, \oplus, \odot, \square\}$$

over $\mathfrak{F}$. We wish to show that the set of all $n \times n$ matrices, together with the matrix operations, form a linear algebra $\mathfrak{M}$ which is isomorphic to $\mathfrak{L}$. Since a linear algebra is a vector space on which is defined a suitable multiplication of vectors, the concept of isomorphism of linear algebras is defined to be a vector space isomorphism which also preserves the multiplication of vectors.

Theorem 4.2. Let $\mathcal{V}$ be an n-dimensional vector space over $\mathfrak{F}$. The set of all $n \times n$ matrices over $\mathfrak{F}$ forms a linear algebra $\mathfrak{M}$ which is isomorphic to the linear algebra $\mathfrak{L}$ of all linear transformations on $\mathcal{V}$.

P R O O F :   Fix a basis $\{\alpha_1, \ldots, \alpha_n\}$ for $\mathcal{V}$. Let $A = (a_{ij})$ be any $n \times n$ matrix over $\mathfrak{F}$. With A we associate the linear transformation $\mathbf{T}$ of $\mathcal{V}$ into $\mathcal{V}$ defined by

$$\alpha_i\mathbf{T} = \sum_{j=1}^{n} a_{ij}\alpha_j, \; i = 1, \ldots, n.$$

It was established in Theorem 3.11 that this correspondence is one-to-one, provided we regard a fixed ordering of the basis vectors. We next show that the correspondence preserves the three operations of scalar multiplication, matrix addition, and matrix multiplication.   The matrix $kA = (ka_{ij})$ determines the linear transformation $\mathbf{S}_1$ defined by

$$\alpha_i \mathbf{S}_1 = \sum_{j=1}^{n} (ka_{ij})\alpha_j = k \sum_{j=1}^{n} a_{ij}\alpha_j = k\alpha_i \mathbf{T} = \alpha_i(k\mathbf{T}),$$

so if A corresponds to $\mathbf{T}$, kA corresponds to $k\mathbf{T}$.   Let $A = (a_{ij})$ correspond to $\mathbf{T}$, and let $B = (b_{ij})$ correspond to $\mathbf{U}$.   Then $A + B = (a_{ij} + b_{ij})$ corresponds to the transformation $\mathbf{S}_2$ defined by

$$\alpha_i \mathbf{S}_2 = \sum_{j=1}^{n} (a_{ij} + b_{ij})\alpha_j = \sum_{j=1}^{n} a_{ij}\alpha_j + \sum_{j=1}^{n} b_{ij}\alpha_j$$

$$= \alpha_i \mathbf{T} + \alpha_i \mathbf{U} = \alpha_i(\mathbf{T} + \mathbf{U}),$$

so $A + B$ corresponds to $\mathbf{T} + \mathbf{U}$.   Finally, the matrix $AB = (c_{ij})$, where $c_{ij} = \sum_{k=1}^{n} a_{ik}b_{kj}$, corresponds to the transformation $\mathbf{S}_3$ defined by

$$\alpha_i \mathbf{S}_3 = \sum_{j=1}^{n} \left(\sum_{k=1}^{n} a_{ik}b_{kj} \right)\alpha_j = \sum_{k=1}^{n} \sum_{j=1}^{n} a_{ik}b_{kj}\alpha_j$$

$$= \sum_{k=1}^{n} a_{ik}\left(\sum_{j=1}^{n} b_{kj}\alpha_j \right)$$

$$= \sum_{k=1}^{n} a_{ik}(\alpha_k \mathbf{U}) = \left(\sum_{k=1}^{n} a_{ik}\alpha_k \right)\mathbf{U}$$

$$= \alpha_i \mathbf{TU}.$$

Hence AB corresponds to $\mathbf{TU}$, and the correspondence is an isomorphism. Theorem 3.1 showed that $\mathcal{L}$ is a linear algebra; hence $\mathfrak{M}$, the set of all $n \times n$ matrices over $\mathfrak{F}$, forms a linear algebra (since $\mathfrak{M}$ and $\mathcal{L}$ are isomorphic), and the proof is complete.

Recall that in Theorem 3.1 it was stated that $\mathcal{L}$ is of dimension n^2, but we deferred the proof that the n^2 linear transformations $\mathbf{T}_{ij}$ form a basis for $\mathcal{L}$. $\mathbf{T}_{ij}$ was defined by

$$(x_1, \ldots, x_n)\mathbf{T}_{ij} = (0, \ldots, 0, x_i, 0, \ldots, 0),$$

where the jth component is x_i.   Now the matrix corresponding to $\mathbf{T}_{ij}$ is the matrix E_{ij} in which every element is zero except the element in the ith row and j^{th} column, which is 1.   It is clear that any matrix is a linear combination of the E_{ij}, $i, j = 1, \ldots, n$, and that the E_{ij} are linearly independent (see Exercise 4, § 4.1).   Hence they form a basis for $\mathfrak{M}$, and by the isomorphism the $\mathbf{T}_{ij}$ form a basis for $\mathcal{L}$.   This completes the proof of Theorem 3.1.

The argument of the preceding paragraph indicates the power and usefulness of Theorem 4.2.   To prove a result about linear transformations we may, if convenient, prove the corresponding result about matrices, and vice versa.   In the next section we list a number of theorems about matrices which have already been proved in the language of linear transformations.

However, we note that Theorem 4.2 concerns only $n \times n$ matrices; for the corresponding theorem for $m \times n$ matrices we recall from Exercise 4, § 3.5, that a linear transformation from $\mathcal{V}_m$ to $\mathcal{W}_n$ is represented, relative to a pair of bases, by an $m \times n$ matrix. Also from Exercise 9, § 3.1, the set of all linear transformations from $\mathcal{V}_m$ to $\mathcal{W}_n$ forms a vector space. It is not difficult to verify that the dimension of this vector space is mn, and that the set of all $m \times n$ matrices forms a vector space isomorphic to it.

As a special case of the discussion of the preceding paragraph, we consider the situation when $\mathcal{W}_n$ is the field $\mathfrak{F}$, in the sense of Example (c), § 2.2. Then $n = 1$, and a linear transformation from $\mathcal{V}_m$ to $\mathfrak{F}$ is simply a scalar-valued function $\mathbf{T}$ on $\mathcal{V}_m$ which satisfies

$$(a\alpha + b\beta)\mathbf{T} = a\alpha\mathbf{T} + b\beta\mathbf{T}.$$

$\mathbf{T}$ is then called a *linear functional* on $\mathcal{V}_m$, and the collection of all linear functionals on $\mathcal{V}_m$ forms an m-dimensional vector space over $\mathfrak{F}$, called the *dual space* of $\mathcal{V}_m$ and denoted $\mathcal{V}_m^*$. Thus an element of $\mathcal{V}_m^*$ is a linear mapping of $\mathcal{V}_m$ into $\mathfrak{F}$, and any such linear mapping is an element of $\mathcal{V}_m^*$. Further properties of the dual space are developed in Exercises 5–8 below.

Exercises

1. Describe the linear transformation on $\mathcal{E}_2$ which is represented by the scalar matrix aI in case

    (i) $a > 1$,
    (ii) $0 < a < 1$,
    (iii) $a < 0$.

2. Describe the linear transformation on $\mathcal{E}_2$ which is represented by each of the following matrices:

    (i) $\begin{pmatrix} 1 & 0 \\ 0 & -1 \end{pmatrix}$,

    (ii) $\begin{pmatrix} 0 & -1 \\ -1 & 0 \end{pmatrix}$,

    (iii) $\begin{pmatrix} 0 & 1 \\ 0 & 0 \end{pmatrix}$,

    (iv) $\begin{pmatrix} 2 & 0 \\ 0 & 3 \end{pmatrix}$,

    (v) $\begin{pmatrix} 2 & 4 \\ -1 & -2 \end{pmatrix}$.

3. (i) Determine all possible 2×2 real matrices which represent idempotent linear transformations on $\mathcal{E}_2$.

(ii) Determine all possible 2×2 real matrices which represent nilpotent linear transformations of index 2 on $\mathcal{E}_2$.

4. Prove that the set of all $m \times n$ matrices over $\mathcal{F}$ forms a vector space of dimension mn which is isomorphic to the space of all linear transformations from $\mathcal{V}_m$ to $\mathcal{W}_n$.

5. If $\{\alpha_1, \ldots, \alpha_n\}$ is a basis for $\mathcal{V}$ and if $(a_1, \ldots, a_n)$ is any n-tuple of elements of $\mathcal{F}$, show that there is one and only one linear functional $\mathbf{f}$ such that $\alpha_i\mathbf{f} = a_i$, $i = 1, \ldots, n$.

6. Given a basis $\{\alpha_1, \ldots, \alpha_m\}$ for $\mathcal{V}$, a linear functional $\mathbf{f}_j \in \mathcal{V}^*$ is defined on $\mathcal{V}$ by prescribing

$$\alpha_i\mathbf{f}_j = \delta_{ij}, \text{ for } i = 1, 2, \ldots, m.$$

Show that $\{\mathbf{f}_1, \ldots, \mathbf{f}_m\}$ is linearly independent and therefore forms a basis for $\mathcal{V}^*$. This basis is called the *dual basis* of $\{\alpha_1, \ldots, \alpha_m\}$.

7. Let $\mathcal{V}$ be any vector space over $\mathcal{F}$ and let $\mathcal{V}^*$ be its dual space; for each $\alpha \in \mathcal{V}$ and each $\mathbf{f} \in \mathcal{V}^*$, $\alpha\mathbf{f}$ is a scalar in $\mathcal{F}$. Since $\mathcal{V}^*$ is a vector space, it too has a dual space, $(\mathcal{V}^*)^*$, which is the space of all linear functionals on $\mathcal{V}^*$.

(i) Show that each $\alpha \in \mathcal{V}$ may be regarded as a linear functional on $\mathcal{V}^*$.

(ii) Deduce that if $\mathcal{V}$ is finite-dimensional, then $\mathcal{V}$ is isomorphic to $(\mathcal{V}^*)^*$.

8. If $\mathfrak{M}$ is an m-dimensional subspace of $\mathcal{V}_n$, show that an $(n - m)$-dimensional subspace $\mathfrak{M}^0$ of $\mathcal{V}_n^*$ is defined by

$$\mathfrak{M}^0 = \{\mathbf{f} \in \mathcal{V}_n^* | \mu\mathbf{f} = 0 \text{ for every } \mu \in \mathfrak{M}\}.$$

(Since each vector of $\mathfrak{M}$ is mapped into 0 by every linear functional of $\mathfrak{M}^0$, $\mathfrak{M}^0$ is called the *annihilator* of $\mathfrak{M}$.)

§4.4. *Rank of a Matrix*

Referring now to § 4.1 we see that properties 1 through 7 of matrices all follow by the isomorphism theorem from the corresponding properties of linear transformations. (See Exercise 1, § 4.1, which asked for direct matrix proofs.) In the same way, other properties of matrices can be derived from the corresponding properties of linear transformations. Before doing this we introduce the notion of the *rank* of a matrix.

First recall that the vector $\xi = \sum_{i=1}^m x_i\alpha_i$ can be represented relative to the α-basis as $\xi = (x_1, \ldots, x_m)$. This representation defines a $1 \times m$ matrix (row vector) $X = (x_1 \ldots x_m)$. If $A = (a_{ij})$ is $m \times n$, then the product XA is defined, and

$$XA = (y_1 \ldots y_n), \text{ where } y_j = \sum_{i=1}^{m} x_i a_{ij}.$$

Let $\eta = \sum_{j=1}^{n} y_j \beta_j$, and let $\mathbf{T}$ be the transformation which corresponds to A, relative to the fixed bases $\{\alpha_1, \ldots, \alpha_m\}$ and $\{\beta_1, \ldots, \beta_n\}$.   Then

$$\xi\mathbf{T} = \left(\sum_{i=1}^{m} x_i \alpha_i \right)\mathbf{T} = \sum_{i=1}^{m} x_i(\alpha_i \mathbf{T})$$

$$= \sum_{i=1}^{m} x_i \left(\sum_{j=1}^{n} a_{ij}\beta_j \right) = \sum_{j=1}^{n} \left(\sum_{i=1}^{m} x_i a_{ij} \right)\beta_j = \sum_{j=1}^{n} y_j\beta_j$$

$$= \eta.$$

Hence *if X represents the vector ξ and A represents the transformation $\mathbf{T}$, then XA represents the vector $\xi\mathbf{T}$.*   This is a generalization of the observation that the image $\alpha_j\mathbf{T}$ of the jth vector of the basis is represented relative to the β-basis by the row vector which is the jth row of the matrix A.

Had we chosen a left hand notation for linear transformations (see the remarks following Definition 3.1), the situation would be different: a vector ξ would be represented by a column vector X, and $\mathbf{T}(\xi)$ would be represented by $A'X$ which is also a column vector.   Note that in this notation, the matrix representing $\mathbf{T}$ is the transpose of our representation matrix A; the image $\mathbf{T}(\alpha_j)$ would be the jth *column vector* of the matrix representing $\mathbf{T}$ in left hand notation, which is the jth *row vector* of the matrix representing $\mathbf{T}$ in right hand notation.   The simplicity of representing $\mathbf{T}$ by the array A of scalars as they stand in the arrangement

$$\alpha_1\mathbf{T} = a_{11}\beta_1 + a_{12}\beta_2 + \ldots + a_{1n}\beta_n$$
$$\alpha_2\mathbf{T} = a_{21}\beta_1 + a_{22}\beta_2 + \ldots + a_{2n}\beta_n$$
$$\vdots \qquad \vdots \qquad \vdots \qquad \qquad \vdots$$
$$\alpha_m\mathbf{T} = a_{m1}\beta_1 + a_{m2}\beta_2 + \ldots + a_{mn}\beta_n$$

is one reason for preferring right hand notation.

Definition 4.9.   The *rank* of a matrix A, denoted $\rho(A)$, is the maximal number of linearly independent row vectors of A.

An immediate question is the following: What is the relation (if any) between the rank of a matrix and the rank of the linear transformation it represents relative to a chosen basis?   Notice that $\rho(A)$ as defined is an intrinsic property of the matrix A and is independent of any bases we choose in order to represent A as a linear transformation.   Likewise, the rank of a linear transformation is defined to be the dimension of its range space and thus is an intrinsic property of the transformation, independent of any choice of bases.

Theorem 4.3.   Let **T** be the transformation corresponding to the $m \times n$ matrix A relative to chosen bases.   Then

$$\rho(\mathbf{T}) = \rho(A).$$

P R O O F :   Let $\{\alpha_1, \ldots, \alpha_m\}$ be any basis for $\mathcal{V}_m$.   Any vector in $\mathfrak{R}_\mathbf{T}$ is a linear combination of the row vectors of A, since if $\xi = \sum_{i=1}^m c_i \alpha_i$, $\xi \mathbf{T} = \sum_{i=1}^m c_i(\alpha_i \mathbf{T})$.   Hence any maximal independent subset of the row vectors of A is a basis for $\mathfrak{R}_\mathbf{T}$.

We conclude this section with a list of theorems, all of which are readily proved by the isomorphism theorem and a corresponding theorem for linear transformations.

Theorem 4.4.   Matrix multiplication is associative and bilinear.

Theorem 4.5.   If $AB = I$, then $BA = I$.

Theorem 4.6.   The following are equivalent for an $n \times n$ matrix A:
(a) A is non-singular,
(b) $\rho(A) = n$,
(c) The row vectors of A are linearly independent.

Theorem 4.7.   If A is non-singular, then
$$\rho(AB) = \rho(B) = \rho(BA).$$

Theorem 4.8. AB is non-singular if and only if A and B are both non-singular.

Theorem 4.9.   If A and B are non-singular then $(AB)^{-1} = B^{-1}A^{-1}$.

$T, S \text{ non-sing} \implies (TS)^{-1} = S^{-1} T^{-1}$

Exercises

1. Using the isomorphism theorem and appropriate theorems for linear transformations, prove Theorems 4.4–4.9.
2. Prove directly by matrix calculations that

$$A(bB + cC) = bAB + cAC$$

for all $n \times n$ matrices A, B, C.
3. Prove that a triangular matrix is non-singular if and only if every diagonal element is different from zero.
4. Let $\xi \in \mathcal{V}_n$, $\xi \neq \theta$.   Prove that the set of all linear transformations $\mathbf{T}$ on $\mathcal{V}_n$ such that $\xi \mathbf{T} = \theta$ forms a linear algebra whose dimension is $n^2 - n$.

  5. Let A, B be $n \times n$ matrices. What statements can you make about $\rho(A + B)$ and $\rho(AB)$?

  6. State as a theorem for matrices the assertion of Theorem 3.6, statements (a), (b), and (c).

  7. State as a theorem for matrices the assertion of Exercise 6, § 3.3.

  8. An $n \times n$ Markov matrix is defined to be any $n \times n$ real matrix $A = (a_{ij})$ which satisfies the two properties

$$0 \le a_{ij} \le 1,$$

$$\sum_{j=1}^{n} a_{ij} = 1 \text{ for } i = 1, 2, \ldots, n.$$

Prove that the product of two Markov matrices is a Markov matrix. Do such matrices form a multiplicative group? No

  9. A Markov (stochastic) matrix is called *doubly stochastic* if the sum of the elements in each column is unity. Is the product of two doubly stochastic matrices doubly stochastic?

  10. If M is a Markov matrix, show that the value of every element of column j of M^2 is between the values of the minimal and maximal elements of column j of M.

  11. In quantum mechanics the Pauli theory of electron spin makes use of linear transformations $\mathbf{T}_x$, $\mathbf{T}_y$, $\mathbf{T}_z$ whose complex matrices in the preferred coordinate system are, respectively,

$$X = \begin{pmatrix} 0 & 1 \\ 1 & 0 \end{pmatrix},$$

$$Y = \begin{pmatrix} 0 & -i \\ i & 0 \end{pmatrix}, \text{ where } i^2 = -1,$$

$$Z = \begin{pmatrix} 1 & 0 \\ 0 & -1 \end{pmatrix}.$$

  (i) Show that $X^2 = Y^2 = Z^2 = I$, and therefore that each is nonsingular.

  (ii) Form a multiplication table of the four matrices I, X, Y, Z, and observe that any product of these matrices is a scalar times one of these matrices.

  (iii) List the elements of the smallest multiplicative group which contains X and Y.

  12. In the special theory of relativity use is made of the Lorentz transformation,

$$x' = b\,(x - vt)$$

$$t' = b\left(-\frac{vx}{c^2} + t\right),$$

where $|v|$ represents the speed of a moving object, c the speed of light, and $b = c(c^2 - v^2)^{-\frac{1}{2}}$. The corresponding matrix is

$$L(v) = b\begin{pmatrix} 1 & -v \\ \dfrac{-v}{c^2} & 1 \end{pmatrix}.$$

(i) Show that $L(v)$ is non-singular for $|v| < c$.

(ii) Show that the set of all $L(v)$ for $|v| < c$ forms a multiplicative group. This group is called the Lorentz group.

§4.5. *Block Multiplication of Matrices*

Although our emphasis in this book is on the theory of matrices rather than on the practical problems which arise in applications, it would be misleading to pretend that such problems do not exist. For example, the form of the product of two matrices may be unfamiliar to a beginner, but it is conceptually simple. In the product of an $m \times n$ matrix and an $n \times p$ matrix there are mp terms to be calculated, and each term requires n binary products and $n - 1$ sums. Hence, there are altogether mpn products and $mp(n - 1)$ sums to be performed. For square matrices, this reduces to n^3 products and $n^3 - n^2$ sums.

In matrices which arise from experimental work the individual entries are decimal numbers which are seldom integral, so that multiplication is considerably more tedious than addition. For this reason the amount of work required for a matrix calculation is usually expressed in terms of the number of multiplications involved. Since the product of two $n \times n$ matrices requires n^3 multiplications, it is clear that a tremendous amount of computation is required when n is large. Even for $n = 10$ the work is sufficiently long to discourage mental computation. The recent development of high speed computers has reduced this problem considerably, and thereby has opened to solution by matric methods many applied problems for which theoretical solutions were known but computationally unfeasible. But even a large electronic computer has a limited storage space, and the practical question of computational technique remains.

We now indicate a device, known as *block multiplication* of matrices, which can be used to decompose the product of two large matrices into numerous products of smaller matrices. Let A be $m \times n$ and B be $n \times p$. Write $n = n_1 + n_2 + \ldots + n_k$, where each n_i is a positive integer; partition the *columns* of A by putting the first n_1 columns in the first block, the next n_2 columns in the second block, and so on. Partition the *rows* of B in exactly the same way. Then

$$A = (A_1|A_2| \ldots |A_k), \qquad B = \begin{pmatrix} B_1 \\ \hline B_2 \\ \cdot \\ \cdot \\ \cdot \\ \hline B_k \end{pmatrix},$$

where A_i is the $m \times n_i$ matrix consisting of columns of A beginning with column $n_1 + \ldots + n_{i-1} + 1$ and ending with column $n_1 + \ldots + n_i$, and where B_j is the $n_j \times p$ matrix consisting of rows of B beginning with row $n_1 + \ldots + n_{j-1} + 1$ and ending with row $n_1 + \ldots + n_j$. Then the method of block multiplication asserts that

$$AB = A_1 B_1 + A_2 B_2 + \ldots + A_k B_k.$$

More generally, suppose that having partitioned the columns of A and the rows of B as described above, we partition the *rows* of A in any manner and the *columns* of B in any manner. We obtain

$$A = \begin{pmatrix} A_{11} & A_{12} \ldots A_{1k} \\ A_{21} & A_{22} \ldots A_{2k} \\ \cdot & \cdot \quad\ \cdot \\ \cdot & \cdot \quad\ \cdot \\ \cdot & \cdot \quad\ \cdot \\ A_{r1} & A_{r2} \ldots A_{rk} \end{pmatrix}, \qquad B = \begin{pmatrix} B_{11} & B_{12} \ldots B_{1s} \\ B_{21} & B_{22} \ldots B_{2s} \\ \cdot & \cdot \quad\ \cdot \\ \cdot & \cdot \quad\ \cdot \\ \cdot & \cdot \quad\ \cdot \\ B_{k1} & B_{k2} \ldots B_{ks} \end{pmatrix},$$

where A_{it} is a matrix (rectangular array) having r_i rows and n_t columns and B_{tj} is a matrix having n_t rows and s_j columns. Then for fixed i, j the product $A_{it}B_{tj}$ is defined and yields an $r_i \times s_j$ matrix; therefore $\sum_{t=1}^{k} A_{it}B_{tj}$ is an $r_i \times s_j$ matrix. The method of block multiplication asserts that

$$AB = \begin{pmatrix} C_{11} & C_{12} \ldots C_{1s} \\ C_{21} & C_{22} \ldots C_{2s} \\ \cdot & \cdot \quad\ \cdot \\ \cdot & \cdot \quad\ \cdot \\ \cdot & \cdot \quad\ \cdot \\ C_{r1} & C_{r2} \ldots C_{rs} \end{pmatrix},$$

where $C_{ij} = \sum_{t=1}^{k} A_{it}B_{tj}$.

This is in the same form as the element-by-element definition of the product of matrices in which each element is considered as a 1×1 block. The important thing to remember in block multiplication of AB is that the column partition of A must coincide with the row partition of B, in order that all the matrix products $A_{it}B_{tj}$ be defined. Since matrix multiplication is non-commutative, it is essential that the proper order be maintained in forming products of blocks.

The proof of this result is not difficult, but it does require care in choosing notation and manipulating indices. Since we do not require the result for the development of theory, a general proof is omitted. To understand the application of block multiplication to the problem of large scale computations, consider two 50×50 matrices. There are 2500 elements in each matrix, while a medium size computer, such as the *IBM* 650, provides storage for only 2500 numbers including the operational instructions to the machine. The multiplication of two such matrices requires 125,000 multiplications and almost as many additions. One method of performing the multiplication on this computer (but certainly not the only method) would be to partition each of the matrices into four 25×25 matrices,

$$A = \left(\begin{array}{c|c} A_{11} & A_{12} \\ \hline A_{21} & A_{22} \end{array} \right), \qquad B = \left(\begin{array}{c|c} B_{11} & B_{12} \\ \hline B_{21} & B_{22} \end{array} \right);$$

each submatrix has 625 entries, so the machine can successively compute the products $A_{11}B_{11}$, $A_{11}B_{12}$, $A_{12}B_{21}$, $A_{12}B_{22}$, etc., record the results on punched cards to clear the machine storage for the next block of calculations, and finally compute $C_{11} = A_{11}B_{11} + A_{12}B_{21}$, etc.

Even for human calculators, block multiplication is useful in case special patterns appear in the matrix. For example, let

$$A = \left(\begin{array}{cc|ccc} 2 & 0 & 0 & 0 & 0 \\ 0 & 2 & 0 & 0 & 0 \\ \hline 1 & 0 & a & b & c \\ 0 & 1 & d & e & f \end{array} \right) = \left(\begin{array}{cc} 2I & Z \\ I & A_0 \end{array} \right),$$

and let

$$B = \left(\frac{B_0}{C_0} \right),$$

where B_0 has two rows and C_0 has three rows. Then

$$AB = \left(\begin{array}{c} 2B_0 \\ B_0 + A_0C_0 \end{array} \right).$$

Hence the only non-trivial computation required for AB is the product of the 2×3 matrix A_0 with the $3 \times p$ matrix C_0.

Exercises

1. Prove the first of the two assertions of the text concerning block multiplication: If $A = (A_1| \ldots |A_k)$ and

$$B = \left(\begin{array}{c} B_1 \\ \cdot \\ \cdot \\ \cdot \\ B_k \end{array} \right),$$

then $AB = A_1B_1 + \ldots + A_kB_k$.

2. Calculate AB in three ways: directly without partition; with the partition indicated; with a different partition of your own choosing.

$$A = \begin{pmatrix} 2 & 3 & 4 & 0 & 0 \\ 3 & 1 & 0 & 0 & 0 \\ \hline 1 & 0 & 1 & 0 & 1 \\ \hline -1 & 0 & 0 & 1 & 0 \\ 0 & -1 & 4 & 0 & 1 \end{pmatrix},$$

$$B = \begin{pmatrix} 1 & 0 & 0 \\ 3 & 0 & 0 \\ \hline 0 & 2 & 1 \\ \hline -1 & 0 & 0 \\ -1 & 0 & 0 \end{pmatrix}.$$

3. Suppose an $n \times n$ matrix A is of the form

$$A = \left(\begin{array}{c|c} A_1 & Z \\ \hline A_3 & A_4 \end{array} \right)$$

where Z is a $k \times (n - k)$ block of zeros.

(i) Consider the linear transformation T determined by A relative to a chosen basis $\{\alpha_1, \ldots, \alpha_n\}$. What is the geometric meaning of the block of zeros?

(ii) Suppose an $n \times n$ matrix B is also of the form described above for the matrix A. Prove by block multiplication that AB has this same property.

(iii) Prove the result of (ii) by a geometric argument.

CHAPTER 5

Linear Equations and Determinants

---

§5.1. *Systems of Linear Equations*

One of the most frequent applications of matrices to modern science arises from the need to solve a system of linear equations:

$$
\begin{aligned}
a_{11}\,x_1 + a_{12}\,x_2 + \ldots + a_{1n}\,x_n &= y_1 \\
a_{21}\,x_1 + a_{22}\,x_2 + \ldots + a_{2n}\,x_n &= y_2 \\
&\;\;\vdots \\
a_{m1}x_1 + a_{m2}x_2 + \ldots + a_{mn}x_n &= y_m.
\end{aligned}
$$

(5.1)

Here we consider the mn scalars a_{ij} and the m scalars y_i as fixed. By a *solution* of the system (*5.1*) we mean an n-tuple of scalars x_j, $j = 1, \ldots, n$, for which each of the m equations is satisfied. To *solve* the system means to find *all* solutions.

The system can be written in compact form by using matrix notation; let

$$
A = \begin{pmatrix} a_{11} & a_{12} & \ldots & a_{1n} \\ a_{21} & a_{22} & \ldots & a_{2n} \\ \vdots & \vdots & & \vdots \\ a_{m1} & a_{m2} & \ldots & a_{mn} \end{pmatrix}, \quad X = \begin{pmatrix} x_1 \\ x_2 \\ \vdots \\ x_n \end{pmatrix}, \quad Y = \begin{pmatrix} y_1 \\ y_2 \\ \vdots \\ y_m \end{pmatrix}.
$$

Then the system is represented by the single matrix equation,

(5.2)
$$
AX = Y.
$$

By taking the transpose of each side we obtain

$$(5.3) \qquad\qquad X'A' = Y',$$

which is in the form we have adopted for linear transformations: X' is a row vector of n components, A' an $n \times m$ matrix, and Y' a row vector of m components. Therefore, if we choose $\{\beta_1, \ldots, \beta_n\}$ as a basis for $\mathcal{W}_n$ and $\{\alpha_1, \ldots, \alpha_m\}$ as a basis for $\mathcal{V}_m$, A' represents a linear transformation $\mathbf{T}$ from $\mathcal{W}_n$ to $\mathcal{V}_m$, X' a vector ξ in $\mathcal{W}_n$, and Y' a vector η in $\mathcal{V}_m$:

$$(5.4) \qquad\qquad \xi\mathbf{T} = \eta.$$

In this section we shall develop the theory concerned with the existence and uniqueness of solutions, deferring several observations concerning specific methods of obtaining solutions until further properties of matrices are established. We remark first about notation; our choice of right hand notation for linear transformations has led to the necessity of considering transposes of the natural arrangement of the scalars of a system of linear equations, in order to reduce the system to right hand matric notation. Thus, while right hand notation seems preferable for the matric representation of linear transformations, left hand notation is more natural for the matric representation of systems of linear equations. This intrinsic difference is the underlying reason for a lack of uniformity in notation for matric representations. Since the passage from either notation to the other is easily performed by means of transposes, no real difficulty is encountered in consulting various references, provided we remember to ascertain which notation is adopted in each case.

In this section we shall make use of one fact about transposes which will be proved independently in Chapter 6: *A matrix and its transpose have the same rank.* Since the rank of a matrix is by definition the maximal number of linearly independent rows, the assertion is that in any matrix the maximal number of linearly independent columns equals the maximal number of linearly independent rows. This equality neutralizes the impression, which might have been created unintentionally, that rows are preferable to columns in some essential way. Any apparent preference for rows (or columns) is a consequence of the choice of notation.

To return to the problem of solving a system of linear equations, we have a given linear transformation $\mathbf{T}$ from $\mathcal{W}_n$ to $\mathcal{V}_m$, a given vector $\eta \in \mathcal{V}_m$, and we seek to find all $\xi \in \mathcal{W}_n$ which are mapped by $\mathbf{T}$ into η:

$$\xi\mathbf{T} = \eta.$$

In solving this problem we shall consider separately the cases $\eta = \theta$ and $\eta \neq \theta$; also, some of our conclusions will depend upon the relative magnitudes of the three positive integers m, n, $\rho(A)$, where (5.1) is a system of m equations in n unknowns whose matrix of coefficients has rank $\rho(A)$. Since $\rho(A) = \rho(A') = \rho(\mathbf{T})$, $\rho(A)$ cannot exceed either m or n.

The homogeneous case.   If $\eta = \theta$, or equivalently $y_1 = y_2 = \ldots = y_m = 0$, the system is said to be *homogeneous*.   In this case the set of all solutions ξ is simply the null space $\mathfrak{N}_\mathbf{T}$, whose dimension is $\nu(\mathbf{T}) = n - \rho(\mathbf{T}) = n - \rho(A) \geq 0$.   The zero vector θ is always a solution, called the *trivial* solution. There will exist non-trivial (non-zero) solutions if and only if $\nu(\mathbf{T}) > 0$.   This simple geometric argument has provided a full description of the solution of a homogeneous system of linear equations.

> **Theorem 5.1.**   If $y_1 = y_2 = \ldots = y_m = 0$, the solutions of *(5.1)* form a vector space of dimension $n - \rho(A)$.   Non-trivial solutions exist if and only if $n - \rho(A) > 0$.   Thus, if $m = n = \rho(A)$, the trivial solution is unique.

For $n = 3$, the geometric interpretation is that either $x_1 = x_2 = x_3 = 0$ is the only solution, or that every point on a certain line through the origin is a solution, or that every point on a certain plane through the origin is a solution.   (The case $\rho(A) = 0$ is not considered, since then $a_{ij} = 0$ for all i, j.)

The non-homogeneous case.   If $\eta \neq \theta$, or equivalently if some $y_j \neq 0$, the system is said to be *non-homogeneous*.   In this case the solution is the set of all vectors ξ which are mapped by $\mathbf{T}$ into η.   Since $\mathbf{T}$ and η are fixed by the given scalars a_{ij} and y_j, there is no assurance that even one solution exists. Clearly, a solution will exist if and only if $\eta \in \mathfrak{R}_\mathbf{T}$.   But $\mathfrak{R}_\mathbf{T}$ is spanned by the rows of A', which are the columns of A.   Hence, a solution exists if and only if the column vector Y is a linear combination of the columns of A.   Let us form a new matrix A_Y, called the *augmented* matrix of the system *(5.1)*, by adjoining the column vector Y to the matrix A: in partitioned form,

$$A_Y = (A|Y).$$

By our previous remark, a solution to *(5.1)* exists if and only if Y is a linear combination of the columns of A.   Taking transposes, Y' must then be a linear combination of the rows of A', so

$$\rho(A_Y) = \rho(A'_Y) = \rho(A') = \rho(A).$$

We have proved the following result.

> **Theorem 5.2.**   A solution of *(5.1)* exists if and only if $\rho(A_Y) = \rho(A)$, where A_Y is the augmented matrix

$$\begin{pmatrix} a_{11} & \cdots & a_{1n} & y_1 \\ a_{21} & \cdots & a_{2n} & y_2 \\ \cdot & & \cdot & \cdot \\ \cdot & & \cdot & \cdot \\ \cdot & & \cdot & \cdot \\ a_{m1} & \cdots & a_{mn} & y_m \end{pmatrix}.$$

Our next theorem describes the set of all solutions of the non-homogeneous system.

Theorem 5.3. If ξ_0 is a solution of the non-homogeneous system (5.4), then ξ is a solution if and only if

$$\xi = \xi_0 + \nu, \text{ for some } \nu \in \mathfrak{N}_T.$$

P R O O F : Let ξ and ξ_0 be solutions. Then $\xi T = \eta = \xi_0 T$. Hence $\xi T - \xi_0 T = (\xi - \xi_0)T = \eta - \eta = \theta$, so $\xi - \xi_0 \in \mathfrak{N}_T$. Conversely, if

$$\xi = \xi_0 + \nu \text{ for some } \nu \in \mathfrak{N}_T,$$

then

$$\xi T = (\xi_0 + \nu)T = \xi_0 T + \nu T = \eta + \theta = \eta,$$

so ξ is a solution.

The geometric meaning of this theorem is interesting. There may be no solutions to (5.4). If one solution ξ_0 exists, then the set of all solutions is a translation by ξ_0 of the subspace $\mathfrak{N}_T$ of all solutions of the associated homogeneous system. Hence, the solution set for $n = 3$ is void, a single point P, a line through P, or a plane through P. These are not subspaces in the non-homogeneous case, because then P is not the origin.

It is appropriate to comment further about Theorem 5.2. The condition that the rank of A equal the rank of the augmented matrix A_Y is called the *consistency condition*, and a system which satisfies this condition is said to be *consistent*. Thus a consistent system is simply one which has a solution. This is equivalent to saying that any linear dependence of the rows of A produces an identical dependence of the components of Y. More precisely, if γ_i denotes the ith row of A,

$$\sum_{i=1}^{m} c_i \gamma_i = \theta, \text{ if and only if } \sum_{i=1}^{m} c_i y_i = 0.$$

We conclude with a uniqueness theorem which is valid for both homogeneous and non-homogeneous systems.

Theorem 5.4.   If $m = n = \rho(A)$, there is a unique solution of (5.1).

P R O O F :   By hypothesis, A is a square matrix which is non-singular. Clearly, $X_0 = A^{-1}Y$ is a solution to (5.2), and for any solution X, $AX = Y$, so $X = A^{-1}Y = X_0$.

Exercises

1. Find a necessary and sufficient condition on $\rho(A)$ that the system (5.2) have a solution for all possible choices of Y.   Prove your result.

2.   (i) Describe geometrically the solutions of the single equation,

$$a_{i1}x_1 + a_{i2}x_2 + a_{i3}x_3 = y_i.$$

What if $y_i = 0$?

(ii) Describe geometrically the solutions of a system of two equations $(i = 1, 2)$ of the type in (i).   Need solutions exist?   Discuss fully.

(iii) In the non-homogeneous case with $m = n = 3$, discuss the geometric meaning of $\rho(A) = 1, 2, 3$, including in your discussion both consistency and non-consistency for each value of $\rho(A)$.

3. Solve the system,

$$
\begin{aligned}
x_1 - & x_2 + & x_3 - & x_4 + & x_5 &= 1 \\
2x_1 - & x_2 + 3x_3 & & + 4x_5 &= 2 \\
3x_1 - & 2x_2 + 2x_3 + & x_4 + & x_5 &= 1 \\
x_1 & & + x_3 + 2x_4 + & x_5 &= 0.
\end{aligned}
$$

4. Solve the system,

$$
\begin{aligned}
x_1 + 2x_2 + & x_3 &= -1 \\
6x_1 + x_2 + & x_3 &= -4 \\
2x_1 - 3x_2 - & x_3 &= 0 \\
-x_1 - 7x_2 - & 2x_3 &= 7 \\
x_1 - x_2 & &= 1.
\end{aligned}
$$

5. Solve the system,

$$
\begin{aligned}
2x_1 + x_2 + 5x_3 &= 4 \\
3x_1 - 2x_2 + 2x_3 &= 2 \\
5x_1 - 8x_2 - 4x_3 &= 1.
\end{aligned}
$$

§5.2. *Determinants*

It is quite likely that the reader has encountered determinants in his previous study of the solution of a system of n linear equations in n unknowns, particularly for the cases $n = 2, 3$.   If so, his estimate of their efficiency as a computational device may be unrealistically high, for while determinants are manageable enough for low values of n, they become quite unwieldy as n

increases. Since more economical methods of solving linear equations are available, determinants actually have little value as a general technique of computation. However, they do possess definite value as a theoretical tool, and for this reason we include a self-contained exposition of the basic properties of a determinant.

Our point of departure may appear at first to be outrageously abstract, but we shall soon see that this abstraction pays handsome dividends in the simplicity of the proofs of the properties of $n \times n$ determinants. This will be especially apparent to anyone who has worked through an inductive definition of determinants.

In formulating any definition abstractly we usually are guided by some knowledge of a special system which we wish to generalize. Here it suffices to consider the determinant of a 2×2 matrix,

$$\begin{vmatrix} a & b \\ c & d \end{vmatrix} = ad - bc.$$

First we recognize that a 2×2 determinant associates a field element with each 2×2 matrix, so this determinant is a function whose domain is the set of all 2×2 matrices over a field and whose range is a subset of the field. Now this function has many properties: of these we mention four, which are easily verified.

1. $\begin{vmatrix} a & kb \\ c & kd \end{vmatrix} = k \begin{vmatrix} a & b \\ c & d \end{vmatrix},$

2. $\begin{vmatrix} a & b + e \\ c & d + f \end{vmatrix} = \begin{vmatrix} a & b \\ c & d \end{vmatrix} + \begin{vmatrix} a & e \\ c & f \end{vmatrix},$

3. $\begin{vmatrix} a & a \\ c & c \end{vmatrix} = 0,$

4. $\begin{vmatrix} 1 & 0 \\ 0 & 1 \end{vmatrix} = 1.$

Since all of these properties, except the last, are assertions about columns, we shall agree to write A_i for the ith column vector of an $n \times n$ matrix; also to make clear the separation between columns, we insert commas:

$$A = (A_1, \ldots, A_n).$$

We are now ready to give an axiomatic definition of determinant.

Definition 5.1. A function "det" whose domain is the set of all $n \times n$ matrices over $\mathfrak{F}$ and whose range is a subset of $\mathfrak{F}$ is called a *determinant*, provided det satisfies three conditions:

(a) det is a linear function of each column; that is, for any $k = 1, 2, \ldots, n$ and all $b, c \in \mathfrak{F}$, if $A_k = bB_k + cC_k$ then

$$\det(A_1, \ldots, bB_k + cC_k, \ldots, A_n)$$
$$= b \det(A_1, \ldots, B_k, \ldots, A_n) + c \det(A_1, \ldots, C_k, \ldots, A_n);$$

(b) if two adjacent columns of A are equal, $\det A = 0$;

(c) $\det I = 1$, where I is the identity matrix and 1 is the unity element of $\mathfrak{F}$.

Notice that (a) combines the first two properties listed for the 2×2 example. It is a remarkable fact that we are able to derive most of the essential properties of determinants from the first and second axioms of Definition 5.1. The third axiom is a normalizing assumption which guarantees that det is uniquely defined, for we must prove that such a function is unique, and even that a function with these properties exists. Three problems are of immediate concern: to prove that det exists, to prove that det is uniquely determined, and to derive properties of det. We shall consider these problems in the reverse order.

Theorem 5.5. If det is a function with properties (a) and (b) of Definition 5.1, then

(a) $\det(A_1, \ldots, cA_k, \ldots, A_n) = c \det(A_1, \ldots, A_k, \ldots, A_n)$,

(b) $\det(A_1, \ldots, B_k + C_k, \ldots, A_n)$
$$= \det(A_1, \ldots, B_k, \ldots, A_n) + \det(A_1, \ldots, C_k, \ldots, A_n),$$

(c) if $A_k = \theta$, then $\det A = 0$,

(d) $\det(A_1, \ldots, A_k, \ldots, A_n) = \det(A_1, \ldots, A_k + cA_{k+1}, \ldots, A_n)$,

(e) $\det(A_1, \ldots, A_k, A_{k+1}, \ldots, A_n) = -\det(A_1, \ldots, A_{k+1}, A_k, \ldots, A_n)$,

(f) if $A_j = A_k$ for any $j \neq k$, then $\det A = 0$,

(g) $\det A = \det(A_1, \ldots, A_k + cA_j, \ldots, A_n)$ for any $j \neq k$,

(h) $\det(A_1, \ldots, A_i, \ldots, A_j, \ldots, A_n)$
$$= -\det(A_1, \ldots, A_j, \ldots, A_i, \ldots, A_n).$$

P R O O F : Before proving each statement, we translate it into words to emphasize its meaning.

(a) *A common factor of each element of a fixed column may be factored out as a multiplicative constant.* Let $b = 0$ in Definition 5.1 (a).

(b) *If a fixed column of A is written as the sum of two column vectors, the determinant of A is the sum of the two determinants as indicated.* Let $b = c = 1$ in Definition 5.1 (a).

(c) *If any column of A consists entirely of zeros, then $\det A = 0$.* Use (a) to factor out 0.

(d) *Any scalar multiple of a column may be added to an adjacent column without changing the value of the determinant.* Use (b) to expand the altered determinant into the sum of two determinants. One of these two is det A; the other is $\det(A_1, \ldots, cA_{k+1}, A_{k+1}, \ldots, A_n) = 0$, since c factors out and then Definition 5.1 (b) may be applied.

(c) *If two adjacent columns are interchanged, the value of the determinant merely changes sign.* First add A_{k+1} to A_k, using (d); then subtract the new k^{th} column from A_{k+1}. This gives

$$\det A = \det(A_1, \ldots, A_k + A_{k+1}, - A_k, \ldots, A_n)$$
$$= \det(A_1, \ldots, A_{k+1}, - A_k, \ldots, A_n)$$
$$= -\det(A_1, \ldots, A_{k+1}, A_k, \ldots, A_n).$$

The interchange of two adjacent columns is called a *transposition*.

(f) *If any two columns are equal, the determinant is zero.* Use (e) repeatedly to bring the equal columns into adjacent position, changing the sign of the determinant at each transposition. Then apply Definition 5.1 (b).

(g) *Any constant multiple of a column may be added to any other column without changing the value of the determinant.* Transpose one of the two columns repeatedly until it is adjacent to the other, and apply (d). Then transpose the moving column back to its original position. The number of transpositions needed to do all of this is even, so the result follows from (e).

(h) *If any two columns are interchanged, the determinant merely changes sign.* Transpose A_j repeatedly until it replaces A_k. If this requires p transpositions, then A_k can be moved from its new position (adjacent to its old one) to the original position of A_j in $p - 1$ transpositions. The interchange can be accomplished in an odd number of adjacent interchanges, and (e) may be applied.

Exercises

1. Consider Definition 5.1 for $n = 2$. Let A, B be any 2×2 matrices.

   (i) Calculate $\det(BA)$ using *only* the properties proved in Theorem 5.5, obtaining an answer in the form $k \det B$, for some scalar k which is a combination of the entries of A.

   (ii) Specialize the result in (i) to the case $B = I$, thus showing that the specific form stated in the text for 2×2 matrices is actually a consequence of Definition 5.1.

2. Show that in $\mathcal{E}_2$ the absolute value of det A is the area of the parallelogram determined by the row vectors of A.

3. Consider the system of equations

$$ax + by = e$$
$$cx + dy = f.$$

$$\begin{bmatrix} a & b & e \\ c & d & f \end{bmatrix} = det \begin{vmatrix} a & b \\ c & d \end{vmatrix}$$

(i) Express the consistency condition in determinant form.

(ii) Express the solution, assuming existence and uniqueness, in determinant form.

§5.3. *An Explicit Form for det A*

We continue with the program declared in the last section—to investigate properties of det, and particularly to show that such a function exists and is uniquely defined by Definition 5.1.   The first step is to obtain an explicit form for det A.   For any $n \times n$ matrix B let $C = BA$; then the kth column of C is given by $C_k = \sum_{j=1}^{n} B_j a_{jk}$, where B_j is the jth column of B.   Hence

$$\det C = \det(C_1, \ldots, C_n) = \det\left(\sum_{j=1}^{n} B_j a_{j1}, \ldots, \sum_{j=1}^{n} B_j a_{jn}\right),$$

where each index of summation runs independently of the others.   Each column is the sum of n columns, and we may use Definition 5.1 (a) on each column in succession to expand det C to a sum of n^n determinants:

$$\det C = \sum \det(B_{j_1} a_{j_1 1}, B_{j_2} a_{j_2 2}, \ldots, B_{j_n} a_{j_n n}),$$

where the summation is extended over all possible values of the indices, each running from 1 to n.   By Theorem 5.5 (f), the only non-zero determinants of this sum are the ones in which $j_1, \ldots, j_n$ are all different—in other words, the subscripts of the various B's form a permutation of $1, \ldots, n$.   Hence

$$\det C = \sum \det(B_{p(1)} a_{p(1)1}, \ldots, B_{p(n)} a_{p(n)n})$$
$$= \sum [a_{p(1)1} \ldots a_{p(n)n} \det(B_{p(1)}, \ldots, B_{p(n)})]$$

since, for each j, $a_{p(j)j}$ factors out of the jth column.   Here the summation is extended over all permutations p of $1, \ldots, n$.   It is well known (see References, 1 or 2) that each permutation p can be classified as even or odd according to whether p can be represented as a product of an even or an odd number of transpositions.   But each transposition of columns of B produces a change in the sign of det B.   Hence

$$\det(B_{p(1)}, \ldots, B_{p(n)}) = \pm \det B,$$

where the $+$ sign is used if p is an even permutation and the $-$ sign is used if p is odd.   Then we have

$$\det C = \det B \cdot \sum_{\text{all } p} [\pm a_{p(1)1} \ldots a_{p(n)n}].$$

$C = AB$ det C = det $B \cdot$ det A

Now *for the first time* we use property (c) of Definition 5.1. Since this last equation is true for all $n \times n$ matrices A and B, we may specify $B = I$. Then $C = IA = A$, and det $B = \det I = 1$, yielding an expression for det A in terms of the elements of A.

We have proved several important results which are now stated explicitly.

Theorem 5.6. If a function det exists with the properties of Definition 5.1, then for every square matrix A,

$$\det A = \sum_p \pm [a_{p(1)1}a_{p(2)2} \ldots a_{p(n)n}],$$

where the sum is extended over all permutations p of the integers $1, 2, \ldots, n$ and where a $+$ or $-$ sign is affixed to each product according to whether p is even or odd.

Thus det A is an algebraic sum of all products of n terms which can be formed by selecting exactly one term from each row and each column of A.

Theorem 5.7. If A' is the transpose of A, then

$$\det A' = \det A.$$

Theorem 5.7 follows from the representation of det A as a sum of products of elements of A, each product containing exactly one element from each row and each column. Hence in Theorem 5.5 the statements about columns are valid for rows.

Theorem 5.8. $\det(AB) = (\det A)(\det B) = \det(BA)$.

PROOF: Exercise.

Theorem 5.6 is a uniqueness theorem because it states that any function det which satisfies Definition 5.1 must assign to A a value det A which is completely described by the elements of A. But we have not yet proved that a function exists which has the properties assumed for det. One way to settle the existence question is to verify that the specific function described by Theorem 5.6 satisfies the three properties of Definition 5.1. Such a proof is possible, but an alternative method is chosen here.

To prove that det exists for every n, we proceed by induction. For $n = 1$, $A = (a)$, and we let det $A = a$. This function trivially satisfies Definition 5.1. Now assume that such a function exists for square matrices of dimension $n - 1$. For an $n \times n$ matrix A define

$$\det A = \sum_{j=1}^{n} a_{ij}|A_{ij}|,$$

where i is any fixed value $1, 2, \ldots, n$, and $|A_{ij}|$ is the $(n-1) \times (n-1)$ determinant obtained by deleting the ith row and the jth column of A and affixing the sign $(-1)^{i+j}$.   Thus,

$$
|A_{ij}| = (-1)^{i+j} \det
\begin{pmatrix}
a_{11} & \ldots & a_{1j} & \ldots & a_{1n} \\
\vdots & & \vdots & & \vdots \\
a_{i1} & \ldots & a_{ij} & \ldots & a_{in} \\
\vdots & & \vdots & & \vdots \\
a_{n1} & \ldots & a_{nj} & \ldots & a_{nn}
\end{pmatrix}
$$

We next verify that det has the three properties of Definition 5.1.

(a) First, suppose $A_k = bB_k + cC_k$.   Then

$$A = (A_1, \ldots, A_k, \ldots, A_n).$$

Let

$$B = (A_1, \ldots, bB_k, \ldots, A_n)$$

and

$$C = (A_1, \ldots, cC_k, \ldots, A_n),$$

so that B and C coincide with A except in the kth column.   If $j = k$, $a_{ik}|A_{ik}| = (bb_{ik} + cc_{ik})|A_{ik}| = bb_{ik}|B_{ik}| + cc_{ik}|C_{ik}|$, since $|A_{ik}| = |B_{ik}| = |C_{ik}|$.   If $j \neq k$,

$$
|A_{ij}| = (-1)^{i+j} \det
\begin{pmatrix}
a_{11} & \ldots & a_{1j} & \ldots & a_{1k} & \ldots & a_{1n} \\
\vdots & & \vdots & & \vdots & & \vdots \\
a_{i1} & \ldots & a_{ij} & \ldots & a_{ik} & \ldots & a_{in} \\
\vdots & & \vdots & & \vdots & & \vdots \\
a_{n1} & \ldots & a_{nj} & \ldots & a_{nk} & \ldots & a_{nn}
\end{pmatrix}
$$

where $a_{hk} = bb_{hk} + cc_{hk}$.   By the induction hypothesis, an $(n-1) \times (n-1)$ determinant is a linear function of any column, so for $j \neq k$

$$a_{ij}|A_{ij}| = a_{ij}(b|B_{ij}| + c|C_{ij}|) = bb_{ij}|B_{ij}| + cc_{ij}|C_{ij}|.$$

Finally,

$$\det A = \sum_{j=1}^{n} a_{ij}|A_{ij}| = \sum_{j=1}^{n} (bb_{ij}|B_{ij}| + cc_{ij}|C_{ij}|) = b \det B + c \det C.$$

(b) Next, suppose $A_k = A_{k+1}$ for some k.   If $j \neq k$, $j \neq k+1$, then $|A_{ij}| = 0$, since two adjacent columns of this determinant are equal.   Hence

$$\det A = a_{ik}|A_{ik}| + a_{i, k+1}|A_{i, k+1}| = 0,$$

since $a_{ik} = a_{i, k+1}$ and $|A_{ik}| = -|A_{i, k+1}|$.

(c) Finally, if $A = I_n$,

$$\det I_n = \sum_{j=1}^{n} a_{ij}|A_{ij}| = |A_{ii}| = \det I_{n-1} = 1.$$

Thus a determinant function exists for all n.

While an existence proof is necessary for logical completeness, the fact that det exists does not surprise us. However, in the proof we have established a useful method of evaluating determinants. In the notation used above, $|A_{ij}|$ is called the *cofactor* of a_{ij}, and the equation

$$\det A = \sum_{j=1}^{n} a_{ij}|A_{ij}|, \text{ for fixed } i,$$

is the rule for expanding det A according to the elements of the ith row. The corresponding result,

$$\det A = \sum_{i=1}^{n} a_{ij}|A_{ij}|, \text{ for fixed } j,$$

holds for columns. These results are summarized below.

Definition 5.2. The *cofactor* $|A_{ij}|$ of a_{ij} in det A is $(-1)^{i+j}$ times the determinant of the matrix obtained by deleting the ith row and j^{th} column of A.

Theorem 5.9.

(i) $\det A = \sum_{j=1}^{n} a_{ij}|A_{ij}|$ for fixed i.

(ii) $\det A = \sum_{i=1}^{n} a_{ij}|A_{ij}|$ for fixed j.

Theorem 5.10.

$$\delta_{ik}\det A = \sum_{j=1}^{n} a_{ij}|A_{kj}|,$$

where δ_{ik} is the Kronecker delta.

PROOF: Exercise.

The following example illustrates some of the properties discussed above. The common notation which replaces det A by $|A|$ is employed here.

$$\begin{vmatrix} 3 & 1 & -2 & 4 \\ 2 & 0 & -5 & 1 \\ 1 & -1 & 2 & 6 \\ -2 & 3 & -2 & 3 \end{vmatrix} \underset{\substack{\text{Add } R_1 \\ \text{to } R_3}}{=} \begin{vmatrix} 3 & 1 & -2 & 4 \\ 2 & 0 & -5 & 1 \\ 4 & 0 & 0 & 10 \\ -2 & 3 & -2 & 3 \end{vmatrix}$$

$$\underset{\substack{\text{Add } -3R_1 \\ \text{to } R_4}}{=} \begin{vmatrix} 3 & 1 & -2 & 4 \\ 2 & 0 & -5 & 1 \\ 4 & 0 & 0 & 10 \\ -11 & 0 & 4 & -9 \end{vmatrix} \underset{\substack{\text{Expand by} \\ \text{elements of } C_2}}{=} (-1) \begin{vmatrix} 2 & -5 & 1 \\ 4 & 0 & 10 \\ -11 & 4 & -9 \end{vmatrix}$$

$$\underset{\substack{\text{Add } -2C_3 \text{ to } C_1 \\ \text{and } 5C_3 \text{ to } C_2}}{=} (-1) \begin{vmatrix} 0 & 0 & 1 \\ -16 & 50 & 10 \\ 7 & -41 & 9 \end{vmatrix} \underset{\substack{\text{Expand by} \\ \text{elements of } R_1}}{=} (-1) \begin{vmatrix} -16 & 50 \\ 7 & -41 \end{vmatrix}$$

$$= -[(-16)(-41) - (50)(7)] = -306.$$

Exercises

1. Prove Theorem 5.8.

2. Prove Theorem 5.10.

3. Illustrate Theorem 5.10 by calculating $\sum_{j=1}^{3} a_{ij}|A_{kj}|$ for $i = 1$, $k = 2$, and for $i = 2$, $k = 2$, given

$$A = \begin{pmatrix} 1 & -1 & -2 \\ -2 & 3 & 1 \\ 2 & -2 & x \end{pmatrix}.$$

4. By applying the remark which immediately follows Theorem 5.6, show that if an $n \times n$ matrix can be partitioned in the form

$$A = \left(\begin{array}{c|c} E & Z \\ \hline G & H \end{array} \right),$$

where E is a square matrix and Z consists entirely of zeros, then $\det A = (\det E)(\det H)$.

5.   (i) How many terms are involved in the representation of $\det A$ by the method of Theorem 5.6?

(ii) How many multiplications are required to evaluate $\det A$ by the method of Theorem 5.6?

(iii) How many multiplications are required to evaluate $\det A$ by the method of Theorem 5.9?

6. The Vandermonde matrix of order n is, by definition,

$$V(x_1, \ldots, x_n) = \begin{pmatrix} 1 & 1 & \ldots 1 \\ x_1 & x_2 & \ldots x_n \\ x_1^2 & x_2^2 & \ldots x_n^2 \\ \cdot & \cdot & \cdot \\ \cdot & \cdot & \cdot \\ \cdot & \cdot & \cdot \\ x_1^{n-1} & x_2^{n-1} & \ldots x_n^{n-1} \end{pmatrix}.$$

(i) For $n = 2, 3$ verify that $\det V = \underset{1 \le i < j \le n}{\Pi} (x_j - x_i)$, where Π denotes "product."

(ii) Prove this statement for all $n > 1$.

§5.4. *The Inverse of a Matrix: Adjoint Method*

One of the most useful properties of the determinant function is that it provides a simple characterization of non-singular matrices. Furthermore, the cofactors of a non-singular matrix can be used to calculate its inverse by a method which is inefficient for large n, but quite easy for $n \leq 4$. Other methods for computing A^{-1} are described in the next chapter.

Theorem 5.11. A is non-singular if and only if det $A \neq 0$. If A is non-singular, $\det(A^{-1}) = (\det A)^{-1}$.

P R O O F :   If A is singular, then its rows are linearly dependent, by Theorem 4.6. Using the results of Theorem 5.5 for rows instead of columns, we can obtain a row of zeros in a determinant whose value is det A. Hence det $A = 0$. Conversely, if A is non-singular, A^{-1} exists and

$$\det A \det A^{-1} = \det (AA^{-1}) = \det I = 1,$$

so det $A \neq 0$.

The first method we describe for calculating A^{-1} is called the *adjoint method*. We now define the term *adjoint*.

Definition 5.3. The *adjoint* of an $n \times n$ matrix $A = (a_{ij})$ is the $n \times n$ matrix adj $A = (a_{ij}^*)$, where $a_{ij}^* = |A_{ji}| = $ cofactor of a_{ji} in det A.

We note in particular two things about the adjoint: first, the elements of adj A are determinants formed from A, each with a suitable sign attached (see Definition 5.2); second, the element in the (i, j) position of adj A is the cofactor of the element in the (j, i) position of A.

Theorem 5.12. If A is non-singular, then

$$A^{-1} = \lfloor \det A \rfloor^{-1} \operatorname{adj} A.$$

P R O O F :   We calculate A adj $A = (b_{ij})$ where

$$b_{ij} = \sum_{k=1}^{n} a_{ik}a_{kj}^* = \sum_{k=1}^{n} a_{ik}|A_{jk}|$$

$$= \delta_{ij} \det A \text{ by Theorem 5.10.}$$

Hence A adj $A = (\delta_{ij} \det A) = (\det A)I$, from which the theorem follows.

EXAMPLE

  Let

$$A = \begin{pmatrix} -2 & 1 & 3 \\ 0 & -1 & 1 \\ 1 & 2 & 0 \end{pmatrix}.$$

Then $\det A = 8$.   To compute a_{12}^* we find the cofactor of a_{21}:

$$|A_{21}| = (-1) \begin{vmatrix} 1 & 3 \\ 2 & 0 \end{vmatrix} = 6.$$

Similar computations yield

$$\text{adj } A = \begin{pmatrix} -2 & 6 & 4 \\ 1 & -3 & 2 \\ 1 & 5 & 2 \end{pmatrix},$$

and therefore

$$A^{-1} = \frac{\text{adj } A}{8} = \begin{pmatrix} -\frac{1}{4} & \frac{3}{4} & \frac{1}{2} \\ \frac{1}{8} & -\frac{3}{8} & \frac{1}{4} \\ \frac{1}{8} & \frac{5}{8} & \frac{1}{4} \end{pmatrix}.$$

It is simpler of course to leave $\frac{1}{8}$ factored in front of adj A.

  Now let us return to the problem of solving a system of n linear equations in n unknowns.   In the notation of § 5.1, $AX = Y$, where A is an $n \times n$ matrix which we here assume to be non-singular.   The unique solution is given by the column vector,

$$X = A^{-1}Y = (\det A)^{-1}(\text{adj } A)Y.$$

Hence

$$x_i = (\det A)^{-1} \sum_{j=1}^{n} a_{ij}^* y_j = (\det A)^{-1} \sum_{j=1}^{n} |A_{ji}| y_j.$$

The terms under the summation sign are easily seen to be the terms of the expansion by elements of the ith column of the determinant

$$\det A_{Y(i)} = \det \begin{pmatrix} a_{11} & \cdots & a_{1,i-1} & y_1 & a_{1,i+1} & \cdots & a_{1n} \\ \cdot & & \cdot & \cdot & \cdot & & \cdot \\ \cdot & & \cdot & \cdot & \cdot & & \cdot \\ \cdot & & \cdot & \cdot & \cdot & & \cdot \\ a_{n1} & \cdots & a_{n,i-1} & y_n & a_{n,i+1} & \cdots & a_{nn} \end{pmatrix},$$

where $A_{Y(i)}$ agrees with A except in the ith column, where Y has replaced A_i. This result is known as Cramer's rule.

  Theorem 5.13.   If the determinant of coefficients of the system of linear equations

$$a_{11}x_1 + \ldots + a_{1n}x_n = y_1$$

$$\cdot \qquad\qquad \cdot \qquad \cdot$$
$$\cdot \qquad\qquad \cdot \qquad \cdot$$
$$\cdot \qquad\qquad \cdot \qquad \cdot$$

$$a_{n1}x_1 + \ldots + a_{nn}x_n = y_n$$

is not zero, then the unique solution is given by

$$x_i = \frac{\det (A_1, \ldots, A_{i-1}, Y, A_{i+1}, \ldots, A_n)}{\det (A_1, \ldots, A_{i-1}, A_i, A_{i+1}, \ldots, A_n)}, \, i = 1, 2, \ldots, n.$$

The amount of work involved in the solution of a linear system by Cramer's rule is the same as in solving by calculating A^{-1} by the adjoint method. Both methods are unnecessarily cumbersome for large n, and for small values of n the method of direct algebraic elimination is often simpler than either the adjoint method or Cramer's rule.

To underline the practical importance of these remarks, consider the problem of solving a system of 25 linear equations in 25 unknowns. Cramer's rule requires the evaluation of 26 determinants of order 25. If either Theorem 5.6 or Theorem 5.9 is used to evaluate these determinants, a total of 26! multiplications are required, a number of the order 10^{26}. A computer which performs 1000 multiplications per second would require 10^{16} years for the calculation. However, by making use of other computational techniques, systems of more than 2000 equations have been solved recently. In the next section a method is described in which a system of n equations can be solved by means of only n^3 multiplications, and $n^3 < n!$ whenever $n > 5$.

Exercises

1. Solve the following system of equations

$$2x_1 - x_2 + 3x_3 = 3$$
$$x_2 = -2$$
$$2x_1 + x_2 + x_3 = 1$$

   (i) by the adjoint method of calculating A^{-1},
   (ii) by Cramer's rule,
   (iii) by direct algebraic elimination.

2. Prove that every square skew-symmetric matrix of odd dimension is singular.

3. In $\mathcal{E}_3$, let $A(a_1, a_2, a_3)$, $B(b_1, b_2, b_3)$, $C(c_1, c_2, c_3)$ be three points, not all on the same line. Prove that an equation for the plane determined by A, B, and C is

$$\begin{vmatrix} x_1 & x_2 & x_3 & 1 \\ a_1 & a_2 & a_3 & 1 \\ b_1 & b_2 & b_3 & 1 \\ c_1 & c_2 & c_3 & 1 \end{vmatrix} = 0.$$

(handwritten margin note: from Thm 5.12 adj $A = (\det A) A^{-1}$ $\det$ adj $A = \det (\det A)$ $\cdot \det (A^{-1})$)

4. Prove that $\det(\text{adj } A) = (\det A)^{n-1}$.

5. For what values of x is the following matrix singular?

$$\begin{pmatrix} 3 - x & 2 & 2 \\ 1 & 4 - x & 1 \\ -2 & -4 & -1 - x \end{pmatrix}$$

6. Show that A is non-singular, where

$$A = \begin{pmatrix} 1^0 & 1^1 & \cdots & 1^{n-1} \\ 2^0 & 2^1 & \cdots & 2^{n-1} \\ \cdot & \cdot & & \cdot \\ \cdot & \cdot & & \cdot \\ \cdot & \cdot & & \cdot \\ (n-1)^0 & (n-1)^1 & \cdots & (n-1)^{n-1} \end{pmatrix}.$$

7. Show that the determinant of a triangular matrix is the product of its diagonal elements. Use this fact to solve Exercise 3, § 4.4.

8. Let A be a singular $n \times n$ matrix.

(i) Prove that if $n = 1, 2$, then A^2 is proportional to A.

(ii) Show that A^2 need not be proportional to A whenever $n > 2$.

(iii) How are these results related to Exercise 6, § 3.3?

9. Read "Solving Linear Equations Can Be Interesting," by G. E. Forsythe, *Bulletin of the American Mathematical Society*, vol. 59 (1953), pp. 299-329.

§5.5. *Operations on Linear Systems*

The solution of the system (*5.1*) of m linear equations in n unknowns by direct algebraic elimination is of such fundamental importance that it deserves analysis here in spite of its apparent simplicity. The idea which underlies most methods is that of horse-trading: to find all the solutions of (*5.1*) we exchange this set of m equations in n unknowns for another set which has exactly the same solutions but which is in some sense preferable. The process can be repeated, in order to obtain an equivalent system of the form

$$x_{1'} = c_1 + b_{1,(r+1)}x_{(r+1)'} + \ldots + b_{1n}x_{n'}$$
$$x_{2'} = c_2 + b_{2,(r+1)}x_{(r+1)'} + \ldots + b_{2n}x_{n'}$$

(5.5)

$$x_{r'} = c_r + b_{r,(r+1)}x_{(r+1)'} + \ldots + b_{rn}x_{n'}$$

where $\{1', 2', \ldots, n'\}$ is a permutation of $\{1, 2, \ldots, n\}$, and where the b's and c's are scalars. Then any solution is obtained by assigning arbitrary values to $x_{i'}$ for $r < i \leq n$ and calculating $x_{1'}, \ldots, x_{r'}$ from (5.5). Of course, r is simply the rank of the matrix A of the coefficients of (5.1).

Now let us formalize these ideas: Two systems of linear equations are said to be *equivalent* if and only if any solution of either system is a solution of the other. In manipulating equations we wish to be certain that any operations we perform will produce a system which is equivalent to the original system. What operations are permissible under this requirement? First, it is apparent that the solution is not affected by the order in which the equations are written. Hence any permutation of the arrangement of the equations will produce an equivalent system. Second, any equation may be replaced by a non-zero scalar multiple of itself. Since such a scalar has a reciprocal, the process can be reversed, and so the two systems are equivalent. Third, an equation can be replaced by the sum of itself and any other equation in the system. In summary, we consider three types of *elementary operations:*

P: permutation of any two equations,

M: multiplication of any equation by a non-zero scalar,

A: addition of one equation to another.

It will be noted that the three elementary operations correspond to row operations which are useful in evaluating determinants by replacing a given determinant by an equal determinant which is simpler. In this connection, "simpler" usually means that the new determinant contains more zeros, or at least a more useful arrangement of zeros. The effect of each of these operations on a determinant is described by Theorem 5.5 (h), (a), and (g), interpreted for rows instead of columns. The effect of each of these row operations on a matrix will be considered in some detail in the next chapter.

There is another general approach to the solution of (5.1) which leads us to a different type of operation on matrices and which has recently received recognition as being the essential arithmetic process of the simplex method for solving problems in linear programming. The system

$$y_1 = a_{11}x_1 + \ldots + a_{1n}x_n$$

(5.6)

$$y_i = a_{i1}x_1 + \ldots + a_{in}x_n$$

$$y_m = a_{m1}x_1 + \ldots + a_{mn}x_n$$

expresses the numbers $y_1, \ldots, y_m$ (usually regarded as known) as known linear combinations of the numbers $x_1, \ldots, x_n$ (usually regarded as unknown). The objective in solving the system is to express the x_i as linear combinations of the y_j—in simplest terms, to reverse the roles of the x_i and the y_j in this system. Suppose that $a_{ij} \neq 0$. Then we can solve for x_j in terms of y_i and the x_k, for $k \neq j$:

$$x_j = a_{ij}^{-1}[-a_{i1}x_1 - \ldots - a_{i,j-1}x_{j-1} + y_i - a_{i,j+1}x_{j+1} - \ldots - a_{in}x_n].$$

This expression may be substituted for x_j in each of the other equations to produce the system

$$y_1 = (a_{11} - a_{ij}^{-1}a_{i1}a_{1j})x_1 + \ldots + a_{ij}^{-1}a_{1j}y_i + \ldots + (a_{1n} - a_{ij}^{-1}a_{in}a_{1j})x_n$$

$$x_j = \quad - a_{ij}^{-1}a_{i1}x_1 \quad - \ldots + a_{ij}^{-1}y_i \quad - \ldots \quad - a_{ij}^{-1}a_{in}x_n$$

$$y_m = (a_{m1} - a_{ij}^{-1}a_{i1}a_{mj})x_1 + \ldots + a_{ij}^{-1}a_{mj}y_i + \ldots + (a_{mn} - a_{ij}^{-1}a_{in}a_{mj})x_n.$$

Such an operation is called a *pivot operation* on a_{ij}. Since the steps are reversible this system is equivalent to (5.6). By a finite succession of such pivot operations it may be possible to obtain an equivalent system in the form (5.5) in which each left hand side is an x_i and each right hand side is a linear combination of the y_j and those x_k which do not appear on the left. If so, the system is thereby solved.

In terms of the matrix of coefficients, a pivot operation on a_{ij} replaces the matrix A of the system (5.6),

$$A = \begin{pmatrix} a_{11} & \ldots & a_{1j} & \ldots & a_{1n} \\ & & & & \\ a_{i1} & \ldots & a_{ij} & \ldots & a_{in} \\ & & & & \\ a_{m1} & \ldots & a_{mj} & \ldots & a_{mn} \end{pmatrix}$$

by the matrix B of the equivalent system, shown above, where

$$b_{rs} = \begin{cases} a_{rs} - a_{ij}^{-1}a_{rj}a_{is} = a_{ij}^{-1}\det\begin{pmatrix} a_{rs} & a_{rj} \\ a_{is} & a_{ij} \end{pmatrix}, & \text{if } r \neq i \text{ and } s \neq j \\ a_{ij}^{-1}a_{rj}, & \text{if } r \neq i \text{ and } s = j \\ -a_{ij}^{-1}a_{is}, & \text{if } r = i \text{ and } s \neq j \\ a_{ij}^{-1}, & \text{if } r = i \text{ and } s = j. \end{cases}$$

The computations of a pivot operation can be arranged so that only 1 division and $mn - 1$ multiplications are required. Since n pivot operations will suffice to invert a non-singular $n \times n$ matrix, the process requires at most n divisions and $n^3 - n$ multiplications.

EXAMPLE

To illustrate the use of pivot operations in solving linear systems, we consider the example of Exercise 1, § 5.4.

$$\begin{aligned} 2x_1 - x_2 + 3x_3 &= \quad 3 \quad y_1 \\ x_2 \quad\quad &= -2 \quad y_2 \\ 2x_1 + x_2 + \ x_3 &= \quad 1. \quad y_3 \end{aligned}$$

The coefficients can be listed in tabular form as follows.

x_1	x_2	x_3		
2	-1	3	$y_1 =$	3
0	1*	0	$y_2 =$	-2
2	1	1	$y_3 =$	1

A pivot on the element marked with an asterisk is equivalent to solving for x_2 in terms of x_1, x_3, and y_2, and produces the following table.

x_1	y_2	x_3	
2	-1	3	y_1
0	1	0	x_2
2	1	1*	y_3

It is an accident due to the numbers of this example that this table is unchanged from the previous one. A second pivot (on the element marked with an asterisk) solves for x_3 in terms of x_1, y_2, and y_3 and produces the following table.

x_1	y_2	y_3	
-4*	-4	3	y_1
0	1	0	x_2
-2	-1	1	x_3

Finally a third pivot solves for x_1 in terms of y_1, y_2, and y_3.

y_1	y_2	y_3	
$-\frac{1}{4}$	-1	$\frac{3}{4}$	x_1
0	1	0	x_2
$\frac{1}{2}$	1	$-\frac{1}{2}$	x_3

The solution is read from this table by writing

$$x_1 = -\tfrac{1}{4}y_1 - 1y_2 + \tfrac{3}{4}y_3 = -\tfrac{3}{4} + 2 + \tfrac{3}{4} = \;\;\; 2$$
$$x_2 = \;\;\; 0y_1 + 1y_2 + 0y_3 = \;\;\; 0 - 2 + 0 = -2$$
$$x_3 = \;\;\; \tfrac{1}{2}y_1 + 1y_2 - \tfrac{1}{2}y_3 = \;\;\; \tfrac{3}{2} - 2 - \tfrac{1}{2} = -1.$$

This scheme provides an effective method of solution, especially for large n, by systematically interchanging an x for a y as long as this is possible. Further examples are suggested in Exercise 1, below.

Pivot operations can be used to define an interesting and useful relation between matrices, called *combinatorial equivalence*. However, since combinatorial equivalence is not used as a central method in the remainder of this book, it is discussed in Appendix B rather than in the next chapter, where we shall study various other equivalence relations.

Exercises

1. Solve the following systems by the use of pivot operations:

    (i) Exercise 3, § 5.1,
    (ii) Exercise 4, § 5.1,
    (iii) Exercise 5, § 5.1.

2. Let A be an $n \times n$ matrix, let $a_{ij} \neq 0$, and let B be the matrix obtained from A by pivoting on a_{ij}. Prove that

$$\det B = a_{ij}^{-1} |A_{ij}|.$$

3. Given $A = \begin{pmatrix} 1 & -2 & -1 \\ 2 & 3 & 1 \\ 0 & 5 & -2 \end{pmatrix}$.

    (i) Compute $\det A$.
    (ii) Pivot on $a_{11} = 1$ to obtain a matrix B, and verify the result of Exercise 2.
    (iii) Pivot B on $b_{22} = 7$ to obtain a matrix C, and again verify the result of Exercise 2.
    (iv) Pivot C on $c_{33} = -\frac{29}{7}$ to obtain a matrix D.
    (v) Show that $D = A^{-1}$.

(vi) Show that det A equals the product of the pivots used in transforming A to A^{-1}.

4. Let A be an $n \times n$ matrix, let $a_{ij} \neq 0$, and let B be the $(n - 1) \times (n - 1)$ matrix obtained by pivoting A on a_{ij} and then deleting the ith row and j^{th} column. Prove that

$$\det A = a_{ij} \det B.$$

5. Let A be an $n \times n$ matrix partitioned as follows:

$$A = \begin{pmatrix} A_1 & \beta \\ \gamma & d \end{pmatrix},$$

where A_1 is a $(n - 1) \times (n - 1)$ matrix, β is an $(n - 1)$ column vector, γ is a $(n - 1)$ row vector, and d is a scalar. Then in terms of matrix multiplication $\beta\gamma$ is an $(n - 1) \times (n - 1)$ matrix.

(i) Show that $\det A = d^{2-n} \det(dA_1 - \beta\gamma)$.

(ii) Show also that $dA_1 - \beta\gamma$ can be computed with at most $2(n - 1)^2$ multiplications, and therefore by successive applications of this method det A can be computed by no more than $2n^3/3$ multiplications.

(iii) For what values of n does this method of evaluating det A require more multiplications than those of Theorem 5.6 and Theorem 5.9?

CHAPTER 6

Equivalence Relations on Matrices

§6.1. *Introduction*

In § 5.5 we skirmished tentatively with the central problem of matrix theory; we now need to describe the problem in more definite terms, because a major portion of the next four chapters will bear directly on its solution.

First we should recognize that we have already used matrices to describe two different mathematical entities: linear transformations and systems of linear equations. In Chapters 9 and 10 we shall see that matrices can represent still other mathematical structures, each of which has its own distinctive problems and methods which in turn can be used to define corresponding matric concepts.

For the case of linear transformations the matric representation is made in terms of pre-selected bases which were fixed throughout the discussion. Presumably then, a different choice of bases would have resulted in a different matric representation of the same transformation. But since a linear transformation is a vector space homomorphism, it is intrinsically independent of the coordinate systems (bases) of the spaces involved, and any matrix which represents a fixed linear transformation reflects the properties of that transformation. Therefore, as we vary the bases we can expect to obtain different representative matrices which share certain common properties. We wonder how such matrices are related to each other, and particularly how we can select a "simplest" matrix to represent that linear transformation.

Now let us return to the problem of solving a system of linear equations. As described in § 5.5, the general method is to exchange the given system for an equivalent system, that is, one with precisely the same solutions as the original.   By so doing we exchange the given coefficient matrix for another matrix.   Since a matrix reflects the properties of the system it represents, different matrices which represent equivalent systems must have certain properties in common.   Again we wonder how such matrices are related to each other and how we can find a "simplest" representative matrix.

In order to deal effectively with such problems we need to use the concept of *equivalence relation*. Relations are discussed generally in Appendix A, § A.2, and equivalence relations are treated in Appendix A, § A.7, but for convenience we summarize here some essential facts concerning equivalence relations.   Let M denote any non-void set; as a specific example we might think of M as the set of all $m \times n$ matrices whose entries are elements of a field $\mathfrak{F}$.   Let the symbol $\sim$ denote a relation between the elements of M. Then the relation $\sim$ is called an *equivalence relation* on M if and only if three properties are satisfied:

1. $\sim$ is *reflexive;* $A \sim A$ for every $A \in M$;
2. $\sim$ is *symmetric;* if $A \sim B$, then $B \sim A$;
3. $\sim$ is *transitive;* if $A \sim B$ and $B \sim C$, then $A \sim C$.

Any equivalence relation, $\sim$, on M separates M into disjoint subsets, called *equivalence classes*.   Each equivalence class $[E]$ has the property that

$$\text{if } A \in [E], \text{ then } B \in [E] \text{ if and only if } B \sim A;$$

that is, all equivalent elements belong to the same equivalence class, and any two elements of the same class are equivalent.

As we shall see, many different equivalence relations arise naturally in the study of matrices.   For each equivalence relation we shall want to describe the matrices which appear in each of the corresponding equivalence classes and, if possible, to find a simple standard form such that each equivalence class of M contains one and only one matrix which is in that form.   Such a form is called *canonical*.   Sometimes we are content to settle for less; namely, it might suffice to obtain a standard form such that each equivalence class contains more then one matrix in standard form, but if two matrices have the same standard form they must be in the same equivalence class.

Exercises

1. Determine which of the three properties of an equivalence relation are satisfied by each of the following relations:

    (i) Similarity of plane triangles.

    (ii) Parallelism of lines on a plane.

(iii) Strict inequality of real numbers.

(iv) Divisibility of integers.

(v) Perpendicularity of lines on a plane.

2. For fixed m and n, consider all real $m \times n$ matrices.   We define $A \sim B$ to mean that A has the same rank as B.

(i) Verify that $\sim$ is an equivalence relation.

(ii) Describe the corresponding equivalence classes.

(iii) Describe a simple canonical form for this notion of equivalence.

3. A student waiter drops a plate, thereby separating it into a finite number of disjoint pieces.   Describe how this act defines an equivalence relation on the molecules of the plate such that the pieces of the decomposition form the equivalence classes.

§6.2. *Elementary Matrices*

We now consider the matric interpretation of the elementary operations which were introduced in § 5.5.   There we were concerned with equivalent systems of linear equations, where two systems were considered equivalent if and only if they have the same solutions.   Clearly, this defines an equivalence relation on the collection of all systems of linear equations with coefficients in a field $\mathfrak{F}$.   Each such system determines a unique rectangular matrix A according to the representation of § 5.1.   The elementary operations were so chosen that the application of each operation to a system produced a new system which was equivalent to the original.   We shall see that a corresponding equivalence relation is induced on the matrices which represent the systems.   For this purpose we focus our attention on three *elementary row operations* for matrices:

P: permutation of two rows,

M: multiplication of a row by a non-zero scalar,

A: addition of one row to another.

We first examine the effect of these operations on the identity matrix.

> **Definition 6.1.**   An *elementary* matrix is any matrix which can be obtained by performing a single elementary row operation on the identity matrix.

There are three types of elementary matrices, one for each type of elementary row operation.   To describe these we recall the notation of § 4.2; E_{rs} denotes the square matrix with $e_{ij} = 0$ if $i \neq r$ or $j \neq s$ and $e_{rs} = 1$.

P: Let P_{ij} denote the matrix obtained from I by permuting the ith and j^{th} rows. Then

$$P_{ij} = I - E_{ii} + E_{ji} - E_{jj} + E_{ij}.$$

M: Let $M_i(c)$ denote the matrix obtained from I by multiplying the ith row by $c \neq 0$. $M_i(c)$ is obtained by adding $c - 1$ to the element in the (i, i) position, so

$$M_i(c) = I + (c - 1)E_{ii}.$$

A: Let A_{ij} denote the matrix obtained from I by adding row i to row j, where $i \neq j$. Clearly,

$$A_{ij} = I + E_{ji}.$$

The usefulness of the three elementary matrices P_{ij}, $M_i(c)$, and A_{ij} stems from the fact that an elementary row operation on an arbitrary rectangular matrix A may be performed by *premultiplying* A (i.e., multiplying A on the left) by the corresponding elementary matrix. But there is more to be said in order to make our meaning precise. Since there is an identity matrix of each dimension, there are three elementary matrices of each dimension. If A is $m \times n$, then any premultiplying matrix B must have m columns for BA to be defined.

Theorem 6.1. Any elementary row operation can be performed on an $m \times n$ matrix A by premultiplying A by the corresponding $m \times m$ elementary matrix.

P R O O F : Exercise.

Theorem 6.2. Every elementary matrix is non-singular.

P R O O F : Exercise. Show that each has n linearly independent rows.

Theorem 6.3. The inverse of an elementary matrix of type P or type M is an elementary matrix of the same type. The inverse of an elementary matrix of type A is the product of elementary matrices of type M and type A.

P R O O F : By expressing each of the elementary matrices in terms of the E_{rs} and using the results of Exercise 1, below, it is easy to verify that

$$P_{ij}^{-1} = P_{ji},$$
$$M_i^{-1}(c) = M_i(c^{-1}),$$
$$A_{ij}^{-1} = I - E_{ji} = M_i(-1)A_{ij}M_i(-1).$$

It should be observed that any type P elementary matrix is a product of elementary matrices of type M and type A (see Exercise 5, below). If we were interested in the most concise axiomatic treatment of row operations, we would consider only the latter two types. However, once we have observed this relationship there is little to be gained by insisting upon using it to replace the natural operation of interchanging rows.

Exercises

1. Prove that $E_{ik}E_{hj} = \delta_{kh}E_{ij}$, and therefore that each E_{ij} is either idempotent or nilpotent of index 2, according to whether $i = j$ or $i \neq j$.

2. Prove Theorem 6.1.

3. Prove Theorem 6.2.

4. Carry out the calculations which establish the statements made in the proof of Theorem 6.3.

5. Using Exercise 1, or otherwise, show that

$$P_{ij} = M_j(-1)A_{ij}M_i(-1)A_{ji}M_j(-1)A_{ij}.$$

6. Write a sequence of elementary row operations whose only effect on A is to add a constant multiple of the ith row of A to the jth row of A.

7. Calculate the determinant of each type of elementary matrix.

§6.3. *Row Equivalence*

The three types of elementary row operations were selected by a consideration of algebraic processes which lead from one system of linear equations to an equivalent system, that is, one with the same solutions as the original. While it is clear that elementary row operations transform any system into an equivalent system, the converse is not so obvious—that any two equivalent systems can be derived from each other by a finite sequence of these elementary row operations. Our investigation of this question will provide a nontrivial example of the general problem of equivalence and canonical forms, as discussed in § 6.1. As is often the case, side results of the investigation will prove to be more important than the answer to the original question.

> **Definition 6.2.**   An $m \times n$ matrix B is said to be *row equivalent* to an $m \times n$ matrix A if and only if B can be obtained by performing a finite number of elementary row operations on A.

The relation of row equivalence of $m \times n$ matrices is easily seen to be an equivalence relation. It is reflexive and transitive by its nature, and symmetric because if B can be obtained from A by elementary row operations, then the reversed sequence of inverse operations applied to B will yield A. The collection of $m \times n$ matrices is thus partitioned into disjoint classes of row equivalent matrices.

Theorem 6.4.   Row equivalent matrices have the same rank.

P R O O F: If B is row equivalent to A, then

$$B = E_k \ldots E_2 E_1 A,$$

where the E_i are elementary matrices and hence non-singular. By Theorem 4.7, A and B have the same rank.

Now let $A = (a_{ij})$ be an $m \times n$ matrix and suppose that the qth column is the first column in which a non-zero element, say a_{pq}, appears. If we multiply row p by a_{pq}^{-1} and then interchange row p and row 1, we obtain a matrix with 1 in row 1 and column q. Then by adding suitable multiples of row 1 to the other rows we obtain a matrix of the following form which is row equivalent to A,

$$B = \begin{pmatrix} 0 \ldots 0 & 1 & * \ldots * \\ 0 \ldots 0 & 0 & \\ \ \vdots & \vdots & \quad R \\ \ \vdots & \vdots & \\ 0 \ldots 0 & 0 & \end{pmatrix}$$

where each $*$ denotes some scalar and where R is an $(m - 1) \times (n - q)$ matrix. We continue the process by operating with the last $m - 1$ rows of B. In R we find the first column in which a non-zero element b_{rs} appears, and multiply row r by b_{rs}^{-1}. We then interchange row r of B with row 2 of B, and as before produce zeros in columns of every row below row 2. Eventually we obtain a matrix which is row equivalent to A and has the following properties:

1. The first k rows are non-zero; the other rows are zero.
2. The first non-zero element in each non-zero row is 1, and it appears in a column to the right of the first non-zero element of any preceding row.

An example of a matrix in this form, for $k = 4$, $m = 5$, $n = 8$, is

$$\begin{pmatrix} 0 & 1 & * & * & * & * & * & * \\ 0 & 0 & 1 & * & * & * & * & * \\ 0 & 0 & 0 & 0 & 1 & * & * & * \\ 0 & 0 & 0 & 0 & 0 & 0 & 0 & 1 \\ 0 & 0 & 0 & 0 & 0 & 0 & 0 & 0 \end{pmatrix}.$$

A matrix which satisfies properties 1 and 2 is said to be in *echelon form*. Suppose B is a matrix in echelon form, and consider any non-zero row. The first non-zero element of that row is $b_{ij} = 1$. In column j above b_{ij} there are elements which may or may not be zero. Below b_{ij} the jth column contains only zeros. Clearly, by a succession of row operations, the elements above

b_{ij} in column j can be replaced by zeros, and the resulting matrix will still be in echelon form with the additional property,

3. The first non-zero element in each non-zero row is the only non-zero element in its column.

Any matrix which is in echelon form and also satisfies property 3 is said to be in *reduced echelon form*.

A reduced echelon form for the matrix of the preceding example is

$$\begin{pmatrix} 0 & 1 & 0 & * & 0 & * & * & 0 \\ 0 & 0 & 1 & * & 0 & * & * & 0 \\ 0 & 0 & 0 & 0 & 1 & * & * & 0 \\ 0 & 0 & 0 & 0 & 0 & 0 & 0 & 1 \\ 0 & 0 & 0 & 0 & 0 & 0 & 0 & 0 \end{pmatrix}.$$

Theorem 6.5. Any $m \times n$ matrix of rank k is row equivalent to a matrix in echelon form (also, reduced echelon form) with k non-zero rows.

P R O O F : Our previous discussion established the row equivalences which the theorem asserts, so we need only prove the statement concerning rank. The rank of any matrix cannot exceed the number of non-zero rows in that matrix, and the non-zero rows of an echelon matrix are linearly independent. Hence its rank is the number of its non-zero rows, and by Theorem 6.4 any matrix row equivalent to it has the same rank.

Theorem 6.6. The number of linearly independent columns of any matrix A equals the number of linearly independent rows of A. Thus $\rho(A) = \rho(A')$.

P R O O F : Let E be a matrix which is row equivalent to A and in reduced echelon form. If $\rho(A) = k$, consider the k column vectors whose only non-zero element is a 1 which is the first non-zero element of the row in which it appears. These k column vectors are linearly independent, and every other column vector is a linear combination of these. Since the columns of E are the rows of E', $\rho(E') = k = \rho(E) = \rho(A)$. Also, $E = E_p E_{p-1} \ldots E_1 A$, so $E' = A' E_1' E_2' \ldots E_p'$. Since the transpose of an elementary matrix is an elementary matrix, $\rho(E') = \rho(A') = \rho(A)$. We have therefore proved the result which was assumed in § 5.1: The rank of a matrix equals the rank of its transpose.

Theorem 6.7. An $n \times n$ matrix is non-singular if and only if it is row equivalent to the identity matrix.

P R O O F: If A is row equivalent to I, then A must have rank n, and thus be non-singular.   Conversely, suppose that A is non-singular. Then it is row equivalent to a matrix E in reduced echelon form and of rank n.   Hence $E = I$.

Theorem 6.8.   A square matrix is non-singular if and only if it is the product of elementary matrices.

P R O O F: If A is non-singular, then by Theorem 6.7

$$E_k \ldots E_2 E_1 A = I$$

for suitable elementary matrices.   Hence $A = E_1^{-1} E_2^{-1} \ldots E_k^{-1}$.   Since the inverse of each elementary matrix is the product of elementary matrices, A is a product of elementary matrices.   The converse is trivial, since the product of non-singular matrices is non-singular.

The usefulness of this theorem actually lies in its proof, because we have

$$E_k \ldots E_2 E_1 I = A^{-1},$$

which gives us a second way of calculating the inverse of a non-singular matrix. We determine the row operations needed to reduce A to I.   Those same row operations when applied to I yield A^{-1}.   A similar method of calculating A^{-1} is given in the next section.

E X A M P L E

To calculate the inverse of

$$A = \begin{pmatrix} 1 & 2 & 3 \\ 2 & 3 & 0 \\ 0 & 1 & 2 \end{pmatrix}$$

we write the block form $(I|A)$ and perform on this 3×6 matrix a sequence of row operations which reduces A to I, yielding $(B|I)$.   Then $B = A^{-1}$.

$$\left(\begin{array}{ccc|ccc} 1 & 0 & 0 & 1 & 2 & 3 \\ 0 & 1 & 0 & 2 & 3 & 0 \\ 0 & 0 & 1 & 0 & 1 & 2 \end{array}\right) \xrightarrow[R_2-2R_1]{} \left(\begin{array}{ccc|ccc} 1 & 0 & 0 & 1 & 2 & 3 \\ -2 & 1 & 0 & 0 & -1 & -6 \\ 0 & 0 & 1 & 0 & 1 & 2 \end{array}\right)$$

$$\xrightarrow[R_3+R_2]{} \left(\begin{array}{ccc|ccc} 1 & 0 & 0 & 1 & 2 & 3 \\ -2 & 1 & 0 & 0 & -1 & -6 \\ -2 & 1 & 1 & 0 & 0 & -4 \end{array}\right) \xrightarrow[-\frac{1}{4}R_3]{-1R_2;} \left(\begin{array}{ccc|ccc} 1 & 0 & 0 & 1 & 2 & 3 \\ 2 & -1 & 0 & 0 & 1 & 6 \\ \frac{1}{2} & -\frac{1}{4} & -\frac{1}{4} & 0 & 0 & 1 \end{array}\right)$$

$$\xrightarrow[R_2-6R_3]{} \left(\begin{array}{ccc|ccc} 1 & 0 & 0 & 1 & 2 & 3 \\ -1 & \frac{1}{2} & \frac{3}{2} & 0 & 1 & 0 \\ \frac{1}{2} & -\frac{1}{4} & -\frac{1}{4} & 0 & 0 & 1 \end{array}\right) \xrightarrow[R_1-2R_2-3R_3]{} \left(\begin{array}{ccc|ccc} \frac{3}{2} & -\frac{1}{4} & \frac{9}{4} & 1 & 0 & 0 \\ -1 & \frac{1}{2} & \frac{3}{2} & 0 & 1 & 0 \\ \frac{1}{2} & -\frac{1}{4} & -\frac{1}{4} & 0 & 0 & 1 \end{array}\right).$$

Thus

$$A^{-1} = \tfrac{1}{4} \begin{pmatrix} 6 & -1 & -9 \\ -4 & 2 & 6 \\ 2 & -1 & -1 \end{pmatrix},$$

a result which should be checked by showing that $A^{-1}A = I$.

Theorem 6.9. B is row equivalent to A if and only if $B = PA$ for some non-singular matrix P.

P R O O F :   Exercise.

Finally we return to the question posed at the beginning of this section: Given any two systems of linear equations having the same solutions, are their corresponding matrices row equivalent?   To answer this we first determine what meaning row equivalence of matrices has for the corresponding linear transformations.   Let A, B be $m \times n$ matrices; choose a basis $\{\alpha_1, \ldots, \alpha_m\}$ for $\mathcal{V}_m$ and $\{\beta_1, \ldots, \beta_n\}$ for $\mathcal{W}_n$.   Let $\mathbf{T}$ and $\mathbf{S}$ be the linear transformations from $\mathcal{V}_m$ to $\mathcal{W}_n$ determined by A and B relative to this choice of bases; that is, $\alpha_i\mathbf{T}$ and $\alpha_i\mathbf{S}$ are respectively represented in the β-basis by the ith rows of A and B, $i = 1, \ldots, m$.

Theorem 6.10.   Relative to a pair of bases, let matrices A and B represent linear transformations $\mathbf{T}$ and $\mathbf{S}$.   Then A and B are row equivalent if and only if $\mathfrak{R}_\mathbf{T} = \mathfrak{R}_\mathbf{S}$.

P R O O F : $\mathfrak{R}_\mathbf{T}$ is the subspace of $\mathcal{W}_n$ which is spanned by the rows of A. If B is row equivalent to A, the rows of B are linear combinations of the rows of A.   Hence $\mathfrak{R}_\mathbf{S} \subseteq \mathfrak{R}_\mathbf{T}$, and equality must hold since row equivalence is a symmetric relation.   Conversely, if $\mathfrak{R}_\mathbf{T} = \mathfrak{R}_\mathbf{S}$, the row vectors of B are linear combinations of the row vectors of A, and each linear combination of rows can be performed by elementary row operations.

Theorem 6.11.   Two matrices A and B in reduced echelon form are row equivalent if and only if $A = B$.

P R O O F :   The one implication is trivial.   For the other let A and B be in reduced echelon form and row equivalent.   As in the previous theorem, if A and B correspond to linear transformations $\mathbf{T}$ and $\mathbf{S}$, then $\mathfrak{R}_\mathbf{T} = \mathfrak{R}_\mathbf{S}$. The row vectors $\alpha_i\mathbf{T}$ span $\mathfrak{R}_\mathbf{T}$ for $i = 1, 2, \ldots, k = \rho(A)$, and from the form of a reduced echelon matrix these k vectors are linearly independent. For $i \leq k$, $\alpha_i\mathbf{S}$ is a non-zero vector of $\mathfrak{R}_\mathbf{S}$, so

$$\alpha_i\mathbf{S} = \sum_{j=1}^{k} c_j\alpha_j\mathbf{T},$$

where not all c_j are zero. Since A, B are in reduced echelon form, the first non-zero element of row i is 1, and it appears in, say, column t_i of A and column s_i of B, for $i \leq k$. Furthermore, these columns contain only this one non-zero entry. Thus the s_i component of $\alpha_i S$ is 1; therefore, at least one of the $\alpha_j T$ must have a non-zero component in the s_i position for which the corresponding c_j is non-zero. The first non-zero component of $\alpha_j T$ occurs in the t_j position, so $t_j \leq s_i$. But if $t_j < s_i$, the first non-zero component of $\alpha_i S$ would appear before the s_i position. Hence $s_i = t_j$ for some j. But this means that the ordered sets of integers $s_1 < s_2 < \ldots < s_k$ and $t_1 < t_2 < \ldots < t_k$ are the same set, and the ordering then implies that

$$s_i = t_i, \qquad i = 1, \ldots, k.$$

Hence A and B must have the leading non-zero elements of non-zero rows in identical positions. Therefore, $c_j = 0$ for $j < i$, $c_i = 1$, and

$$\alpha_i S = \alpha_i T + \sum_{j=i+1}^{k} c_j \alpha_j T;$$

this can be written in equivalent form in terms of the elements of A and B,

(6.1) $$b_{ir} = a_{ir} + \sum_{j=i+1}^{k} c_j a_{jr}.$$

Suppose $a_{qr} \neq 0$ for some q, $i < q \leq k$. Since the first non-zero element of the qth row of A appears in column t_q, we have

$$a_{qt_q} = 1 \text{ for some } t_q, \ t_i < t_q \leq r.$$

Since A and B are in reduced echelon form with the first non-zero elements of non-zero rows in identical positions,

$$b_{qt_q} = 1,$$
$$b_{pt_q} = 0 = a_{pt_q} \text{ whenever } p \neq q.$$

Since $i \neq q$, we apply (6.1) to obtain

$$b_{it_q} = a_{it_q} + \sum_{j=i+1}^{k} c_j a_{jt_q},$$
$$0 = 0 \quad + c_q$$

Hence if $a_{qr} \neq 0$, then $c_q = 0$. It follows that $b_{ir} = a_{ir}$ for all r and for $i \leq k$. But for $i > k$, $b_{ir} = a_{ir} = 0$ for all r. Hence $A = B$.

From this theorem we draw two conclusions:

There is one and only one reduced echelon matrix which is row equivalent to a given matrix A; that is, the reduced echelon form is *canonical* with respect to row equivalence.

Two homogeneous systems of m linear equations in n unknowns are equivalent (have the same solutions) if and only if their coefficient matrices are row equivalent.

We note also that if row equivalence had been defined to include the trivial row operations of adding or deleting a zero row, then the latter statement above would be valid for any two homogeneous systems of linear equations in n unknowns.

Exercises

1. Use the method of this section to calculate the inverse of each of the following matrices:

(i)
$$\begin{pmatrix} -2 & 1 & 3 \\ 0 & -1 & 1 \\ 1 & 2 & 0 \end{pmatrix},$$

(ii)
$$\begin{pmatrix} 1 & -1 & 1 & -1 \\ 0 & 1 & 0 & 1 \\ 1 & 0 & -1 & 0 \\ 0 & 1 & 0 & -1 \end{pmatrix}.$$

2. Determine which of the following matrices are row equivalent:

$$A = \begin{pmatrix} 5 & 3 & 8 \\ 3 & 1 & 4 \\ -1 & 3 & 2 \end{pmatrix},$$

$$B = \begin{pmatrix} -1 & -3 & -2 \\ 5 & 7 & 2 \\ -3 & 1 & 4 \end{pmatrix},$$

$$C = \begin{pmatrix} -1 & 5 & 6 \\ 1 & 2 & 1 \\ -1 & -3 & -2 \end{pmatrix}.$$

3. Prove Theorem 6.9.

4. Show in detail how the two statements at the end of this section follow from previous theorems.

5. Prove that if A is $m \times n$ and P_{ij} is $n \times n$ then AP_{ij} coincides with A except that columns i and j are interchanged.

6. (i) Let A be an $m \times (m + n)$ matrix of rank m, and let E be the reduced echelon form of A. Show that a permutation of the columns of E transforms E into block form $(I|B)$ where B is $m \times n$.

(ii) Using Exercise 5, or otherwise, show that there exist non-singular matrices P and Q such that
$$PAQ = (I|B).$$

§6.4. *Equivalence*

If we consider matrices as rectangular arrays, without regard to any systems which they represent, it is as natural to perform elementary operations on *columns* as on rows. For this purpose we observe that a column operation on A is the same as a row operation on A'. Hence A may be transformed into B by a succession of elementary column operations if and only if A' can be transformed into B' by the same succession of row operations. That is, if

$$B' = PA',$$

then

$$B = (PA')' = AP' = AQ,$$

where Q is non-singular, since Q is the transpose of the non-singular matrix P. Hence column operations can be performed on A by *postmultiplying* A by a suitable non-singular matrix.

We next propose to study the effect of changing A by both column operations and row operations. If B is the resulting matrix, then

$$B = PAQ,$$

where P is the non-singular matrix which performs the row operations and Q is the non-singular matrix which performs the column operations.

Definition 6.3. B is said to be *equivalent* to A if and only if B can be obtained from A by a finite number of elementary row and column operations.

Theorem 6.12. B is equivalent to A if and only if $B = PAQ$ for suitable non-singular matrices P and Q.
P R O O F: See the remarks preceding Definition 6.3.

Theorem 6.13. Equivalence of matrices is an equivalence relation.
P R O O F: Exercise.

Theorem 6.14. An $m \times n$ matrix of rank k is equivalent to the $m \times n$ matrix B in which $b_{11} = b_{22} = \ldots = b_{kk} = 1$, and $b_{ij} = 0$ otherwise.
P R O O F: Let A be of rank k. If $k = 0$, then $A = Z$ and there is nothing to prove. Otherwise, some $a_{ij} \neq 0$, and by row and column interchanges a_{ij} can be moved to the $(1, 1)$ position and replaced by 1 by a row multiplication by a_{ij}^{-1}. Then column operations are used to produce zeros in the remainder of the first row, and row operations are used to produce zeros in the remainder of the first column. Hence for non-singular P and Q we have

$$PAQ = \begin{pmatrix} 1 & 0 \ldots 0 \\ 0 & \\ \vdots & R \\ \vdots & \\ 0 & \end{pmatrix},$$

where R is an $(m-1) \times (n-1)$ matrix.   The argument is now repeated, letting the first row and column remain fixed, bringing 1 into the
$(2, 2)$ position if $R \neq Z$, and producting zeros elsewhere in the second
row and column.   Finally, we obtain a matrix B which is equivalent to A
and which has 1 in a certain number of the (i, i) positions and 0 elsewhere.
The rank of B is precisely the number of non-zero elements, and this is
also the rank of A.

Theorem 6.15.   Two $m \times n$ matrices are equivalent if and only if
they have the same rank.
P R O O F :   If A and B are equivalent, $\rho(A) = \rho(B)$ since $B = PAQ$.
Conversely, if A and B have rank k, each is equivalent to the matrix
described in Theorem 6.14.

From Theorem 6.15 we derive two immediate corollaries.   The first is
that the form described in Theorem 6.14 is *canonical* with respect to equivalence.   The second we state formally.

Theorem 6.16.   A square matrix is non-singular if and only if it is
equivalent to the identity matrix.
P R O O F :   Apply Theorem 6.15.

Therefore if A is non-singular, there exist non-singular matrices P and Q
such that

$$I = PAQ,$$
$$P^{-1}Q^{-1} = A,$$
$$A^{-1} = QP.$$

Recall that P is obtained by performing on I the same row operations which
were performed on A, and that Q is obtained by performing on I the same
column operations which were performed on A, the combination of row and
column operations transforming A into I.   This gives us another method of
computing A^{-1}, and the following scheme simplifies the calculation of P and
Q.   Write I to the left of A and below A, as shown:

$$\begin{array}{c|c} I & A \\ \hline & I \end{array}.$$

Perform row and column operations on A as needed to transform A into I. As each row operation is performed on A, perform the same row operation on the matrix at the upper left of the array. Similarly, as each column operation is performed on A, perform the same column operation on the lower right hand matrix. Then the final array is

$$\frac{P \mid I}{\quad \mid Q},$$

and $A^{-1} = QP$.

EXAMPLE

Let

$$A = \begin{pmatrix} 2 & -1 & 0 \\ 1 & 2 & 1 \\ -1 & 0 & 3 \end{pmatrix}.$$

$$
\left.\begin{array}{ccc|ccc}
1 & 0 & 0 & 2 & -1 & 0 \\
0 & 1 & 0 & 1 & 2 & 1 \\
0 & 0 & 1 & -1 & 0 & 3 \\
\hline
 & & & 1 & 0 & 0 \\
 & & & 0 & 1 & 0 \\
 & & & 0 & 0 & 1
\end{array}\right.,
$$

Interchange R_1 and R_2

$$
\left.\begin{array}{ccc|ccc}
0 & 1 & 0 & 1 & 2 & 1 \\
1 & 0 & 0 & 2 & -1 & 0 \\
0 & 0 & 1 & -1 & 0 & 3 \\
\hline
 & & & 1 & 0 & 0 \\
 & & & 0 & 1 & 0 \\
 & & & 0 & 0 & 1
\end{array}\right.,
$$

$C_2 - 2C_1;$
$C_3 - C_1$

$$
\left.\begin{array}{ccc|ccc}
0 & 1 & 0 & 1 & 0 & 0 \\
1 & 0 & 0 & 2 & -5 & -2 \\
0 & 0 & 1 & -1 & 2 & 4 \\
\hline
 & & & 1 & -2 & -1 \\
 & & & 0 & 1 & 0 \\
 & & & 0 & 0 & 1
\end{array}\right.,
$$

$R_2 - 2R_1;$
$R_3 + R_1$

$$
\left.\begin{array}{ccc|ccc}
0 & 1 & 0 & 1 & 0 & 0 \\
1 & -2 & 0 & 0 & -5 & -2 \\
0 & 1 & 1 & 0 & 2 & 4 \\
\hline
 & & & 1 & -2 & -1 \\
 & & & 0 & 1 & 0 \\
 & & & 0 & 0 & 1
\end{array}\right.,
$$

$\frac{1}{2}R_3;$
interchange R_2 and R_3

$$
\left.\begin{array}{ccc|ccc}
0 & 1 & 0 & 1 & 0 & 0 \\
0 & \frac{1}{2} & \frac{1}{2} & 0 & 1 & 2 \\
1 & -2 & 0 & 0 & -5 & -2 \\
\hline
 & & & 1 & -2 & -1 \\
 & & & 0 & 1 & 0 \\
 & & & 0 & 0 & 1
\end{array}\right.,
$$

$C_3 - 2C_2$

$$
\left.\begin{array}{ccc|ccc}
0 & 1 & 0 & 1 & 0 & 0 \\
0 & \frac{1}{2} & \frac{1}{2} & 0 & 1 & 0 \\
1 & -2 & 0 & 0 & -5 & 8 \\
\hline
 & & & 1 & -2 & 3 \\
 & & & 0 & 1 & -2 \\
 & & & 0 & 0 & 1
\end{array}\right.,
$$

$R_3 + 5R_2$

$$
\left.\begin{array}{ccc|ccc}
0 & 1 & 0 & 1 & 0 & 0 \\
0 & \frac{1}{2} & \frac{1}{2} & 0 & 1 & 0 \\
1 & \frac{1}{2} & \frac{5}{2} & 0 & 0 & 8 \\
\hline
 & & & 1 & -2 & 3 \\
 & & & 0 & 1 & -2 \\
 & & & 0 & 0 & 1
\end{array}\right.,
$$

$\frac{1}{8}R_3$

$$
\left.\begin{array}{ccc|ccc}
0 & 1 & 0 & 1 & 0 & 0 \\
0 & \frac{1}{2} & \frac{1}{2} & 0 & 1 & 0 \\
\frac{1}{8} & \frac{1}{16} & \frac{5}{16} & 0 & 0 & 1 \\
\hline
 & & & 1 & -2 & 3 \\
 & & & 0 & 1 & -2 \\
 & & & 0 & 0 & 1
\end{array}\right..
$$

$$\text{Now } P = \tfrac{1}{16}\begin{pmatrix} 0 & 16 & 0 \\ 0 & 8 & 8 \\ 2 & 1 & 5 \end{pmatrix} \text{ and } Q = \begin{pmatrix} 1 & -2 & 3 \\ 0 & 1 & -2 \\ 0 & 0 & 1 \end{pmatrix}, \text{ so}$$

$$A^{-1} = QP = \tfrac{1}{16}\begin{pmatrix} 6 & 3 & -1 \\ -4 & 6 & -2 \\ 2 & 1 & 5 \end{pmatrix}.$$

This method of calculating A^{-1} is tedious to write, but all calculations are easy ones.

Exercises

1. Use the method of § 6.4 to calculate the inverse of each matrix of Exercise 1, § 6.3.

2. Prove Theorem 6.13.

3. Show that the form described by Theorem 6.14 is canonical for matrix equivalence.

4. Which of the matrices of Exercise 2, § 6.3, are equivalent?

5. Show that if A is a symmetric $n \times n$ matrix of complex numbers, then there exists a non-singular matrix P such that PAP' is in canonical form for matrix equivalence.

6. Given that A and B are equivalent, determine whether or not each of the following pairs are equivalent:

   (i) A' and B',
   (ii) A^2 and B^2,
   (iii) AB and BA.

§6.5. *Similarity*

Thus far we have introduced two different equivalence relations for matrices which were suggested by processes for solving a system of linear equations. In this section we resume the study of linear transformations and their representative matrices. In so doing we discover an important interpretation of equivalence of matrices, a special case of which leads us to a third equivalence relation, called *similarity*. Other equivalence relations will be considered in Chapter 9, where matrices are used to represent still another mathematical structure.

In § 4.1 we derived the matric representation of a linear transformation $\mathbf{T}$ under the agreement that our discussion pertained to a fixed basis $\{\alpha_1, \ldots, \alpha_m\}$ of the domain $\mathbf{\mathcal{U}}_m$ of $\mathbf{T}$ and a fixed basis $\{\beta_1, \ldots, \beta_n\}$ of a space $\mathbf{\mathcal{W}}_n$ which contained the range of **T**. With this understanding, **T** is represented uniquely by a matrix, but the matric representation of **T** depends upon the choice of bases. Now we are ready to determine the relationship between two matrices, each of which represents the same **T** with respect to an independent choice of bases for $\mathcal{V}_m$ and $\mathcal{W}_n$.

Let **T** be a linear transformation from $\mathcal{V}_m$ to $\mathcal{W}_n$. With respect to bases $\{\alpha_1, \ldots, \alpha_m\}$ and $\{\beta_1, \ldots, \beta_n\}$, **T** is represented by a uniquely determined matrix A. With respect to bases $\{\gamma_1, \ldots, \gamma_m\}$ and $\{\delta_1, \ldots, \delta_n\}$, **T** is represented by a matrix C. Thus

$$\alpha_i \mathbf{T} = \sum_{k=1}^{n} a_{ij}\beta_j,$$

$$\gamma_j \mathbf{T} = \sum_{k=1}^{n} c_{jk}\delta_k.$$

Let **R** be the linear transformation which maps γ_i onto α_i in $\mathcal{V}_m$. Since **R** maps a basis onto a basis it is non-singular, and relative to the γ-basis it is represented by a non-singular matrix P, where

$$\alpha_i = \gamma_i \mathbf{R} = \sum_{j=1}^{m} p_{ij}\gamma_j.$$

Similarly, let **S** be the linear transformation which maps δ_j onto β_j in $\mathcal{W}_n$. **S** is represented relative to the δ-basis by a non-singular matrix Q, where

$$\beta_j = \delta_j \mathbf{S} = \sum_{k=1}^{n} q_{jk}\delta_k.$$

The situation is represented graphically by the following scheme, where subscripts on the matrices indicate the bases concerned.

$$\mathcal{V}_m = [\alpha] \xrightarrow[A_{\alpha,\beta}]{\mathbf{T}} \mathcal{W}_n = [\beta]$$

$$\mathbf{R}\uparrow P_\gamma \qquad\qquad Q_\delta\uparrow \mathbf{S}$$

$$\mathcal{V}_m = [\gamma] \xrightarrow[\mathbf{T}]{C_{\gamma,\delta}} \mathcal{W}_n = [\delta]$$

Figure 6.1

We compute the **T**-image of α_i in two ways:

$$\alpha_i \mathbf{T} = \sum_{j=1}^{n} a_{ij}\beta_j = \sum_{j=1}^{n} a_{ij}\left(\sum_{k=1}^{n} q_{jk}\delta_k\right) = \sum_{k=1}^{n}\left(\sum_{j=1}^{n} a_{ij}q_{jk}\right)\delta_k,$$

$$\alpha_i \mathbf{T} = \left(\sum_{j=1}^{m} p_{ij}\gamma_j\right)\mathbf{T} = \sum_{j=1}^{m} p_{ij}\left(\sum_{k=1}^{n} c_{jk}\delta_k\right) = \sum_{k=1}^{n}\left(\sum_{j=1}^{m} p_{ij}c_{jk}\right)\delta_k,$$

for $i = 1, 2, \ldots, m$. Since $\alpha_i \mathbf{T}$ is a unique linear combination of the δ_k,

$$\sum_{j=1}^{n} a_{ij}q_{jk} = \sum_{j=1}^{m} p_{ij}c_{jk}.$$

The left hand side is the (i, k) element of AQ, and the right hand side is the (i, k) element of PC.   Hence

$$AQ = PC,$$

$$A = PCQ^{-1};$$

or in a form which reminds us of the bases used to obtain each matrix,

$$A_{\alpha,\beta} = P_\gamma C_{\gamma,\delta} Q_\delta^{-1}.$$

Theorem 6.17.   Two $m \times n$ matrices A and C represent the same linear transformation from $\mathcal{V}_m$ to $\mathcal{W}_n$ relative to two pairs of bases if and only if A and C are equivalent.

P R O O F: Our previous discussion has shown that if A and C represent the same linear transformation, then

$$A = PCQ^{-1}$$

for some non-singular $m \times m$ matrix P and some non-singular $n \times n$ matrix Q.   Hence A and C are equivalent.   Conversely, if A and C are equivalent, then for suitable non-singular matrices P, Q

$$A = PCQ.$$

Choose any basis pair, $\{\gamma\}$ for $\mathcal{V}_m$ and $\{\delta\}$ for $\mathcal{W}_n$, and let $\mathbf{T}$ be the linear transformation represented by C relative to this choice of bases.   Let $\mathbf{R}$ be the linear transformation on $\mathcal{V}_m$ defined by the matrix P relative to the γ-basis, and let $\mathbf{S}$ be the linear transformation on $\mathcal{W}_n$ defined by the matrix Q^{-1} relative to the δ-basis.   Since

$$A = PC(Q^{-1})^{-1},$$

our previous calculations show that A represents $\mathbf{T}$ relative to the bases $\{\gamma\mathbf{R}\}$ for $\mathcal{V}_m$ and $\{\delta\mathbf{S}\}$ for $\mathcal{W}_n$.

Now let us reverse the roles of matrices and linear transformations in this discussion.   Suppose we have a single $m \times n$ matrix A and two pairs of bases, α,β and γ,δ.   Relative to each basis pair, A determines a linear transformation, say $\mathbf{T}_1$ and $\mathbf{T}_2$.   How are these transformations related?

As before, we let $\mathbf{R}$ and $\mathbf{S}$ be the linear transformations defined by $\gamma_i\mathbf{R} = \alpha_i$ and $\delta_j\mathbf{S} = \beta_j$.   We have

$$\gamma_i\mathbf{T}_2 = \sum_{j=1}^{n} a_{ij}\delta_j,$$

$$\alpha_i\mathbf{T}_1 = \sum_{j=1}^{n} a_{ij}\beta_j.$$

Hence

$$\gamma_i \mathbf{R} \mathbf{T}_1 = \alpha_i \mathbf{T}_1 = \sum_{j=1}^{m} a_{ij}\beta_j = \sum_{j=1}^{m} a_{ij}\delta_j \mathbf{S} = \gamma_i \mathbf{T}_2 \mathbf{S}.$$

Therefore

$$\mathbf{R} \mathbf{T}_1 = \mathbf{T}_2 \mathbf{S},$$

$$\mathbf{T}_1 = \mathbf{R}^{-1} \mathbf{T}_2 \mathbf{S}.$$

Now the pictorial scheme is especially helpful.

$$\mathcal{V}_m = [\alpha] \xrightarrow[A_{\alpha,\beta}]{\mathbf{T}_1} \mathcal{W}_n = [\beta]$$

$$\mathbf{R} \uparrow \qquad\qquad\qquad \uparrow \mathbf{S}$$

$$\mathcal{V}_m = [\gamma] \xrightarrow[\mathbf{T}_2]{A_{\gamma,\delta}} \mathcal{W}_n = [\delta]$$

Figure 6.2

$\mathbf{T}_1$ has the same effect on $\mathcal{V}_m$ as a change of coordinates in $\mathcal{V}_m$ ($\mathbf{R}^{-1}$ indicated by going against the arrow), followed by $\mathbf{T}_2$, followed by a change of coordinates $\mathbf{S}$ in $\mathcal{W}_n$. Notice that in Figure 6.1 a similar interpretation can be made only by considering the vertical arrows as being reversed. We have proved the following analogue of Theorem 6.17.

Theorem 6.18. Two linear transformations $\mathbf{T}_1$ and $\mathbf{T}_2$ are represented relative to two pairs of bases by the same matrix if and only if nonsingular linear transformations $\mathbf{R}$ and $\mathbf{S}$ exist such that $\mathbf{T}_2 = \mathbf{R}\mathbf{T}_1\mathbf{S}^{-1}$.

We now specialize our consideration to linear transformations of an n-dimensional space into itself; many of the important transformations of mathematics and physics are of this type. The matrices which represent such transformations will be square, say $n \times n$, and our work of the next four chapters will principally concern square matrices.

For the present discussion, if $\mathcal{V}_m = \mathcal{W}_n$ we can take the α- and β-bases to be the same, and the γ- and δ-bases to be the same. In this case the transformations $\mathbf{R}$ and $\mathbf{S}$ are equal, and the relation between the two matrices A and C which represent the same linear transformation relative to the α-basis and the γ-basis, respectively, is

$$A = PCP^{-1},$$

where P represents relative to the γ-basis the transformation which changes bases from γ to α. This relation between matrices exists only for square matrices and is a special type of equivalence wherein $Q = P^{-1}$.

Definition 6.4. Two $n \times n$ matrices A and B are said to be *similar* if and only if

$$A = PBP^{-1}$$

for some non-singular matrix P.

Theorem 6.19. Two square matrices are similar if and only if they represent the same linear transformation relative to suitably chosen bases.

P R O O F: Apply the proof of Theorem 6.17 to the case of square matrices.

The notion of similarity is particularly important because of Theorem 6.19. Since similar matrices represent the same linear transformation, they must share all properties of the transformation which are independent of any coordinate system. These are the intrinsic geometric properties of the transformation. A problem of special interest is to find a simple canonical form for every similarity class; this problem is the same as that of selecting a coordinate system in which a given linear transformation assumes a simple form which is determined by intrinsic geometric properties. The next two chapters are concerned with its solution.

Exercises

1. Prove that similarity of matrices is an equivalence relation.
2. Prove that if A and B are similar, then

   (i) $\rho(A) = \rho(B)$,
   (ii) $\det A = \det B$.

3. Are AB and BA similar for all $n \times n$ matrices? What can be said if either A or B is non-singular?

4. In the analysis of three-phase power systems, an impedance matrix often occurs in the form

$$C = \begin{pmatrix} z_1 & z_2 & z_3 \\ z_3 & z_1 & z_2 \\ z_2 & z_3 & z_1 \end{pmatrix},$$

where z_j is a complex number for $j = 1, 2, 3$. Let

$$P = \begin{pmatrix} 1 & 1 & 1 \\ 1 & e & e^2 \\ 1 & e^2 & e \end{pmatrix}$$

where $e = \frac{1}{2}(-1 + i\sqrt{3})$. Show that C is similar to a diagonal matrix D and compute D. (Observe that $e^3 = 1$, so that $e^2 + e + 1 = 0$.)

5. Let **T** be a linear transformation of $\mathcal{E}_2$ into $\mathcal{E}_3$ whose matrix relative to the bases $\{\epsilon_1, \epsilon_2\}$ and $\{\epsilon_1, \epsilon_2, \epsilon_3\}$ is

$$A = \begin{pmatrix} 1 & 0 & -3 \\ 2 & 1 & -1 \end{pmatrix}.$$

Let new bases be defined by

$$\begin{cases} \alpha_1 = \epsilon_1 - 2\epsilon_2 \\ \alpha_2 = \epsilon_1 + \epsilon_2, \end{cases}$$

and

$$\begin{cases} \beta_1 = \epsilon_1 + \epsilon_2 \\ \beta_2 = \quad\ \epsilon_2 + \epsilon_3 \\ \beta_3 = \epsilon_1 \quad\ + \epsilon_3. \end{cases}$$

Compute the matrix which represents **T** relative to the α-, β-bases.

6. (i) Show that any two idempotent matrices of the same dimension and rank are similar.

(ii) Describe a form for idempotent matrices which is canonical with respect to similarity.

7. Given that A and B are similar, determine whether or not each of the following pairs are similar:

(i) A^k and B^k,

(ii) A' and B',

(iii) A^{-1} and B^{-1}, assuming A is non-singular.

CHAPTER 7

Characteristics of a Linear Transformation

For the remainder of this book we shall restrict our investigation in two ways, sometimes by necessity and sometimes for convenience:

We shall consider only square matrices, unless otherwise noted; thus linear transformations will be regarded as mapping a space into itself.

We shall assume that the scalar field is either the real or complex numbers.

By this time you should have little difficulty in discerning which theorems can be extended beyond the limits imposed by these restrictions.

§7.1. *Characteristic Vectors and Values*

The general problem which we undertake in this chapter and the next was stated at the end of § 6.5. We consider a linear transformation $\mathbf{T}$ on $\mathcal{U}_n$. From the dynamic (alibi) point of view (see § 3.5), $\mathbf{T}$ may be regarded as a rearrangement of the points of the space, without reference to particular coordinate systems. Indeed, those properties which distinguish $\mathbf{T}$ intrinsically must hold in any coordinate system and hence must be invariant under a change of coordinates. Since equal transformations are represented by similar matrices, our investigation will make heavy use of similarity, with a major objective being the derivation in Chapter 8 of a canonical form for similarity. One problem which we shall solve in this chapter is to determine under what conditions a given matrix is similar to a diagonal matrix. Since calculations with diagonal matrices are quite easy, the relation of this problem to the simple representation of a linear transformation is apparent.

When we regard $\mathbf{T}$ as a rearrangement of the vectors of $\mathcal{U}$, it is natural to

126

look for vectors which are mapped by **T** in some simple way.   The null space, for example, is the set of vectors mapped into θ.   Also we might look for a *fixed point*—a vector which is mapped into itself.   More generally, we search for any vector which is mapped by **T** into a *scalar multiple* of itself:

$$\xi\mathbf{T} = \lambda\xi, \text{ for some scalar } \lambda.$$

(The use of the Greek letter λ for a scalar is an exception to the notation previously adopted for this book.   It is used for characteristic values to conform with generally accepted notation.)   Clearly, for any **T**, θ is such a vector (indeed, a fixed point), so we are interested only in non-zero vectors which have this property.

Definition 7.1.   A non-zero vector ξ such that

$$\xi\mathbf{T} = \lambda\xi, \text{ for some scalar } \lambda,$$

is called a *characteristic vector* of **T**.   The scalar λ is called the *characteristic value* of **T** which is associated with the characteristic vector ξ.

In the literature of matrices there is a wide variety of synonyms for characteristic vectors (eigenvectors, proper vectors, proper states) and for characteristic values (eigenvalues, proper values, characteristic numbers, characteristic roots, latent roots).

Suppose that **T** is represented by $A = (a_{ij})$ and ξ is represented by the row vector $X = (x_1 \ldots x_n)$, relative to a fixed basis.   If ξ is a characteristic vector associated with the characteristic value λ, then

$$\xi\mathbf{T} = \lambda\xi,$$

$$XA = \lambda X,$$

$$X(A - \lambda I) = Z.$$

This is the matric form of a system of n linear homogeneous equations, and by Theorem 5.1 a non-zero solution X exists if and only if $A - \lambda I$ is singular. This occurs if and only if

$$\det(A - \lambda I) = 0.$$

From our knowledge of determinants we see that

$$\det(A - \lambda I) = \begin{vmatrix} a_{11} - \lambda & a_{12} & \cdots & a_{1n} \\ a_{21} & a_{22} - \lambda & \cdots & a_{2n} \\ \cdot & \cdot & & \cdot \\ \cdot & \cdot & & \cdot \\ \cdot & \cdot & & \cdot \\ a_{n1} & a_{n2} & \cdots & a_{nn} - \lambda \end{vmatrix} = 0$$

is a polynomial equation of degree n in λ, say

$$(-1)^n\lambda^n + b_1\lambda^{n-1} + \ldots + b_{n-1}\lambda + b_n = 0,$$

where the b's are sums of products of the a_{ij}. If the scalar field is the field of real or complex numbers, we know by the fundamental theorem of algebra and its corollaries that there are exactly n complex numbers λ (not necessarily distinct from one another) which satisfy this equation. In order that we may be sure that the characteristic values λ are in the scalar field of $\mathcal{V}$, we shall make the simplifying assumption during the remainder of this chapter that $\mathcal{F}$ is the field of complex numbers.

> **Definition 7.2.** The polynomial $\det(A - \lambda I)$ is called the *characteristic polynomial* of the matrix A. The equation $\det(A - \lambda I) = 0$ is called the *characteristic equation* of A.

> **Definition 7.3.** The *characteristic values of a matrix A* are the roots of the characteristic equation of A.

Our discussion has established the following result:

> **Theorem 7.1.** The characteristic values of a matrix A are the characteristic values of the linear transformation represented by A in any coordinate system.

> **Theorem 7.2.** If A and B are similar, then A and B have the same characteristic polynomial and hence the same characteristic values.
> FIRST PROOF: If $A = PBP^{-1}$, then

$$A - \lambda I = PBP^{-1} - \lambda I = P(B - \lambda I)P^{-1}$$
$$\det(A - \lambda I) = (\det P)\det(B - \lambda I)(\det P^{-1}) = \det(B - \lambda I).$$

SECOND PROOF: If A and B are similar, they represent the same transformation **T** relative to different bases. The characteristic values of **T** depend only on **T** and are independent of the coordinate system. Hence A and B have the same characteristic values, so their characteristic polynomials are alike except possibly for a multiplicative constant. Thus $\det(A - \lambda I) = k \det(B - \lambda I)$ for all λ. For $\lambda = 0$ we have $\det A = k \det B$, so $k = 1$, since similar matrices have the same determinant.

> **Theorem 7.3.** The characteristic values of a triangular matrix are the diagonal elements. Thus the characteristic values of a diagonal matrix are the diagonal elements.
> PROOF: Exercise.

So far we have found out how to determine the characteristic values $\lambda_1, \ldots, \lambda_n$ of A. To determine characteristic vectors associated with the value λ_i we solve for X the matric equation

$$X(A - \lambda_i I) = Z.$$

Suppose that X_i is the matric representation of a characteristic vector associated with λ_i. Then for any scalar c, cX_i is also a characteristic vector associated with λ_i. Likewise, if Y_i is a characteristic vector associated with λ_i, then $(X_i + Y_i)$ is also a characteristic vector associated with λ_i. From these statements we obtain the following theorem.

Theorem 7.4.   The characteristic vectors associated with the characteristic value λ, together with the zero vector, form a subspace $\mathcal{C}_\lambda$ of $\mathcal{V}$.

Exercises

1. Find the characteristic polynomial, the characteristic values, and the characteristic vectors of each of the following matrices:

(i)
$$\begin{pmatrix} 0 & 3 \\ 2 & -1 \end{pmatrix},$$

(ii)
$$\begin{pmatrix} 3 & 2 & 4 \\ 2 & 0 & 2 \\ 4 & 2 & 3 \end{pmatrix},$$

(iii)
$$\begin{pmatrix} 3 & 0 & 0 & 0 \\ 2 & 1 & 2 & 0 \\ 1 & 0 & 1 & 0 \\ 0 & 1 & 0 & 1 \end{pmatrix}.$$

2. Prove that if X is a row vector and D a diagonal matrix such that $XD^2 = Z$, then $XD = Z$.

3. Prove Theorem 7.3.

4. Verify in detail the proof of Theorem 7.4.

5. Referring to Theorem 7.4, show that $\mathcal{C}_\lambda$ is a subspace of the range space of the transformation if $\lambda \neq 0$, and of the null space if $\lambda = 0$.

6. Prove that if A is non-singular then the characteristic values of A^{-1} are the reciprocals of the characteristic values of A. What can be said about the corresponding characteristic vectors?

7. Show that if X is a characteristic vector of A associated with the value λ, then for any natural number k, X is a characteristic vector of A^k associated with the characteristic value λ^k.

8. If $\lambda_1, \ldots, \lambda_n$ are the characteristic values of A, show that

$$\det A = \lambda_1 \lambda_2 \ldots \lambda_n$$

by relating each side to the constant term of the characteristic polynomial of A.

9. A Markov matrix was defined in Exercise 8, § 4.4. Prove that every characteristic value of a Markov matrix satisfies $|\lambda| \leq 1$.

10. Prove that $\lambda = 1$ is a characteristic value of every Markov matrix.

§7.2. *A Method of Diagonalization*

As a start on the problem of determining what matrices are similar to a diagonal matrix, the next theorem gives us a sufficient condition, which is later proved to be necessary also.   In addition, we obtain a method of diagonalizing A; that is, we find P such that PAP^{-1} is diagonal.

Theorem 7.5.   Let $X_i = (x_{i1}, \ldots, x_{in})$ be a characteristic vector of A associated with λ_i, $i = 1, 2, \ldots, n$. If the vectors X_i span $\mathcal{V}$, then the matrix $P = (x_{ij})$ is such that

$$PAP^{-1} = \begin{pmatrix} \lambda_1 & 0 & . & . & 0 \\ 0 & \lambda_2 & . & . & 0 \\ . & . & . & & . \\ . & . & & . & \\ 0 & 0 & . & . & \lambda_n \end{pmatrix} = \mathrm{diag}(\lambda_1, \ldots, \lambda_n) = D.$$

P R O O F :   Notice that the row vectors of P are characteristic vectors X_i. If these n vectors span $\mathcal{V}$, they are linearly independent, so P is non-singular.   We have

$$X_i A = \lambda_i X_i,$$

so

$$\sum_{k=1}^{n} x_{ik} a_{kj} = \lambda_i x_{ij}$$

for $j = 1, 2, \ldots, n$.   Furthermore,

$$PA = (c_{ij}), \text{ where } c_{ij} = \sum_{k=1}^{n} x_{ik} a_{kj} = \lambda_i x_{ij},$$

and

$$DP = (b_{ij}), \text{ where } b_{ij} = \lambda_i x_{ij}.$$

(You should verify these calculations.)   Hence $PA = DP$.

E X A M P L E

We shall find the characteristic values, characteristic vectors, and a diagonalizing matrix P for the matrix

$$A = \begin{pmatrix} 1 & 0 & -2 \\ 0 & 0 & 0 \\ -2 & 0 & 4 \end{pmatrix}.$$

The characteristic equation of A is

$$0 = \det(A - \lambda I) = \begin{vmatrix} 1 - \lambda & 0 & -2 \\ 0 & -\lambda & 0 \\ -2 & 0 & 4 - \lambda \end{vmatrix}$$

$$= (1 - \lambda)(-\lambda)(4 - \lambda) - (-2)(-\lambda)(-2)$$

$$= -\lambda^3 + 5\lambda^2.$$

Hence the characteristic values of A are $\lambda_1 = 0$, $\lambda_2 = 0$, $\lambda_3 = 5$. Let $X = (x_1, x_2, x_3)$. Then

$$XA = (x_1 - 2x_3, 0, -2x_1 + 4x_3)$$

and

$$\lambda X = (\lambda x_1, \lambda x_2, \lambda x_3).$$

Necessary and sufficient conditions that X be a characteristic vector associated with λ are therefore

$$x_1 - 2x_3 = \lambda x_1$$
$$0 = \lambda x_2$$
$$-2x_1 + 4x_3 = \lambda x_3.$$

For $\lambda = 0$ these reduce to

$$x_1 = 2x_3.$$

Hence any vector of the form $(2c, b, c)$ is characteristic. Two such vectors which are linearly independent are

$$X_1 = (2, 0, 1),$$
$$X_2 = (0, 1, 0).$$

Notice in this case that it is possible to select two linearly independent characteristic vectors both of which are associated with the same characteristic value. For $\lambda_3 = 5$ the conditions reduce to

$$-2x_1 = x_3,$$
$$x_2 = 0.$$

Hence any vector of the form $(a, 0, -2a)$ is characteristic. As a simple vector of this form we choose

$$X_3 = (1, 0, -2)$$

as a characteristic vector associated with $\lambda_3 = 5$. Then

$$P = \begin{pmatrix} 2 & 0 & 1 \\ 0 & 1 & 0 \\ 1 & 0 & -2 \end{pmatrix},$$

and det $P = -5$, which checks the linear independence of X_1, X_2, and X_3. You should check the calculations which show that

$$P^{-1} = -\tfrac{1}{5}\begin{pmatrix} -2 & 0 & -1 \\ 0 & -5 & 0 \\ -1 & 0 & 2 \end{pmatrix},$$

and

$$PAP^{-1} = \begin{pmatrix} 0 & 0 & 0 \\ 0 & 0 & 0 \\ 0 & 0 & 5 \end{pmatrix}.$$

The geometric interpretation of these calculations is that in $\mathcal{E}_3$ each point η on the line determined by the origin and $\xi_3 = (1, 0, -2)$ is mapped by **T** into 5η, while each point ζ on the plane determined by the origin, $\xi_1 = (2, 0, 1)$, and $\xi_2 = (0, 1, 0)$ is mapped by **T** into $0 \cdot \zeta = \theta$. The three characteristic vectors ξ_1, ξ_2, and ξ_3 are linearly independent and may be chosen as a basis for $\mathcal{U}_3$. Relative to that basis, **T** is represented by the diagonal matrix $D = \mathrm{diag}(0, 0, 5)$.

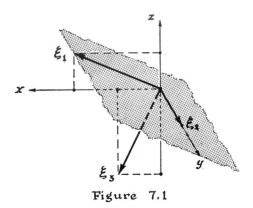

Figure 7.1

When we attempt to diagonalize a given matrix A by the preceding method there are three possible situations:

If the characteristic values are all distinct, then there exist n linearly independent characteristic vectors; thus A can be diagonalized. (Proved later.)

If the characteristic values are not distinct, as in the preceding example, it might still be possible to find n linearly independent characteristic vectors so that A can be diagonalized.

If the characteristic values are not distinct, it can happen that no set of n linearly independent characteristic vectors exists. Then A cannot be diagonalized.

These three cases are illustrated in Exercise 1, below.

Exercises

1. For each of the following matrices determine the characteristic values and corresponding characteristic vectors; if the matrix is similar to a diagonal matrix, find P and show that PAP^{-1} is diagonal:

(i)
$$\begin{pmatrix} 2 & -2 & 3 \\ 1 & 1 & 1 \\ 1 & 3 & -1 \end{pmatrix},$$

(ii)
$$\begin{pmatrix} 7 & 4 & -1 \\ 4 & 7 & -1 \\ -4 & -4 & 4 \end{pmatrix},$$

(iii)
$$\begin{pmatrix} 2 & -2 & 3 \\ 10 & -4 & 5 \\ 5 & -4 & 6 \end{pmatrix}.$$

2. Which matrices of Exercise 1, § 7.1, are similar to a diagonal matrix? Without computing P write the diagonal form of each such matrix.

3. Prove that a transformation is singular if and only if it has zero as a characteristic value.

4. Prove that a transformation is nilpotent if and only if all of its characteristic values are zero.

5. (i) Without expanding a 4×4 determinant show that $a - b$, $a - c$, and $a - d$ are characteristic values of the matrix

$$A = \begin{pmatrix} a & b & c & d \\ b & a & c & d \\ b & c & a & d \\ b & c & d & a \end{pmatrix}.$$

(ii) What is the fourth characteristic value?

(iii) Find general conditions on the numbers a, b, c, d which are sufficient that A be similar to a diagonal matrix.

6. Prove that AB and BA have the same characteristic values by establishing the following assertions:

(i) If $D = PAQ$ is the canonical matrix equivalent to A (Theorem 6.14) then DC and CD have the same characteristic polynomial for all C.

(ii) $PABP^{-1}$ and $QBAQ^{-1}$ have the same characteristic equation if P and Q are as given in (i).

(iii) AB and BA have the same characteristic equation.

7. (i) Prove that if either A or B is non-singular, then AB and BA are similar.

(ii) Combine Exercises 6 and 7(i) to show that matrices with the same characteristic values need not be similar. Give an example which illustrates this observation.

8 Prove Theorem 7.5 by means of a geometric argument.

§7.3. *Minimal Polynomial of a Matrix*

In Theorem 4.2 and subsequent remarks it was proved that the set of all $n \times n$ matrices over a field forms a linear algebra of dimension n^2. Hence in this algebra the $n^2 + 1$ elements

$$I = A^0, A, A^2, \ldots, A^{n^2}$$

are linearly dependent for any $n \times n$ matrix A. By Theorem 2.7, a set is dependent only if some "vector" of the set is a linear combination of the ones which precede it. Let m be the integer such that $(I, A, \ldots, A^{m-1})$ is independent but $(I, A, \ldots, A^m)$ is dependent. For suitable scalars we have

$$a_0 A^m + a_1 A^{m-1} + \ldots + a_{m-1} A + a_m I = Z,$$

where $a_0 \neq 0$. Hence for $b_k = a_k a_0^{-1}$ we have

$$A^m + b_1 A^{m-1} + \ldots + b_{m-1} A + b_m I = Z.$$

This is a polynomial equation in the matrix A. The corresponding scalar polynomial is

$$M(x) = x^m + b_1 x^{m-1} + \ldots + b_m.$$

A polynomial, such as M, which has 1 as the coefficient of its largest power is called *monic*.

Definition 7.4.   The *minimal polynomial* of the matrix A is the monic scalar polynomial

$$M(x) = x^m + a_1 x^{m-1} + \ldots + a_m$$

of least degree such that

$$A^m + a_1 A^{m-1} + \ldots + a_m I = Z.$$

We have seen that each matrix has a minimal polynomial, and as an exercise you may prove that the minimal polynomial of A is unique. A word of caution is justified at this point. The form of Definition 7.4 tempts us to define the minimal polynomial of A as "the monic polynomial of least degree for which A is a zero." However, we must distinguish between *matric* polynomials and *scalar* polynomials. Since the properties of matrices and scalars are quite different, there is no *a priori* justification for substituting the matrix A for the scalar x. But every scalar polynomial determines a matric polynomial which is formed by replacing the scalar x by the matrix X and each scalar coefficient a_i by the scalar matrix $a_i I$. In this sense it is correct to say that the minimal polynomial of A is the monic polynomial M of least degree and with scalar matrices as coefficients such that $M(A) = Z$.

The difficulties which arise in handling polynomials having matrices as coefficients are due principally to the existence of zero divisors and the lack of commutativity.   For example, the matric polynomial equation

$$(X - A)(X - B) = Z$$

does not imply that $X = A$ or $X = B$, because a product of non-zero matrices may be zero.   Also, the matric polynomial

$$X^2 - AX - BX + AB$$

cannot be factored as

$$(X - A)(X - B)$$

unless it is known that X and B commute.   On the other hand, we know that any scalar matrix $B = bI$ commutes with any matrix, so that any factorization of a scalar polynomial

$$x^m + a_1 x^{m-1} + \ldots + a_m = (x - r_1) \ldots (x - r_m)$$

determines a like factorization of the corresponding matric polynomial,

$$X^m + a_1 X^{m-1} + \ldots + a_m I = (X - r_1 I) \ldots (X - r_m I).$$

A remarkable result concerning matric polynomials is the Hamilton-Cayley theorem which may be stated loosely as "Every square matrix satisfies its characteristic equation."   To see that this is so, consider a square matrix A and assume for the present that its characteristic vectors span $\mathcal{U}$.   Let the characteristic polynomial of A be

$$(-1)^n \lambda^n + b_1 \lambda^{n-1} + \ldots + b_n.$$

Let B be the matrix defined by

$$B = (-1)^n A^n + b_1 A^{n-1} + \ldots + b_n I.$$

If X is a characteristic vector of A associated with the characteristic value λ, then by direct calculation using Exercise 7, § 7.1, we have

$$XB = [(-1)^n \lambda^n + b_1 \lambda^{n-1} + \ldots + b_n]X = 0 \cdot X = Z.$$

The transformation **S** associated with B maps every characteristic vector of A into zero.   By assumption, the characteristic vectors of A span $\mathcal{U}$, so **S** is the zero transformation, and B must be the zero matrix.   In the next chapter we shall prove the same result for any square matrix.

Theorem 7.6.   (Hamilton-Cayley.)   If A is a matrix with characteristic equation

$$(-1)^n \lambda^n + b_1 \lambda^{n-1} + \ldots + b_n = 0,$$

then

$$(-1)^n A^n + b_1 A^{n-1} + \ldots + b_n I = Z.$$

The Hamilton-Cayley theorem gives us a little more information concerning the minimal polynomial of A, for we now know that its degree does not exceed n. It can be proved that the minimal polynomial of A divides any polynomial p such that $p(A) = Z$; hence the minimal polynomial divides the characteristic polynomial.

Exercises

1. Show that the minimal polynomial of A is unique.

2. Prove that a matrix and its transpose have the same characteristic polynomial.

3. Prove the Hamilton-Cayley theorem for 2×2 matrices by direct calculations with matrices.

4. Prove that if A is similar to B and if $p(X)$ is any matric polynomial with scalar coefficients, then $p(A)$ is similar to $p(B)$.

5. Prove that if A is similar to the scalar matrix cI, then $A = cI$.

6.   (i) Determine all real 2×2 matrices A which satisfy $A^2 = -I$.

   (ii) Show that no real 3×3 matrix A satisfies $A^2 = -I$.

7.   (i) Let C be a square matrix with 1 in every position on the superdiagonal $(c_{i,i+1} = 1)$, $c_{n1}, \ldots, c_{nn}$ in the last row, and zeros elsewhere. Show that the characteristic polynomial of C is

$$(-1)^n[\lambda^n - c_{nn}\lambda^{n-1} - c_{n,n-1}\lambda^{n-2} - \ldots - c_{n2}\lambda - c_{n1}].$$

   (ii) Deduce that every polynomial whose leading coefficient is ± 1, according to whether its degree is even or odd, is the characteristic polynomial of some matrix.

8. Use the Hamilton-Cayley theorem to solve Exercise 8, § 5.4.

§7.4. *Diagonalization Theorems*

In this section we shall establish a variety of criteria for determining whether a given matrix A is similar to a diagonal matrix D. Since the diagonal elements of D are the characteristic values of D (hence of A), we need only know that such a D exists in order to write one, merely by placing the characteristic values of A along the diagonal.

Theorem 7.7.   Each of the following conditions is necessary and sufficient that A be similar to a diagonal matrix.

(a) There exist n linearly independent characteristic vectors of A.

(b) For every row vector X and scalar λ, if $X(A - \lambda I)^2 = Z$, then $X(A - \lambda I) = Z$.

(c) If X_0 is a characteristic row vector corresponding to the characteristic value λ_0, then there is no row vector Y such that $Y(A - \lambda_0 I) = X_0$.

(d) There exists a scalar polynomial P with distinct zeros such that $P(A) = Z$.

(e) There exist an integer r, scalars $a_1, \ldots, a_r$, and non-zero matrices $E_1, \ldots, E_r$ such that

$$\sum_{j=1}^{r} a_j E_j = A,$$

$$\sum_{j=1}^{r} E_j = I.$$

$$E_i E_j = Z \text{ if } i \neq j.$$

P R O O F :   Theorem 7.5 has established that (a) implies that A can be diagonalized. We shall show that diagonalization implies (b), (b) implies (c), (c) implies (d), (d) implies (e), and (e) implies (a), thus completing the cycle.

Diagonalization implies (b): Let $D = PAP^{-1}$ be diagonal, let $Y = XP^{-1}$ for a given row vector X, and suppose $X(A - \lambda I)^2 = Z$ for some scalar λ. Then

$$Z = YP(A - \lambda I)^2 = YP(P^{-1}DP - \lambda I)^2 = Y(D - \lambda I)^2 P.$$

Since P is non-singular, $Y(D - \lambda I)^2 = Z$, and hence $Y(D - \lambda I) = Z$ since $D - \lambda I$ is diagonal (Exercise 2, § 7.1). Thus $X(A - \lambda I)P^{-1} = Z$, so $X(A - \lambda I) = Z$.

(b) implies (c): Let λ_0 be a characteristic value and X_0 a corresponding characteristic row vector. Then $X_0 A = \lambda_0 X_0$. If a vector Y exists such that $Y(A - \lambda_0 I) = X_0$, then we have

$$Y(A - \lambda_0 I)^2 = X_0(A - \lambda_0 I) = Z,$$

so by (b) we have

$$Y(A - \lambda_0 I) = Z = X_0.$$

This contradicts the hypothesis that X_0 is a characteristic row vector, so no vector Y exists with the stated property.

(c) implies (d): We prove that the minimal polynomial M of A has distinct zeros if (c) is satisfied. Assume that M has λ_0 as a repeated zero. Then

$$M(x) = f(x)(x - \lambda_0)^2.$$

Since M is minimal, $f(A)(A - \lambda_0 I)$ is a non-zero matrix, and for some row vector Y_0,

$$Y_0[f(A)(A - \lambda_0 I)] \neq Z.$$

Let us call this non-zero row vector X_0.   Then

$$X_0(A - \lambda_0 I) = Y_0 f(A)(A - \lambda_0 I)^2 = Y_0 M(A) = Z$$

since $M(A) = Z$.   Hence X_0 is characteristic, corresponding to λ_0. But then the equation

$$Y(A - \lambda_0 I) = X_0$$

has the solution $Y_0 f(A)$, which contradicts (c).

(d) implies (e): Let P be a scalar polynomial of degree r such that its zeros $a_1, \ldots, a_r$ are distinct and such that $P(A) = Z$.   We define r other polynomials p_i by the relations

$$P(x) = (x - a_i)p_i(x), \qquad i = 1, \ldots, r.$$

Then $p_i(a_j) = 0$ if and only if $i \neq j$.   Let the polynomial g be defined by

$$g(x) = 1 - \sum_{i=1}^{r} [p_i(a_i)]^{-1} p_i(x),$$

and observe that g is a polynomial of degree less than r such that $g(a_k) = 0$ for $k = 1, \ldots, r$.   Hence $g(x) = 0$ for every x, and each coefficient of g is zero.   Hence $g(B) = Z$ for every matrix B.   Now consider the r matrices

$$E_i = [p_i(a_i)]^{-1} p_i(A), \qquad i = 1, \ldots, r.$$

We have $\sum_{i=1}^{r} E_i = I$.   Also

$$P(A) = (A - a_i I)p_i(A) = Z,$$

so

$$a_i p_i(A) = A p_i(A).$$

Thus

$$\sum_{i=1}^{r} a_i E_i = \sum_{i=1}^{r} [p_i(a_i)]^{-1} A p_i(A) = A \sum_{i=1}^{r} E_i = A.$$

Finally, if $i \neq j$, we have

$$E_i E_j = [p_i(a_i)p_j(a_j)]^{-1} p_i(A)p_j(A)$$
$$= cP(A)h(A),$$

where c is a scalar and $h(A)$ is the product of the $r - 2$ matrices $A - a_k I$, where $k \neq i$ and $k \neq j$.   Therefore $E_i E_j = Z$ if $i \neq j$.

(e) implies (a): Assuming (e) we shall show that for an arbitrary vector X, XE_i is characteristic:

$$(XE_i)A = XE_i\left(\sum_{j=1}^{r} a_j E_j\right) = X \sum_{j=1}^{r} a_i E_i E_j$$

$$= a_i X E_i^2 = a_i(XE_i).$$

The last equality follows from the fact that the matrices E_i are idempotent. (See Exercise 4). In addition, we have

$$X = XI = X \sum_{i=1}^{r} E_i = \sum_{i=1}^{r} (XE_i),$$

so that any vector is a linear combination of characteristic vectors, which means that there are n linearly independent characteristic vectors. The proof of Theorem 7.7 is now complete.

Of these five criteria for diagonability the first is perhaps the most useful for the problems we are considering. Given an $n \times n$ matrix A we need only compute the characteristic vectors and see if there are n of these which are linearly independent. This usually requires a considerable amount of computation. However, if the n characteristic values of A are distinct, the diagonalization problem is easily solved. In that event, A is similar to a diagonal matrix because the characteristic values are the distinct zeros of the characteristic polynomial f, and $f(A) = Z$ by the Hamilton-Cayley theorem. In case the characteristic values are not all distinct, n linearly independent vectors might still exist. This will occur whenever k linearly independent characteristic vectors correspond to each characteristic value of multiplicity k.

Theorem 7.8. A sufficient (but not necessary) condition that A be similar to a diagonal matrix is that the characteristic values of A are distinct.

Let us summarize the results concerning diagonalization obtained thus far. Any square matrix is *equivalent* to a diagonal matrix, and a matrix is *similar* to a diagonal matrix if and only if the characteristic vectors span the full space. Since similar matrices represent the same transformation, we are particularly interested in the second result, and we recall that the diagonal entries must be the characteristic values. The next question is this: Suppose A cannot be diagonalized by a change of coordinates; how close can we come to diagonalizing A? Or, is there some simple matric form such that every matrix is similar to a matrix in this canonical form and such that the form is *almost* diagonal? This question is answered affirmatively in the next chapter.

Exercises

1. Determine whether each of the following matrices is similar to a diagonal matrix. (Exercise 7, § 7.3, may be of assistance.)

(i)
$$\begin{pmatrix} 2 & 0 & 0 \\ 0 & 1 & 2 \\ 0 & 0 & 2 \end{pmatrix},$$

(ii)
$$\begin{pmatrix} 0 & 1 & 0 \\ 0 & 0 & 1 \\ -1 & -3 & -3 \end{pmatrix},$$

(iii)
$$\begin{pmatrix} 0 & 1 & 0 \\ 0 & 0 & 1 \\ 0 & -9 & 6 \end{pmatrix},$$

(iv)
$$\begin{pmatrix} 0 & 1 & 0 & 0 \\ 0 & 0 & 1 & 0 \\ 0 & 0 & 0 & 1 \\ 0 & -4 & 4 & 1 \end{pmatrix}.$$

2. Show that the following $n \times n$ matrices are similar:

$$A = \begin{pmatrix} 1 & 1 \dots 1 \\ 1 & 1 \dots 1 \\ . & . & . \\ . & . & . \\ . & . & . \\ 1 & 1 \dots 1 \end{pmatrix}, \qquad B = \begin{pmatrix} n & 0 \dots 0 \\ 0 & 0 \dots 0 \\ . & . & . \\ . & . & . \\ . & . & . \\ 0 & 0 \dots 0 \end{pmatrix}.$$

3. Show that the following $n \times n$ matrices are similar:

$$A = \begin{pmatrix} 0 & 1 & 0 \dots 0 \\ 0 & 0 & 1 \dots 0 \\ . & . & . & . \\ . & . & . & . \\ . & . & . & . \\ 0 & 0 & 0 \dots 1 \\ 1 & 0 & 0 \dots 0 \end{pmatrix}, \qquad B = \begin{pmatrix} e_1 & 0 & 0 \dots 0 \\ 0 & e_2 & 0 \dots 0 \\ . & . & . & . \\ . & . & . & . \\ . & . & . & . \\ 0 & 0 & 0 \dots e_n \end{pmatrix},$$

where $e_1, e_2, \dots, e_n$ are the n distinct n^{th} roots of unity,

$$e_k = \cos \frac{2\pi k}{n} + i \sin \frac{2\pi k}{n}.$$

4. Let $E_1, \dots, E_r$ be a set of matrices which have the second and third properties of Theorem 7.7 (e).   Prove that each E_i is idempotent.

5. Show that if $A = \sum_{i=1}^{r} a_i E_i$, where the E_i have the properties listed in Theorem 7.7 (e), then each a_i is a characteristic value of A.   Find a corresponding characteristic vector.

6. Prove that if $S = \{\xi_1, \ldots, \xi_k\}$ is a set of characteristic vectors of **T** associated respectively with distinct characteristic values $\lambda_1, \ldots, \lambda_k$, then S is linearly independent.

7. Give a necessary and sufficient condition for the diagonability of the block matrix

$$\begin{pmatrix} A & Z \\ Z & D \end{pmatrix}$$

in terms of the diagonability of the square blocks A and D.

CHAPTER 8

A Canonical Form for Linear Transformations

§8.1. *Direct Sums and Invariant Spaces*

In this chapter we shall answer the question which was raised at the end of Chapter 7: How close can we come to diagonalizing an arbitrary matrix A by a suitable change of coordinates? We shall show that A is similar to a matrix J which is the sum of two matrices, $J = D + N$, where D has zeros everywhere except on the main diagonal and N has zeros everywhere except on the superdiagonal. Thus N is nilpotent. Furthermore, the diagonal elements of D are the characteristic values of A, and the superdiagonal elements of N are either 0 or 1. An example of a matrix in this form is

$$J = \begin{pmatrix} \lambda_1 & 1 & 0 & 0 & 0 \\ 0 & \lambda_1 & 0 & 0 & 0 \\ 0 & 0 & \lambda_1 & 0 & 0 \\ 0 & 0 & 0 & \lambda_2 & 1 \\ 0 & 0 & 0 & 0 & \lambda_2 \end{pmatrix}.$$

The precise arrangement of the superdiagonal elements will also be derived.

A proof of this result is best understood in terms of vector spaces and linear transformations, and indeed the canonical form is an assertion about the effect of a linear transformation on a space, relative to a well-chosen basis. In addition to the concepts of nilpotent transformations, range space, and null space, we need two further notions: the direct sum of subspaces, and invariant subspaces.

142

Definition 8.1.   Let $\mathfrak{M}$ and $\mathfrak{N}$ be subspaces of a vector space $\mathcal{V}$. $\mathcal{V}$ is said to be the *direct sum* of $\mathfrak{M}$ and $\mathfrak{N}$, written

$$\mathcal{V} = \mathfrak{M} \oplus \mathfrak{N},$$

if and only if $\mathfrak{M} + \mathfrak{N} = \mathcal{V}$ and $\mathfrak{M} \cap \mathfrak{N} = [\theta]$.

Theorem 8.1. $\mathcal{V} = \mathfrak{M} \oplus \mathfrak{N}$ if and only if every vector $\xi \in \mathcal{V}$ has a unique representation

$$\xi = \mu + \nu,$$

for some $\mu \in \mathfrak{M}$ and some $\nu \in \mathfrak{N}$.

P R O O F :   Assume that $\mathcal{V} = \mathfrak{M} \oplus \mathfrak{N}$.   Then since $\mathcal{V} = \mathfrak{M} + \mathfrak{N}$, each $\xi \in \mathcal{V}$ can be expressed as $\xi = \mu + \nu$ for suitable $\mu \in \mathfrak{M}$ and $\nu \in \mathfrak{N}$, and we need only prove uniqueness.   Suppose also that $\xi = \mu_1 + \nu_1$. Then

$$\mu_1 + \nu_1 = \mu + \nu,$$

$$\mu_1 - \mu = \nu - \nu_1.$$

But $\mu_1 - \mu \in \mathfrak{M}$ and $\nu - \nu_1 \in \mathfrak{N}$, and by hypothesis $\mathfrak{M}$ and $\mathfrak{N}$ have only the zero vector in common.   Hence $\mu_1 = \mu$ and $\nu_1 = \nu$, so the representation is unique.   To prove the converse, assume that each $\xi \in \mathcal{V}$ is expressed uniquely as the sum of some $\mu \in \mathfrak{M}$ and $\nu \in \mathfrak{N}$.   Clearly, $\mathfrak{M} + \mathfrak{N} = \mathcal{V}$.   Let $\alpha \in \mathfrak{M} \cap \mathfrak{N}$.   Then

$$\alpha = \alpha + \theta, \text{ where } \alpha \in \mathfrak{M} \text{ and } \theta \in \mathfrak{N}$$

$$= \theta + \alpha, \text{ where } \theta \in \mathfrak{M} \text{ and } \alpha \in \mathfrak{N}.$$

Since any such representation of α is unique, we have $\alpha = \theta$.   Hence $\mathfrak{M} \cap \mathfrak{N} = [\theta]$, and therefore $\mathcal{V} = \mathfrak{M} \oplus \mathfrak{N}$.

Closely associated with the concept of direct sum is a type of linear transformation $\mathbf{E}$, called a *projection*, which is nothing more or less than an idempotent transformation:

$$\mathbf{E}^2 = \mathbf{E}.$$

In Exercise 5, § 3.5, it was shown that any projection is the identity transformation on its range space $\mathfrak{R}_{\mathbf{E}}$.   Let $\mathbf{E}_1, \ldots, \mathbf{E}_k$ be a set of projections. These projections are called *orthogonal* if and only if

$$\mathbf{E}_i \mathbf{E}_j = \mathbf{Z} \text{ whenever } i \neq j,$$

and *supplementary* if and only if

$$\mathbf{I} = \sum_{i=1}^{k} \mathbf{E}_i.$$

An example of a set of orthogonal supplementary projections occurred in Theorem 7.7 (e).

Projections have many important properties, some of which are developed in Exercise 6 of this section; in particular, parts (iv) and (v) disclose their relation to direct sum and show that this purely algebraic formulation of a projection is an accurate description of the familiar geometric concept of a projection.   Although we do not make systematic use of projections, you are urged to read Exercise 6 carefully and to solve the problems stated there.

The second notion we need is that of a subspace which is invariant under a transformation.

> **Definition 8.2.**   Let $\mathbf{T}$ be a linear transformation on $\mathcal{V}$.   A subspace $\mathfrak{M}$ of $\mathcal{V}$ is said to be *invariant under* $\mathbf{T}$ (or $\mathbf{T}$-invariant) if and only if $\xi\mathbf{T} \in \mathfrak{M}$ for every $\xi \in \mathfrak{M}$.

A $\mathbf{T}$-invariant subspace therefore has the property that each vector of the subspace is mapped by $\mathbf{T}$ into a vector in the same subspace.   Clearly the range space of $\mathbf{T}$ is invariant and so is the null space.   A useful notation is to let $\mathfrak{M}\mathbf{T}$ denote the set of all images of the vectors of $\mathfrak{M}$.   Then a space $\mathfrak{M}$ is invariant under $\mathbf{T}$ if and only if $\mathfrak{M}\mathbf{T} \subseteq \mathfrak{M}$.   If $\mathfrak{M}$ is a $\mathbf{T}$-invariant subspace of $\mathcal{V}$, it is possible to study the behavior of $\mathfrak{M}$ under $\mathbf{T}$, ignoring the effect of $\mathbf{T}$ on the rest of $\mathcal{V}$, since vectors of $\mathfrak{M}$ are mapped into vectors of $\mathfrak{M}$.   The transformation $\mathbf{T}$ on $\mathcal{V}$ thus defines a transformation $\mathbf{T}_{\mathfrak{M}}$ on $\mathfrak{M}$, called $\mathbf{T}$ *restricted to* $\mathfrak{M}$.

The matric interpretation of this notion is illuminating.   Let $\{\alpha_1, \ldots, \alpha_k\}$ be a basis for the invariant space $\mathfrak{M}$, and let $\{\alpha_1, \ldots, \alpha_n\}$ be a basis for $\mathcal{V}$. Then $\alpha_i\mathbf{T} = \sum_{j=1}^{k} a_{ij}\alpha_j$ for $i = 1, \ldots, k$, and the matrix of $\mathbf{T}$ in this new basis is of the block form

$$\begin{pmatrix} A_1 & Z \\ A_3 & A_2 \end{pmatrix},$$

where A_1 is a $k \times k$ matrix.

In the event that $\mathcal{V} = \mathfrak{M} \oplus \mathfrak{N}$ where $\mathfrak{M}$ and $\mathfrak{N}$ are both invariant under $\mathbf{T}$, a basis for $\mathfrak{M}$ together with a basis for $\mathfrak{N}$ form a basis for $\mathcal{V}$, and relative to that basis $\mathbf{T}$ is represented by a matrix of the form

$$\begin{pmatrix} A_1 & Z \\ Z & A_2 \end{pmatrix},$$

where A_1 is a square array of dimension equal to the dimension of $\mathfrak{M}$ and A_2 is a square array of dimension equal to the dimension of $\mathfrak{N}$.

Exercises

1. Refer to the linear transformation $\mathbf{T}_3$ of Example (c), § 3.1.

(i) Find two invariant subspaces such that $\mathcal{E}_2$ is the direct sum of these subspaces.

(ii) Write the matrix A for $\mathbf{T}_3$ relative to the $\{\epsilon_1, \epsilon_2\}$ basis.

(iii) Write the matrix B for $\mathbf{T}_3$ relative to a basis $\{\beta_1, \beta_2\}$, where each β_i spans one of the invariant subspaces of (i).

(iv) Find a matrix P for which

$$B = PAP^{-1}.$$

2. Let $\mathcal{C}_\lambda$ be the space spanned by all characteristic vectors of a linear transformation $\mathbf{T}$ which are associated with a single characteristic value λ. Prove that $\mathcal{C}_\lambda$ is $\mathbf{T}$-invariant.

3. Let $\mathbf{T}$ be a linear transformation and ξ an arbitrary vector. Let $\mathcal{S} = [\xi, \xi\mathbf{T}, \xi\mathbf{T}^2, \ldots, \xi\mathbf{T}^k, \ldots]$. $\mathcal{S}$ is called the *cyclic subspace generated by* ξ. Prove that $\mathcal{S}$ is $\mathbf{T}$-invariant.

4. Prove that if $\mathcal{S}$ and $\mathcal{R}$ are $\mathbf{T}$-invariant subspaces, then so are $\mathcal{S} \cap \mathcal{R}$ and $\mathcal{S} + \mathcal{R}$.

5. Let $\{\alpha_1, \ldots, \alpha_n\}$ be a basis for $\mathcal{V}$, let $\mathcal{S} = [\alpha_1, \ldots, \alpha_k]$, and let $\mathfrak{J} = [\alpha_{k+1}, \ldots, \alpha_n]$.

(i) Show that $\mathcal{V} = \mathcal{S} \oplus \mathfrak{J}$.

(ii) Show how any subspace of $\mathcal{V}$ can be a component of a direct sum for $\mathcal{V}$.

6. Develop the following information about projections.

(i) $\mathbf{E}$ is a projection if and only if $\mathbf{I} - \mathbf{E}$ is a projection.

(ii) If $\mathbf{E}$ is a projection, then $\mathbf{E}$ and $\mathbf{I} - \mathbf{E}$ are orthogonal and supplementary.

(iii) If $\mathbf{E}_1, \ldots, \mathbf{E}_k$ are orthogonal projections but not supplementary, then $\mathbf{E}_1, \ldots, \mathbf{E}_k, \mathbf{I} - \sum_{i=1}^{k} \mathbf{E}_i$ are orthogonal and supplementary.

(iv) If $\mathbf{E}_1, \ldots, \mathbf{E}_k$ are orthogonal and supplementary projections, then $\mathcal{V} = \mathcal{R}_{\mathbf{E}_1} \oplus \mathcal{R}_{\mathbf{E}_2} \oplus \ldots \oplus \mathcal{R}_{\mathbf{E}_k}$.

(v) If $\mathcal{V} = \mathcal{S}_1 \oplus \mathcal{S}_2 \oplus \ldots \oplus \mathcal{S}_k$, we know that every $\xi \in \mathcal{V}$ has a unique representation $\xi = \xi_1 + \xi_2 + \ldots + \xi_k$, where $\xi_i \in \mathcal{S}_i$. Prove that the mappings $\mathbf{E}_i$, $i = 1, 2, \ldots, k$, defined by

$$\xi\mathbf{E}_i = \xi_i,$$

are linear transformations which form a set of orthogonal and supplementary projections.

(vi) What matrix represents $\mathbf{E}_i$ relative to a basis for $\mathcal{V}$ formed by the union of a basis for each $\mathcal{R}_{\mathbf{E}_i}$ in (iv)?

(vii) What are the possible characteristic values of a projection?

(viii) Let $\mathcal{S}_1$ be a subspace of $\mathcal{V}$ and let $\mathcal{V} = \mathcal{S}_1 \oplus \mathcal{S}_2$. Let $\mathbf{E}_1$ be the projection on $\mathcal{S}_1$ defined in (v). Show that $\mathcal{S}_1$ is $\mathbf{T}$-invariant if and only if

$$\mathbf{E}_1 \mathbf{T} \mathbf{E}_1 = \mathbf{E}_1 \mathbf{T}.$$

§8.2. *Nilpotent Transformations*

As the next stage of preparation to prove the result announced at the beginning of the previous section we now investigate the nature of nilpotent transformations.

Theorem 8.2.   Let $\mathbf{T}$ be a nilpotent linear transformation of index p, and let ξ be a vector such that $\xi \mathbf{T}^{p-1} \neq \theta$. The set $\{\xi, \xi \mathbf{T}, \ldots, \xi \mathbf{T}^{p-1}\}$ is linearly independent.

P R O O F :   Assume that the set is not linearly independent; then

$$\sum_{i=0}^{p-1} c_i \xi \mathbf{T}^i = \theta,$$

where not all c_i are zero. Let c_k be the first non-zero scalar; then

$$\xi \mathbf{T}^k = -c_k^{-1} \sum_{k+1}^{p-1} c_i \xi \mathbf{T}^i,$$

$$\xi \mathbf{T}^{p-1} = \xi \mathbf{T}^k \mathbf{T}^{p-1-k} = -c_k^{-1} \sum_{k+1}^{p-1} c_i \xi \mathbf{T}^{i+p-1-k}.$$

Since $i > k$ in the summation, every power of $\mathbf{T}$ is at least p, and $\mathbf{T}^p = \theta$ by hypothesis. Hence $\xi \mathbf{T}^{p-1} = \theta$, which is a contradiction.

Theorem 8.3.   Let $\mathbf{T}$ be nilpotent of index p, let $\xi \mathbf{T}^{p-1} \neq \theta$, and let $\mathfrak{M} = [\xi, \xi \mathbf{T}, \ldots, \xi \mathbf{T}^{p-1}]$. Then there exists an invariant subspace $\mathfrak{N}$ such that $\mathcal{V} = \mathfrak{M} \oplus \mathfrak{N}$.

P R O O F :   From Theorem 8.2 we see that $\mathfrak{M}$ is of dimension p. Furthermore, $\mathfrak{M}$ is clearly invariant under $\mathbf{T}$. Our job therefore is to find another invariant subspace $\mathfrak{N}$ such that $\mathfrak{M} + \mathfrak{N} = \mathcal{V}$ and $\mathfrak{M} \cap \mathfrak{N} = [\theta]$. We use induction on the index of nilpotency p. If $p = 1$, then $\mathbf{T}$ is the zero transformation, and the theorem is trivial. We therefore assume the conclusion of the theorem for any nilpotent transformation of index $p - 1$. If we consider $\mathbf{T}$ as a transformation restricted to the range space $\mathcal{R}_{\mathbf{T}}$ of $\mathbf{T}$, then $\mathbf{T}_{\mathcal{R}_{\mathbf{T}}}$ is nilpotent of index $p - 1$. Applying the induction hypothesis we have

$$\mathcal{R}_{\mathbf{T}} = \mathfrak{M}_0 \oplus \mathfrak{N}_0,$$

where $\mathfrak{M}_0 = [\xi\mathbf{T}, \ldots, \xi\mathbf{T}^{p-1}]$ and $\mathfrak{N}_0$ are $\mathbf{T}$-invariant.

We shall adjust $\mathfrak{N}_0$ in several steps to obtain the space $\mathfrak{N}$ desired for the theorem. Since several subspaces are defined, subspace diagrams are given at each stage to clarify the construction. First let

$$\mathfrak{N}_1 = \{\alpha \in \mathcal{V} \,|\, \alpha\mathbf{T} \in \mathfrak{N}_0\}.$$

Then $\mathfrak{N}_0 \subseteq \mathfrak{N}_1$, since $\mathfrak{N}_0$ is $\mathbf{T}$-invariant, and $\mathfrak{N}_1\mathbf{T} = \mathfrak{N}_0$.

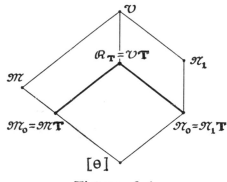

Figure 8.1

We now show that $\mathcal{V} = \mathfrak{M} + \mathfrak{N}_1$. Let $\alpha \in \mathcal{V}$; then since $\alpha\mathbf{T} \in \mathcal{R}_\mathbf{T}$,

$$\alpha\mathbf{T} = \mu_0 + \nu_0$$

for some $\mu_0 \in \mathfrak{M}_0$, $\nu_0 \in \mathfrak{N}_0$.
But

$$\mu_0 = \sum_{i=1}^{p-1} c_i\xi\mathbf{T}^i = \left(\sum_{i=1}^{p-1} c_i\xi\mathbf{T}^{i-1}\right)\mathbf{T} = \mu\mathbf{T}$$

for some $\mu \subset \mathfrak{M}$. Hence

$$\nu_0 = \alpha\mathbf{T} - \mu_0 = \alpha\mathbf{T} - \mu\mathbf{T} = (\alpha - \mu)\mathbf{T} \in \mathfrak{N}_0.$$

Therefore $\alpha - \mu \in \mathfrak{N}_1$, and $\alpha = \mu + \nu_1$, where $\mu \in \mathfrak{M}$ and $\nu_1 \in \mathfrak{N}_1$. Thus $\mathcal{V} = \mathfrak{M} + \mathfrak{N}_1$; if we could prove that $\mathfrak{M} \cap \mathfrak{N}_1 = [\theta]$, we would be through. Unfortunately, $\mathfrak{N}_1$ may be too large, and it is not true in general that $\mathfrak{M} \cap \mathfrak{N}_1 = [\theta]$.

Let $\beta \in \mathfrak{M} \cap \mathfrak{N}_1$; since $\mathfrak{M}\mathbf{T} \subseteq \mathfrak{M}_0$ and $\mathfrak{N}_1\mathbf{T} \subseteq \mathfrak{N}_0$, $\beta\mathbf{T} \subset \mathfrak{M}_0 \cap \mathfrak{N}_0$. But $\mathcal{R}_\mathbf{T}$ is the direct sum of $\mathfrak{M}_0$ and $\mathfrak{N}_0$, so $\beta\mathbf{T} = \theta$. This implies that $\beta = c\xi\mathbf{T}^{p-1} \in \mathfrak{M}_0$. Thus $\mathfrak{M} \cap \mathfrak{N}_1 \subseteq \mathfrak{M}_0$, so $(\mathfrak{M} \cap \mathfrak{N}_1) \cap \mathfrak{N}_0 = [\theta]$. Therefore, we can form the direct sum of $\mathfrak{M} \cap \mathfrak{N}_1$ and $\mathfrak{N}_0$ to form a subspace $\mathcal{S}$ of $\mathfrak{N}_1$,

$$\mathcal{S} = (\mathfrak{M} \cap \mathfrak{N}_1) \oplus \mathfrak{N}_0 \subseteq \mathfrak{N}_1.$$

Let $\mathfrak{N}_0'$ be any space such that

$$\mathcal{S} \oplus \mathfrak{N}_0' = (\mathfrak{M} \cap \mathfrak{N}_1) \oplus \mathfrak{N}_0 \oplus \mathfrak{N}_0' = \mathfrak{N}_1,$$

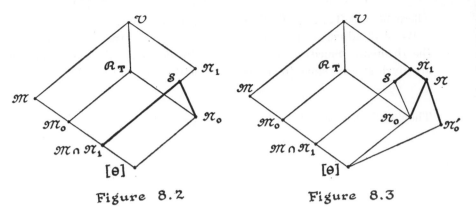

Figure 8.2   Figure 8.3

and let

$$\mathfrak{N} = \mathfrak{N}_0 \oplus \mathfrak{N}_0'.$$

We shall show that this space $\mathfrak{N}$ has the properties stated in the theorem. Clearly, $\mathfrak{N}_0 \subseteq \mathfrak{N} \subseteq \mathfrak{N}_1$, so $\mathfrak{N}\mathbf{T} \subseteq \mathfrak{N}_1\mathbf{T}$. But as observed after the definition of $\mathfrak{N}_1$, $\mathfrak{N}_1\mathbf{T} \subseteq \mathfrak{N}_0$. Hence $\mathfrak{N}\mathbf{T} \subseteq \mathfrak{N}_0 \subseteq \mathfrak{N}$, and $\mathfrak{N}$ is **T**-invariant. Next we have $\mathfrak{M} \cap \mathfrak{N} = \mathfrak{M} \cap (\mathfrak{N} \cap \mathfrak{N}_1) = (\mathfrak{M} \cap \mathfrak{N}_1) \cap \mathfrak{N} = [\theta]$, since $\mathfrak{N}$ was defined by means of a direct sum with $\mathfrak{M} \cap \mathfrak{N}_1$. Finally, let $\alpha \in \mathcal{V}$. Then

$$\alpha = \mu_0 + \nu_1 \text{ for } \mu_0 \in \mathfrak{M} \text{ and } \nu_1 \in \mathfrak{N}_1.$$

But by the direct sum decomposition of $\mathfrak{N}_1$,

$$\nu_1 = \mu_1 + \nu_0 + \nu_0',$$

where

$$\mu_1 \in \mathfrak{M} \cap \mathfrak{N}_1, \ \nu_0 \in \mathfrak{N}_0 \text{ and } \nu_0' \in \mathfrak{N}_0'.$$

Hence

$$\alpha = (\mu_0 + \mu_1) + (\nu_0 + \nu_0')$$

$$= \mu + \nu,$$

where

$$\mu = \mu_0 + \mu_1 \in \mathfrak{M} \text{ and } \nu = \nu_0 + \nu_0' \in \mathfrak{N}.$$

Therefore $\mathcal{V} = \mathfrak{M} \oplus \mathfrak{N}$, where $\mathfrak{M}$ is of dimension p and both $\mathfrak{M}$ and $\mathfrak{N}$ are **T**-invariant, and the proof is complete.

The matric interpretation of Theorem 8.3 is interesting and enlightening. Let A be a nilpotent matrix which corresponds in a given coordinate system to a nilpotent transformation **T**, and let $\mathfrak{M}$ and $\mathfrak{N}$ be **T**-invariant spaces such that $\mathcal{V} = \mathfrak{M} \oplus \mathfrak{N}$. Let $\{\alpha_1, \ldots, \alpha_p\}$ be a basis for $\mathfrak{M}$ and $\{\alpha_{p+1}, \ldots, \alpha_n\}$

be a basis for $\mathfrak{N}$. Then $\{\alpha_1, \ldots, \alpha_n\}$ is a basis for $\mathfrak{V}$, and relative to this basis $\mathbf{T}$ is represented by a matrix of the form

$$\begin{pmatrix} A_1 & Z \\ Z & B_1 \end{pmatrix},$$

where A_1 and B_1, respectively, are $p \times p$ and $(n - p) \times (n - p)$ arrays. We can say more; A_1 describes the behavior of $\mathbf{T}$ on $\mathfrak{M}$. If we choose as a basis for $\mathfrak{M}$ the vectors $\alpha_i = \xi\mathbf{T}^{i-1}$, then

$$\alpha_i\mathbf{T} = \xi\mathbf{T}^i = \alpha_{i+1} \text{ for } i = 1, \ldots, p - 1,$$

and $\alpha_p\mathbf{T} = \theta$. Hence we can select a basis such that

$$A_1 = \begin{pmatrix} 0 & 1 & & & & \\ & 0 & 1 & & & \\ & & 0 & \cdot & & \\ & & & \cdot & \cdot & \\ & & & & \cdot & 1 \\ & & & & & 0 \end{pmatrix},$$

where every superdiagonal element is 1 and all other elements are 0. Next, what about B_1? Since $\mathbf{T}$ is nilpotent of index p on $\mathfrak{V}$, $\mathbf{T}$ is nilpotent of index $p' \le p$ on any subspace of $\mathfrak{V}$. In particular, let $p_2 \le p$ be the index of nilpotency of $\mathbf{T}$, considered as a transformation restricted to the invariant space $\mathfrak{N}$. As before, let $\xi_2 \in \mathfrak{N}$ be such that $\xi_2\mathbf{T}_{\mathfrak{N}}^{p_2-1} \ne \theta$. The space $\mathfrak{N}$ can be written as a direct sum

$$\mathfrak{N} = \mathfrak{M}_2 \oplus \mathfrak{N}_2$$

of invariant spaces, and a basis for $\mathfrak{M}_2$ is $\{\xi_2, \xi_2\mathbf{T}_{\mathfrak{N}}, \ldots, \xi_2\mathbf{T}_{\mathfrak{N}}^{p_2-1}\}$. Relative to this basis for $\mathfrak{M}_2$ and any basis for $\mathfrak{N}_2$, the behavior of $\mathbf{T}_{\mathfrak{N}}$ is represented by the matrix

$$\begin{pmatrix} A_2 & Z \\ Z & B_2 \end{pmatrix},$$

where A_2 is a $p_2 \times p_2$ array with 1 in every superdiagonal position and zeros elsewhere. Again, we consider $\mathbf{T}$ restricted to $\mathfrak{N}_2$ and repeat the argument. Since $\mathfrak{V}$ is finite-dimensional, the process can be iterated until we have chosen a basis for $\mathfrak{V}$ relative to which $\mathbf{T}$ is represented in the new basis by the matrix

$$\begin{pmatrix} A_1 & & & & \\ & A_2 & & & \\ & & \cdot & & \\ & & & \cdot & \\ & & & & A_k \end{pmatrix},$$

where each A_i is a square block with 1 in each superdiagonal position and zeros elsewhere.   Therefore any nilpotent matrix A is similar to a matrix of the form

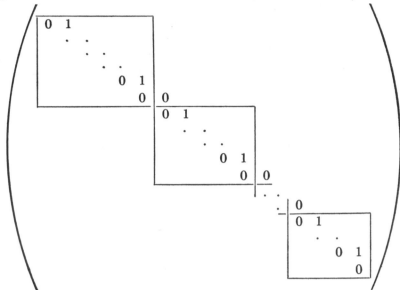

where every element off the superdiagonal is 0 and the superdiagonal consists of several chains of 1, each chain followed by at least one 0.

In the language of transformations therefore, a nilpotent transformation on $\mathcal{V}$ decomposes $\mathcal{V}$ into a direct sum of k spaces

$$\mathcal{V} = \mathfrak{M}_1 \oplus \mathfrak{M}_2 \oplus \ldots \oplus \mathfrak{M}_k.$$

Each $\mathfrak{M}_i$ is **T**-invariant, **T** is nilpotent of index p_i on $\mathfrak{M}_i$, and a basis for each $\mathfrak{M}_i$ is determined by a vector ξ_i such that $\xi_i \mathbf{T}^{p_i-1} \neq \theta$.   In Theorem 8.6 we shall show that the integers $k, p_1, \ldots, p_k$ completely characterize **T**; that is, two nilpotent matrices are similar if and only if these integers are the same for the two matrices.   Notice that k gives the number of blocks in the canonical form for A, while p_i is the dimension of the ith block.   Thus the following two results have been proved.

Theorem 8.4.   If **T** is a nilpotent transformation of index p_1, then there exist an integer k, k distinct vectors $\xi_1, \ldots, \xi_k$, and k integers $p_1 \geq p_2 \geq \ldots \geq p_k$ such that

(a)
$$\xi_1, \ \xi_1\mathbf{T}, \ldots, \xi_1\mathbf{T}^{p_1-1}$$
$$\xi_2, \ \xi_2\mathbf{T}, \ldots, \xi_2\mathbf{T}^{p_2-1}$$
$$\cdot \quad \cdot \qquad \quad \cdot$$
$$\cdot \quad \cdot \qquad \quad \cdot$$
$$\xi_k, \ \xi_k\mathbf{T}, \ldots, \xi_k\mathbf{T}^{p_k-1}$$

forms a basis for $\mathcal{V}$,

(b) for each i, $[\xi_i, \xi_i\mathbf{T}, \ldots, \xi_i\mathbf{T}^{p_i-1}] = \mathfrak{M}_i$ is a **T**-invariant subspace of $\mathcal{U}$,

(c) $\mathcal{U} = \mathfrak{M}_1 \oplus \ldots \oplus \mathfrak{M}_k$.

Theorem 8.5. Any nilpotent matrix is similar to a matrix with a certain arrangement of 0 and 1 along the superdiagonal and 0 elsewhere.

Theorem 8.6. Let **T** and **S** be nilpotent linear transformations on $\mathcal{U}_n$. In the notation of Theorem 8.4 let **T** determine the integers k, $p_1 \geq p_2 \geq \ldots \geq p_k$; let **S** determine the integers j, $q_1 \geq q_2 \geq \ldots \geq q_j$. Then $k = j$ and $p_i = q_i$ for $i = 1, \ldots, k$ if and only if there exists a non-singular transformation **R** on $\mathcal{U}_n$ such that

$$\mathbf{S} = \mathbf{RTR}^{-1}.$$

P R O O F :   Suppose $k = j$ and $p_i = q_i$ for $i = 1, \ldots, k$. As in Theorem 8.4, choose as a basis for $\mathcal{U}_n$ the vectors

$$\xi_1, \ \xi_1\mathbf{T}, \ldots, \ \xi_1\mathbf{T}^{p_1-1}$$
$$\xi_2, \ \xi_2\mathbf{T}, \ldots, \ \xi_2\mathbf{T}^{p_2-1}$$
$$\cdot \qquad \cdot \qquad\qquad \cdot$$
$$\cdot \qquad \cdot \qquad\qquad \cdot$$
$$\xi_k, \ \xi_k\mathbf{T}, \ldots, \ \xi_k\mathbf{T}^{p_k-1}.$$

Relative to this basis, **T** is represented by a matrix N whose superdiagonal has 1 in the first $p_1 - 1$ positions, followed by 0, then 1 in the next $p_2 - 1$ positions, followed by 0, and so on. All other entries of N are zero. In the same way, choose a basis according to the properties of **S**. The matrix representing **S** in this basis will also be N, so by Theorem 6.18, $\mathbf{S} = \mathbf{RTR}^{-1}$ for some non-singular linear transformation **R**.

Conversely, suppose $\mathbf{S} = \mathbf{RTR}^{-1}$. Choose as a basis for $\mathcal{U}_n$ the vectors,

$$\eta_1, \ \eta_1\mathbf{S}, \ldots, \ \eta_1\mathbf{S}^{q_1-1}$$
$$\eta_2, \ \eta_2\mathbf{S}, \ldots, \ \eta_2\mathbf{S}^{q_2-1}$$
$$\cdot \qquad \cdot \qquad\qquad \cdot$$
$$\cdot \qquad \cdot \qquad\qquad \cdot$$
$$\eta_j, \ \eta_j\mathbf{S}, \ldots, \ \eta_j\mathbf{S}^{q_j-1},$$

as guaranteed by Theorem 8.4. Since **R** is non-singular, we obtain a new basis by mapping each of these basis vectors by **R**. But if $j > 0$,

$$\eta_i\mathbf{S}^j\mathbf{R} = \eta_i\mathbf{S}^{j-1}(\mathbf{SR}) = \eta_i\mathbf{S}^{j-1}(\mathbf{RT}) = (\eta_i\mathbf{S}^{j-1}\mathbf{R})\mathbf{T}.$$

Hence if we let $\xi_i = \eta_i\mathbf{R}$, the new basis can be written

$$\xi_1, \ \xi_1\mathbf{T}, \ldots, \ \xi_1\mathbf{T}^{q_1-1}$$
$$\xi_2, \ \xi_2\mathbf{T}, \ldots, \ \xi_2\mathbf{T}^{q_2-1}$$

$$\xi_j, \ \xi_j\mathbf{T}, \ldots, \ \xi_j\mathbf{T}^{q_i-1}.$$

But

$$\xi_i\mathbf{T}^{q_i-1}\mathbf{T} = \eta_i\mathbf{RTT}^{q_i-1} = \eta_i\mathbf{SRT}^{q_i-1} = \eta_i\mathbf{S}^2\mathbf{RT}^{q_i-2}$$

$$= \ldots = \eta_i\mathbf{S}^q\mathbf{R} = \theta\mathbf{R} = \theta.$$

Hence the ξ-basis is of the form of Theorem 8.4, and therefore $\mathbf{T}$ determines the same integers as does $\mathbf{S}$.

According to Theorem 6.18, specialized to the case in which $\mathcal{U}_m = \mathcal{W}_n$, the assertion of Theorem 8.6 is that two nilpotent linear transformations determine the same set of integers if and only if the two transformations are represented by the same matrix relative to suitably chosen bases. Thus the integers $k, p_1, \ldots, p_k$ of Theorem 8.4 are uniquely determined by a nilpotent transformation even though the vectors $\xi_1, \ldots, \xi_k$ are not uniquely determined by the transformation.

The matric analogue of Theorem 8.6 is that two nilpotent matrices determine the same set of integers if and only if the matrices are similar. Thus the superdiagonal block form described in the text following Theorem 8.3 is canonical for the equivalence relation of similarity for nilpotent matrices.

Exercises

1. Prove that any matrix which is similar to a nilpotent matrix of index p is itself nilpotent of index p.

2. Let

$$A = \begin{pmatrix} 0 & 2 & 1 \\ 0 & 0 & 3 \\ 0 & 0 & 0 \end{pmatrix}$$

be the matrix of a transformation $\mathbf{T}$ on $\mathcal{E}_3$.

(i) Find the rank of A, the null space of A, and the index of nilpotency of A.

(ii) Following the method of Theorem 8.4 and starting with $\xi_1 = (1, -1, 0)$, find a basis for $\mathcal{E}_3$ such that with respect to this basis $\mathbf{T}$ is represented by a matrix in the canonical form of Theorem 8.5.

(iii) Calculate this new matrix from the new basis, and find the integers $k, p_1, \ldots, p_k$.

3. Let N be the $n \times n$ matrix which has 1 in each superdiagonal position and zeros elsewhere.

(i) Prove that A and N commute if and only if A is of the form

$$\begin{pmatrix} a_1 & a_2 & a_3 & \ldots & a_n \\ 0 & a_1 & a_2 & \ldots & a_{n-1} \\ 0 & 0 & a_1 & \ldots & a_{n-2} \\ \cdot & \cdot & \cdot & & \cdot \\ \cdot & \cdot & \cdot & & \cdot \\ \cdot & \cdot & \cdot & & \cdot \\ 0 & 0 & 0 & \ldots & a_1 \end{pmatrix}.$$

(ii) If A is of the form above and if $a_2 \neq 0$, show that the space spanned by the characteristic vectors of A is one-dimensional.

(iii) Let $k \geq 2$. If $a_2 = a_3 = \ldots = a_k = 0$ and $a_{k+1} \neq 0$, show that the space spanned by the characteristic vectors of A is k-dimensional.

4. Find necessary and sufficient conditions that the matrix C of Exercise 7, § 7.3, be nilpotent.

§8.3. *Jordan Canonical Form*

We have referred at various times to the difference between the properties of field elements and the properties of matrices of field elements. One more contrast is worth examining, namely, the existence of inverses. The inverse of a field element b exists if and only if $b \neq 0$, so "inverse" and "non-zero" are closely related notions. For a matrix B, the existence of B^{-1} certainly implies $B \neq Z$, but the reverse implication is not valid since non-zero matrices may be singular. Again, the concept of nilpotency with positive index never arises in a field, but it has come into our study of matrices in an essential way. A non-zero nilpotent matrix, we feel, is an example of something which barely escapes being zero, while a non-singular matrix is quite the opposite. It is of interest therefore to show that every matrix is a combination of a non-singular matrix and a nilpotent matrix.

Theorem 8.7. Let $\mathbf{T}$ be any linear transformation on $\mathcal{V}$. There exist subspaces $\mathcal{R}$ and $\mathcal{S}$ such that

(a) $\mathcal{R}$ and $\mathcal{S}$ are $\mathbf{T}$-invariant,

(b) $\mathcal{V} = \mathcal{R} \oplus \mathcal{S}$,

(c) $\mathbf{T}$, restricted to $\mathcal{R}$, is non-singular, and $\mathbf{T}$, restricted to $\mathcal{S}$, is nilpotent.

P R O O F : We consider successive powers of $\mathbf{T}$. From Theorem 3.5 we recall that the range and null spaces of powers of $\mathbf{T}$ form chains such that

$$\mathcal{V} \supset \mathcal{R}_{\mathbf{T}} \supset \mathcal{R}_{\mathbf{T}^2} \supset \ldots \supset \mathcal{R}_{\mathbf{T}^k} = \mathcal{R}_{\mathbf{T}^{k+1}} = \ldots$$
$$[\theta] \subset \mathcal{N}_{\mathbf{T}} \subset \mathcal{N}_{\mathbf{T}^2} \subset \ldots \subset \mathcal{N}_{\mathbf{T}^k} = \mathcal{N}_{\mathbf{T}^{k+1}} = \ldots$$

for some integer $k \geq 0$. Let $\mathcal{R} = \mathcal{R}_{\mathbf{T}^k}$ and $\mathcal{S} = \mathfrak{N}_{\mathbf{T}^k}$, and suppose $\xi \in \mathcal{R} \cap \mathcal{S}$. Then $\xi = \eta \mathbf{T}^k$ for some $\eta \in \mathcal{V}$, and $\xi \mathbf{T}^k = \theta$. Hence $\theta = \xi \mathbf{T}^k = (\eta \mathbf{T}^k) \mathbf{T}^k$. Hence $\eta \in \mathfrak{N}_{\mathbf{T}^{2k}} = \mathfrak{N}_{\mathbf{T}^k}$, so $\theta = \eta \mathbf{T}^k = \xi$. Now $\mathcal{R}$ and $\mathcal{S}$ have only θ in common, and the sum of their dimensions is n. Hence

$$\mathcal{V} = \mathcal{R} \oplus \mathcal{S}.$$

Also, $\mathcal{R}_{\mathbf{T}^k} \mathbf{T} = \mathcal{R}_{\mathbf{T}^{k+1}} = \mathcal{R}_{\mathbf{T}^k}$, and similarly for $\mathcal{S}$, so $\mathcal{R}$ and $\mathcal{S}$ are $\mathbf{T}$-invariant. Now $\mathbf{T}$ maps $\mathcal{R}$ onto $\mathcal{R}$, so $\mathbf{T}_\mathcal{R}$ is non-singular. The vectors of $\mathcal{S}$ are mapped into θ by $\mathbf{T}^k$, so $\mathbf{T}_\mathcal{S}$ is nilpotent.

The next theorem, which is stated in terms of linear transformations, is the one which gives us the Jordan canonical form for a matrix, as stated in § 8.1.

Theorem 8.8.   Let $\mathbf{T}$ be a linear transformation with the distinct characteristic values $\lambda_1, \ldots, \lambda_r$, and let s_i be the multiplicity of λ_i for $i = 1, \ldots, r$.   Then $\mathcal{V}$ is the direct sum of r subspaces,

$$\mathcal{V} = \mathcal{S}_1 \oplus \mathcal{S}_2 \oplus \ldots \oplus \mathcal{S}_r,$$

such that for $i = 1, \ldots, r$

(a) $\mathcal{S}_i$ is $\mathbf{T}$-invariant,
(b) $\mathcal{S}_i$ is of dimension s_i,
(c) when restricted to the space $\mathcal{S}_i$, $\mathbf{T}$ has the form $\mathbf{T}_{\mathcal{S}_i} = \lambda_i \mathbf{I} + \mathbf{N}_i$, where $\mathbf{N}_i$ is nilpotent.

P R O O F :   Given $\mathbf{T}$, we consider the linear transformation $\mathbf{T}_1$ defined by

$$\mathbf{T}_1 = \mathbf{T} - \lambda_1 \mathbf{I}$$

and apply Theorem 8.7 to obtain $\mathbf{T}_1$-invariant subspaces $\mathcal{S}_1$ and $\mathcal{R}_1$ such that

$$\mathcal{V} = \mathcal{S}_1 \oplus \mathcal{R}_1,$$

where $\mathbf{T}_1$ is nilpotent on $\mathcal{S}_1$ and non-singular on $\mathcal{R}_1$.   Clearly, $\mathcal{S}_1$ and $\mathcal{R}_1$ are $\mathbf{T}$-invariant, since $\mathbf{T} = \mathbf{T}_1 + \lambda_1 \mathbf{I}$; also $\mathbf{T}_{\mathcal{S}_1} = (\mathbf{T}_1 + \lambda_1 \mathbf{I})_{\mathcal{S}_1}$ is of the form (c), since $\mathbf{T}_1$ is nilpotent on $\mathcal{S}_1$.   We next prove $s_1 = \dim \mathcal{S}_1$. Since $\mathcal{S}_1$ and $\mathcal{R}_1$ form a direct sum, we may choose any basis for $\mathcal{S}_1$ and any basis for $\mathcal{R}_1$, combining them to give a basis for $\mathcal{V}$.   With respect to any such basis, $\mathbf{T}$ is represented by a matrix of the block form

$$A = \begin{pmatrix} A_{\mathcal{S}_1} & Z \\ Z & A_{\mathcal{R}_1} \end{pmatrix},$$

where $A_{\mathcal{S}_1}$ and $A_{\mathcal{R}_1}$ represent $\mathbf{T}$ restricted to the $\mathbf{T}$-invariant spaces $\mathcal{S}_1$ and $\mathcal{R}_1$, respectively.   Hence $A_{\mathcal{R}_1} - \lambda_1 I_{\mathcal{R}_1}$ represents $\mathbf{T}_1$ on $\mathcal{R}_1$.   Now for any λ,

$$\det(A - \lambda I) = \det(A_{S_1} - \lambda I_{S_1}) \cdot \det(A_{\mathcal{R}_1} - \lambda I_{\mathcal{R}_1}).$$

Since $\mathbf{T}_1$ is non-singular on $\mathcal{R}_1$, $\det(A_{\mathcal{R}_1} - \lambda_1 I_{\mathcal{R}_1}) \neq 0$, and the dimension of S_1 is at least as great as the multiplicity of the characteristic value λ_1;

$$\dim S_1 \geq s_1.$$

On the other hand, $\mathbf{T}_1$ is nilpotent on S_1 and we apply Theorem 8.5 to choose a basis for S_1 such that $\mathbf{T}_1$ restricted to S_1 is represented by a matrix with zeros and ones on the superdiagonal and zeros elsewhere. Since $\mathbf{T}_{S_1} = (\mathbf{T}_1 + \lambda_1\mathbf{I})_{S_1}$, the matrix A_{S_1} has λ_1 in every diagonal position, zeros and ones on the superdiagonal, and zeros elsewhere. Thus A_{S_1} has λ_1 as its only characteristic value, so

$$\dim S_1 \leq s_1.$$

Part (b) of the theorem follows from the two inequalities which we have obtained.

Now all parts of the theorem are established for the case $i = 1$. We next consider the transformation $\mathbf{T}_{\mathcal{R}_1}$ and repeat the argument, using

$$\mathbf{T}_2 = \mathbf{T}_{\mathcal{R}_1} - \lambda_2\mathbf{I}_{\mathcal{R}_1}.$$

By finite-dimensionality the theorem follows after r steps.

The matric interpretation of this theorem gives the Jordan canonical form for a matrix. Let A be a matrix with distinct characteristic values λ_i, each of multiplicity s_i for $i = 1, \ldots, r$. Then A is similar to a matrix in the block form

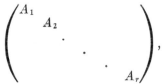

where A_i is $s_i \times s_i$ with λ_i in every diagonal position, zeros and ones on the superdiagonal in a certain arrangement, and zeros elsewhere.

Theorem 8.9. A matrix with characteristic values λ_i, $i = 1, \ldots, n$ is similar to a matrix with these characteristic values in the diagonal positions, zeros and ones along the superdiagonal, and zeros elsewhere.

We shall now make several observations which add real information to the rather loose statement of Theorem 8.9. Any Jordan matrix which is similar to A has r major blocks A_i on the diagonal whenever A has r distinct characteristic values. A_i is a square block of dimension s_i, the multiplicity of λ_i as a characteristic value. Each diagonal element of A_i is λ_i, and any other non-zero entry of A_i must be 1 and must occur on the superdiagonal of A_i. Furthermore, λ_i can appear as a diagonal element of no block other than A_i. Hence if A and B are similar, and therefore have the same characteristic polynomial, the Jordan form of each must contain the same number of blocks, each of the same dimension. Except for possible permutations of the blocks along the diagonal, the two Jordan matrices can possibly differ only on the superdiagonal.

Now consider the distribution of 0's and 1's on the superdiagonal of the block A_i:

$$
A_i = \begin{pmatrix}
\lambda_i & \delta & 0 & \cdots & 0 & 0 \\
0 & \lambda_i & \delta & \cdots & 0 & 0 \\
\cdot & \cdot & \cdot & & \cdot & \cdot \\
\cdot & \cdot & \cdot & & \cdot & \cdot \\
\cdot & \cdot & \cdot & & \cdot & \cdot \\
\cdot & \cdot & \cdot & & \cdot & \cdot \\
0 & 0 & 0 & \cdots & \lambda_i & \delta \\
0 & 0 & 0 & \cdots & 0 & \lambda_i
\end{pmatrix}, \quad \delta = 0 \text{ or } 1.
$$

Since $A_i - \lambda_i I$ is nilpotent of index s_i, we can apply the matric form of Theorem 8.4 to decompose $A_i - \lambda_i I$ into sub-blocks B_{ij} along the diagonal, $j = 1, 2, \ldots, k(i)$:

$$
A_i - \lambda_i I = \begin{pmatrix}
B_{i1} & & & & \\
& B_{i2} & & & \\
& & \cdot & & \\
& & & \cdot & \\
& & & & B_{ik(i)}
\end{pmatrix}.
$$

The dimensions of these blocks are given by the numbers

$$
p_{i1} \geq p_{i2} \geq \cdots \geq p_{ik(i)}
$$

of Theorem 8.4 which, according to Theorem 8.6, are uniquely determined. This implies that the distribution of 0's and 1's on the superdiagonal of each A_i and hence of A (except for permutations of the blocks along the diagonal of A) is uniquely determined by the transformation represented by A. Hence, two matrices are similar if and only if they have the same Jordan form. This is the assertion that the Jordan form is canonical for similar matrices.

This means that a linear transformation $\mathbf{T}$ determines r numbers, $s_1, \ldots, s_r$, where each s_i is the multiplicity of λ_i as a root of the characteristic equation. Each s_i determines other numbers p_{ij}, in decreasing order,

$$
p_{i1} \geq p_{i2} \geq \cdots \geq p_{ik(i)},
$$
$$
s_i = p_{i1} + p_{i2} + \ldots + p_{ik(i)}, \qquad i = 1, \ldots, r.
$$

The number p_{ij} is the dimension of the block B_{ij} within the block A_i. The superdiagonal elements of A are a string of $p_{11} - 1$ ones followed by a zero, then $p_{12} - 1$ ones, and another zero, and so on. Finally, the Jordan form is completely determined by the numbers,

$$\lambda_1, \ldots, \lambda_r$$
$$s_1, \ldots, s_r$$
$$p_{11}, \ldots, p_{1k(1)}$$
$$\cdot \qquad \cdot$$
$$\cdot \qquad \cdot$$
$$\cdot \qquad \cdot$$
$$p_{r1}, \ldots, p_{rk(r)}.$$

The numbers p_{ij} are often written in the form

$$\{(p_{11}, p_{12}, \ldots, p_{1k(1)})(p_{21}, p_{22}, \ldots, p_{2k(2)}) \ldots (p_{r1}, p_{r2}, \ldots, p_{rk(r)})\},$$

and this form is called the *Segre characteristic* of A.

We state a few more facts which are of importance but which are not pursued in this book. Let the characteristic polynomial of A be

$$P(\lambda) = (\lambda - \lambda_1)^{s_1}(\lambda - \lambda_2)^{s_2} \ldots (\lambda - \lambda_r)^{s_r}.$$

The polynomials $D_{ij}(\lambda) = (\lambda - \lambda_i)^{p_{ij}}$ are called *elementary divisors* of A, since each is a divisor of $P(\lambda)$. It can be shown that the minimal polynomial of A is

$$M(\lambda) = (\lambda - \lambda_1)^{p_{11}}(\lambda - \lambda_2)^{p_{21}} \ldots (\lambda - \lambda_r)^{p_{r1}},$$

the product of the distinct elementary divisors of highest power. From this it is clear that $P(\lambda)$ is a multiple of $M(\lambda)$ and that $P(A) = Z$ since $M(A) = Z$. We shall give an independent proof of this, the Hamilton-Cayley theorem, in the next section.

Finally, we remind ourselves that the theory of the Jordan form depended upon a factorization of $P(\lambda)$ into linear factors. This is always possible if the base field is the field of complex numbers, but other canonical forms must be used if we are restricted to work, for example, entirely within the field of real numbers.

Exercises

1. Use the Jordan canonical form to solve the following problems:
    (i) Exercse 8, § 7.1.
    (ii) Exercise 3, § 7.2.
    (iii) Exercise 4, § 7.2.
    (iv) Prove Theorem 7.8.

2. Determine whether or not the following matrices are similar:

$$A = \begin{pmatrix} 1 & 4 \\ -1 & -3 \end{pmatrix}, \qquad B = \begin{pmatrix} -1 & 1 \\ 0 & -1 \end{pmatrix}.$$

3. Determine necessary and sufficient conditions on a, b, c, d that the matrix

$$\begin{pmatrix} a & b \\ c & d \end{pmatrix}$$

is *not* similar to a diagonal matrix.

4. Determine the Jordan form of the following matrices:

(i) Exercise 1 (iii), § 7.2.

(ii) Exercise 1 (ii), § 7.4.

(iii) $\begin{pmatrix} 0 & 1 & 0 \\ 0 & 0 & 1 \\ -1 & 1 & 1 \end{pmatrix}$.

5. State and prove a theorem which gives a matric interpretation of Theorem 8.7.

6. Prove that the inverse of a non-singular Jordan matrix has non-zero entries only on the diagonal and superdiagonal but in general is not in Jordan form.

7. Given the 12×12 Jordan matrix J whose diagonal elements in order are 2, 2, 2, 2, 2, 2, 0, 0, 0, 0, 1, 1 and whose superdiagonal elements in order are 1, 1, 1, 0, 1, 0, 1, 1, 1, 0, 0. In the terminology of the discussion following Theorem 8.9, supply the following information.

(i) Write J in block form, showing the sub-blocks of each major block.

(ii) Write the characteristic values and the multiplicity of each.

(iii) Write the numbers p_{ij}.

(iv) Write the Segre characteristic of J.

(v) Write the characteristic polynomial of J.

(vi) Write the minimal polynomial of J.

(vii) Write the elementary divisors of J.

(viii) By examining the block form of J, show that $M(J) = Z$ for the polynomial M of (vi).

8. Write a matrix whose characteristic values are 2, 3, 4, 5 and whose Segre characteristic is $\{(2, 1, 1)(1, 1, 1)(3, 2)(1)\}$.

§8.4. *An Application of the Hamilton-Cayley Theorem*

We are now able to give an easy proof of the Hamilton-Cayley theorem. Let A be a matrix with characteristic polynomial

$$P(\lambda) = (-1)^n(\lambda - \lambda_1)(\lambda - \lambda_2) \ldots (\lambda - \lambda_n),$$

and let J be a Jordan matrix which is similar to A.

$$J = \begin{pmatrix} \lambda_1 & \delta & & & \\ & \lambda_2 & \delta & & \\ & & \lambda_3 & \cdot & \\ & & & \cdot & \cdot \\ & & & & \cdot & \delta \\ & & & & & \lambda_n \end{pmatrix}, \text{ where } \delta = 0 \text{ or } \mathbf{1}.$$

Let $J_i = J - \lambda_i I$, $i = 1, 2, \ldots, n$, so that

$$P(J) = (-1)^n J_1 J_2 \ldots J_n,$$

since the factoring for $P(\lambda)$ holds for the matrix polynomial $P(X)$. Now the ith row of J_i has δ in the $i + 1$ column and zeros elsewhere. Therefore the nth row of J_n is a zero row; the last two rows of $J_{n-1}J_n$ are zero; the last three rows of $J_{n-2}J_{n-1}J_n$ are zero rows, and so on. Therefore successive multiplication of the J_i gives

$$P(J) = Z.$$

By Exercises 4 and 5, § 7.3, $P(A)$ is similar to $P(J) = Z$, and hence $P(A) = Z$, which is the desired conclusion.

We now apply the Hamilton-Cayley theorem to obtain another method of calculating the inverse of a non-singular matrix A. Let the characteristic polynomial of A be

$$(-1)^n(\lambda^n + c_1\lambda^{n-1} + \ldots + c_n).$$

Since A is non-singular, $\lambda = 0$ is not a characteristic value, so $c_n \neq 0$. We have

$$A^n + c_1 A^{n-1} + \ldots + c_n I = Z,$$
$$(A^n + c_1 A^{n-1} + \ldots + c_{n-1}A) = -c_n I,$$

and therefore

$$A^{-1} = -c_n^{-1}(A^{n-1} + c_1 A^{n-2} + \ldots + c_{n-1}I).$$

Thus A^{-1} may be calculated as a combination of powers of A and the coefficients of the characteristic polynomial of A. For large values of n the c_1 may be very hard to compute directly, but an alternate method is described below.

Definition 8.3. The *trace* of A, denoted tr A, is the sum of the n characteristic values of A;

$$\text{tr } A = \sum_{i=1}^{n} \lambda_i.$$

In addition to the present application, the concept of trace is quite useful. We recall that similar matrices have equal characteristic values and therefore have equal traces.   Thus the trace of a linear transformation **T** can be defined to be the trace of any matrix which represents **T**.   We now prove that tr A is the sum of the diagonal elements of A.

Theorem 8.10.   tr $A = \sum\limits_{i=1}^{n} a_{ii}$,

and hence if A and B are similar,

$$\sum_{i=1}^{n} a_{ii} = \sum_{i=1}^{n} b_{ii}.$$

P R O O F :   Consider the characteristic polynomial of A,

$$\det(A - \lambda I) = (-1)^n(\lambda^n + c_1\lambda^{n-1} + \ldots + c_n)$$
$$= (-1)^n(\lambda - \lambda_1) \ldots (\lambda - \lambda_n).$$

From the determinant form, the coefficient of λ^{n-1} is seen to be

$$(-1)^{n-1} \sum_{i=1}^{n} a_{ii} = (-1)^n c_1,$$

while from the factored form we get

$$(-1)^{n+1} \sum_{i=1}^{n} \lambda_i = (-1)^n c_1.$$

Hence

$$\text{tr } A = \sum_{i=1}^{n} \lambda_i = \sum_{i=1}^{n} a_{ii}.$$

As a corollary we have the equation

$$c_1 = -\text{tr } A.$$

The other c_i can be determined similarly to give the following set of equations:

$$c_1 = -\text{tr } A$$
$$c_2 = -2^{-1}[c_1 \text{ tr } A + \text{tr } A^2]$$
$$c_3 = -3^{-1}[c_2 \text{ tr } A + c_1 \text{ tr } A^2 + \text{tr } A^3]$$
$$\vdots$$
$$c_n = -n^{-1}[c_{n-1} \text{ tr } A + c_{n-2} \text{ tr } A^2 + \ldots + c_1 \text{ tr } A^{n-1} + \text{tr } A^n].$$

These equations permit us to calculate A^{-1} by calculating $A, A^2, \ldots, A^{n-1}$ and the diagonal elements of A^n.   From these matrices we can calculate the traces as sums of the diagonal elements, determine the c_i, and finally use the equation

$$A^{-1} = -c_n^{-1}(A^{n-1} + c_1 A^{n-2} + \ldots + c_{n-1} I).$$

This method for finding A^{-1} requires fewer than n^4 multiplications and is easily described in the language of high speed computers.   Also we obtain the characteristic polynomial of A as a by-product of the computation of A^{-1}.

Exercises

1. Use the preceding method to calculate the inverse and the characteristic polynomial of the matrix of Exercise 1 (ii), § 6.3.

2. Prove that the trace of A^k is the sum of the kth powers of the characteristic values of A.

3. Verify that
$$c_2 = -\tfrac{1}{2}(c_1 \operatorname{tr} A + \operatorname{tr} A^2).$$

4. Prove the following properties of the trace.

   (i) If A is nilpotent, $\operatorname{tr} A = 0$.

   (ii) If A is idempotent, $\operatorname{tr} A = \rho(A)$.

   (iii) $\operatorname{tr}(A + B) = \operatorname{tr} A + \operatorname{tr} B$.

   (iv) $\operatorname{tr}(kA) = k \operatorname{tr} A$.

   (v) $\operatorname{tr} A' = \operatorname{tr} A$.

   (vi) $\operatorname{tr}(AB) = \operatorname{tr}(BA)$.

5. Let A and B be 2×2 matrices for which $\det A = \det B$ and $\operatorname{tr} A = \operatorname{tr} B$.

   (i) Do A and B have the same characteristic values?   Prove your answer.

   (ii) Are A and B similar?   Prove your answer.

   (iii) Would your answers to (i) or (ii) be different if A and B were 3×3 matrices?

6.   (i) Prove that if **T** is a projection, then for any matrix which represents **T**, the sum of the diagonal elements is a non-negative integer.

   (ii) Prove that any projection can be represented by a diagonal matrix whose non-zero entries must be 1.

CHAPTER 9

Metric Concepts

§9.1. *Bilinear Functions*

Up to this point our study of vector spaces has been accomplished without any reference to the customary concepts of geometric measurement such as length, distance, angle, and perpendicularity. This is in sharp contrast to the usual development of the geometry of the plane or three-dimensional space which from the start assumes a rectangular coordinate system and defines distance in terms of that system; for an abstract n-dimensional space in which we wish to consider a variety of coordinate systems, such an approach would be too confining. We shall now see how metric notions can be derived generally. In so doing we shall discover an interpretation of matrices which is distinct from the matric representations of linear transformations and linear equations studied previously.

A moment's reflection makes it clear that length, distance, and angle are scalar quantities which are attached to each vector or each pair of vectors of a space. Thus, it is natural that we consider various functions from vector spaces to the scalar field. We recall that one such function was discussed briefly at the end of § 4.3, where the dual space of $\mathcal{V}$ was defined to consist of all *linear functionals*, linear mappings from $\mathcal{V}$ to $\mathcal{F}$.

We now consider the more general case of functions which map the cartesian product $\mathcal{V}_m \times \mathcal{W}_n$ of two vector spaces into the scalar field $\mathcal{F}$. Since the properties of $\mathcal{F}$ come into greater prominence here than before, we distinguish two cases according to whether $\mathcal{F}$ is the real or the complex field. The corresponding theories are parallel, and we choose to emphasize the real case in the text discussion, commenting on the corresponding results for the complex case but listing those proofs as exercises.

162

Definition 9.1.   A *bilinear function* f is a function which assigns to each pair of vectors (ξ, η), where $\xi \in \mathcal{U}_m$ and $\eta \in \mathcal{W}_n$, a scalar value $f(\xi, \eta) \in \mathfrak{F}$ in such a way that for all $a, b \in \mathfrak{F}$ the following properties hold:

(a) $f(a\xi_1 + b\xi_2, \eta) = af(\xi_1, \eta) + bf(\xi_2, \eta)$,

(b) $f(\xi, a\eta_1 + b\eta_2) = af(\xi, \eta_1) + bf(\xi, \eta_2)$.

Conditions (a) and (b) simply state that f is a linear function of each of its variables (which are vectors).   First we see how bilinear functions may be represented by matrices; the work we do here will bear a striking similarity to the corresponding matric representation of linear transformations.   Let $\{\alpha_1, \ldots, \alpha_m\}$ be a basis for $\mathcal{U}_m$ and $\{\beta_1, \ldots, \beta_n\}$ be a basis for $\mathcal{W}_n$.   Let $\xi = \sum_{i=1}^{m} x_i\alpha_i \in \mathcal{U}_m$, and $\eta = \sum_{j=1}^{n} y_j\beta_j \in \mathcal{W}_n$.   Then

$$f(\xi, \eta) = f\left(\sum_{i=1}^{m} x_i\alpha_i, \eta\right) = \sum_{i=1}^{m} x_i f(\alpha_i, \eta)$$

$$= \sum_{i=1}^{m} x_i f\left(\alpha_i, \sum_{j=1}^{n} y_j\beta_j\right) = \sum_{i=1}^{m} x_i \left[\sum_{j=1}^{n} y_j f(\alpha_i, \beta_j)\right]$$

$$= \sum_{i=1}^{m} \sum_{j=1}^{n} x_i y_j f(\alpha_i, \beta_j).$$

The mn scalars $f(\alpha_i, \beta_j)$ therefore completely determine the value of the bilinear function f.   Now consider the $m \times n$ matrix

$$A = (a_{ij}), \text{ where } a_{ij} = f(\alpha_i, \beta_j),$$

which is uniquely determined by f relative to the α-, β-bases.   Then an easy calculation shows that

$$f(\xi, \eta) = XAY'.$$

Definition 9.2.   An expression of the type

$$\sum_{i=1}^{m} \left(\sum_{j=1}^{n} a_{ij} x_i y_j\right)$$

is called a *bilinear form* in the $m + n$ variables $x_1, \ldots, x_m, y_1, \ldots, y_n$.

Thus each bilinear function f on $\mathcal{U}_m \times \mathcal{W}_n$ determines, relative to chosen bases, a bilinear form whose coefficient matrix represents f relative to those bases.   For a different choice of bases we can expect to obtain a bilinear form with different coefficients and therefore a different matric representation of A.   As in § 6.5, suppose that $\{\gamma_1, \ldots, \gamma_m\}$ is a basis for $\mathcal{U}_m$ and that $\{\delta_1, \ldots, \delta_n\}$ is a basis for $\mathcal{W}_n$.   Let $\mathbf{T}, \mathbf{S}$ be the linear transformations $\gamma_i\mathbf{T} = \alpha_i$ and $\delta_j\mathbf{S} = \beta_j$; suppose that $\mathbf{T}$ is represented relative to the γ-basis by P and that $\mathbf{S}$ is represented relative to the δ-basis by Q.   Then

$$\xi = \sum_{i=1}^{m} x_i \alpha_i = \sum_{i=1}^{m} x_i \gamma_i \mathbf{T} = \sum_{i=1}^{m} x_i \left(\sum_{k=1}^{m} p_{ik} \gamma_k \right)$$

$$= \sum_{k=1}^{m} \left(\sum_{i=1}^{m} x_i p_{ik} \right) \gamma_k;$$

similarly,

$$\eta = \sum_{k=1}^{n} \left(\sum_{j=1}^{n} y_j q_{jk} \right) \delta_k.$$

Thus ξ is represented relative to the γ-basis by $U = XP$; η is represented relative to the δ-basis by $V = YQ$. Let C be the matrix representing the bilinear function f relative to the γ-, δ-bases:

$$C = (c_{ij}), \text{ where } c_{ij} = f(\gamma_i, \delta_j).$$

Then

$$f(\xi, \eta) = XAY' = UCV' = (XP)C(YQ)' = X(PCQ')Y'.$$

Thus A and C are equivalent matrices. We now summarize the results obtained.

Theorem 9.1. A bilinear function f from $\mathcal{V}_m \times \mathcal{W}_n$ to $\mathfrak{F}$ is represented uniquely relative to a pair α, β of bases by the $m \times n$ matrix

$$A = (a_{ij}), \text{ where } a_{ij} = f(\alpha_i, \beta_j);$$

if ξ, η are represented by X, Y, then

$$f(\xi, \eta) = XAY'.$$

Furthermore, $m \times n$ matrices A and C represent the same bilinear function relative to different bases if and only if A and C are equivalent. P R O O F : The representation of f by A was established by the previous discussion. Uniqueness follows easily since two functions are different if their functional values differ at any point. The discussion also shows that the same f is represented relative to two pairs of bases by equivalent matrices. Conversely, if A and C are equivalent matrices, let $A = PCR$ for non-singular P, R. Let $Q' = R$, and retrace the calculations already made to show that if C represents f relative to the γ-, δ-bases, then A represents f relative to the bases $\gamma \mathbf{T}$, $\delta \mathbf{S}$ obtained from the non-singular linear transformations represented by P and Q.

Since a bilinear function is represented in different coordinate systems by equivalent matrices, and since equivalent matrices have the same rank, we define the *rank* of a bilinear function (or a bilinear form) to be the rank of any representative matrix.

Theorem 9.2. Let f be a bilinear function of rank r from $\mathcal{U}_m \times \mathcal{W}_n$ into $\mathfrak{F}$, where $r \leq m,n$. There exist bases for $\mathcal{U}_m$ and $\mathcal{W}_n$ such that if $\xi \in \mathcal{U}_m$ and $\eta \in \mathcal{W}_n$, then

$$f(\xi, \eta) = x_1 y_1 + x_2 y_2 + \ldots + x_r y_r.$$

P R O O F : Let f be represented by an $m \times n$ matrix A of rank r relative to some pair of bases for $\mathcal{U}_m$ and $\mathcal{W}_n$. Any matrix equivalent to A has the same rank and represents the same bilinear function f. By Theorem 6.14, A is equivalent to the canonical matrix C which has the block I_r in the upper left corner and zeros elsewhere. Then from the proof of Theorem 9.1,

$$f(\xi, \eta) = XCY' = x_1 y_1 + x_2 y_2 + \ldots + x_r y_r.$$

We are particularly interested in the case in which the two spaces $\mathcal{U}_m$ and $\mathcal{W}_n$ are the same. Then a bilinear function f maps each pair of vectors of $\mathcal{U}$ into a scalar in $\mathfrak{F}$. An example of such a function is the familiar *dot product* of vectors in $\mathcal{E}_n$:

$$(x_1, x_2, \ldots, x_n) \cdot (y_1, y_2, \ldots, y_n) = x_1 y_1 + \ldots + x_n y_n.$$

Theorem 9.2 shows that any bilinear function of rank n from $\mathcal{U}_n \times \mathcal{U}_n$ into $\mathfrak{F}$ assumes the form of the dot product in a suitable coordinate system.

It is important to notice the sharpening of Theorem 9.1 which occurs in case $\mathcal{U}_m$ and $\mathcal{W}_n$ are the same space, $\mathcal{U}$. Instead of having two bases (one for each space) we can describe a bilinear function f from $\mathcal{U} \times \mathcal{U}$ to $\mathfrak{F}$ in terms of a single basis for $\mathcal{U}$. This is equivalent to saying that in the proof of Theorem 9.1 we can now consider α and β to be the same, and γ and δ to be the same. Then $R = S$ and $P = Q$, and we obtain the following result.

Theorem 9.3. A bilinear function f from $\mathcal{U}_n \times \mathcal{U}_n$ to $\mathfrak{F}$ is represented relative to two bases for $\mathcal{U}_n$ by two $n \times n$ matrices A, C if and only if there exists a non-singular matrix P such that

$$A = PCP'.$$

It is clear that the relation $A = PCP'$ is a special type of matrix equivalence, and therefore we give it a special name.

Definition 9.3. Two $n \times n$ matrices A and B with elements in $\mathfrak{F}$ are said to be *congruent* over $\mathfrak{F}$ if and only if

$$A = PBP'$$

for some non-singular matrix P with elements in $\mathfrak{F}$.

It is easy to verify that congruence of matrices is yet another example of an equivalence relation on matrices, and it is distinct from the equivalence relations we have considered previously: row equivalence, equivalence, and similarity.   Another equivalence relation, called *conjunctivity* or *Hermitian congruence* is defined for complex matrices in Exercise 7, § 9.5.   The definition is such that conjunctivity reduces to congruence when the matrices are real.

In terms of row and column operations, the description of congruence of matrices is easily stated.   Since P describes a sequence of elementary row operations, P' describes the same sequence of elementary column operations. Hence A and B are congruent if and only if A can be obtained by transforming B by a sequence of changes, each change being an elementary operation on rows followed by the same operation on the corresponding columns.

To develop a theory of canonical forms for congruence we first recall from § 4.2 that any matrix is the sum of a symmetric matrix and a skew matrix, provided that $1 + 1 \neq 0$ in $\mathfrak{F}$:

$$A = \tfrac{1}{2}[(A + A') + (A - A')].$$

The canonical forms under congruence for symmetric matrices and skew matrices are different, and for reasons which will become apparent in § 9.5 we are more interested in the symmetric case.   For an $n \times n$ skew matrix K it can be shown (Exercise 7, § 9.1) that the rank must be an even number, $2t$, and that K is congruent to a matrix which has t blocks B_i along the diagonal, and zeros elsewhere, each block being

$$B_i = \begin{pmatrix} 0 & -1 \\ 1 & 0 \end{pmatrix}, \qquad i = 1, 2, \ldots, t.$$

Now we consider the symmetric case and obtain a simple standard form which is not, however, canonical.

Theorem 9.4.   Every symmetric matrix with elements in $\mathfrak{F}$ is congruent over $\mathfrak{F}$ to a diagonal matrix, provided $1 + 1 \neq 0$ in $\mathfrak{F}$.

P R O O F :   Since the rank of a diagonal matrix is the number of non-zero elements, a symmetric matrix of rank r will be congruent to a diagonal matrix with r non-zero elements; the proof will show that these can be placed in the first r diagonal positions.   Let A be symmetric; then for every non-singular P, $(PAP')' = P''A'P' = PAP'$, so a symmetric matrix will always result from applying to A an elementary row operation followed by the same elementary column operation.   If all the diagonal elements of A are zero, let $a_{ij} \neq 0$.   Add row i to row j, and then add column i to column j.   The result will be a symmetric matrix $B = P_1 A P_1'$ for which $b_{jj} = a_{ij} + a_{ji} = 2a_{ij}$.   If some diagonal element of A is non-zero, take $B = A$.   Interchange row j and row 1 of B, and similarly interchange column j and column 1 of the resulting matrix.   The result is $C = P_2 A P_2'$, where C is symmetric and $c_{11} \neq 0$.   Apply row and the corresponding column operations to C to produce zeros in the $(1, j)$ and $(j, 1)$ positions, $j = 2, \ldots, n$.   The resulting matrix is

$$D = P_s A P_s' = \begin{pmatrix} d_{11} & 0 \ldots 0 \\ 0 & \\ \cdot & \\ \cdot & A_1 \\ \cdot & \\ 0 & \end{pmatrix}, \qquad d_{11} \neq 0.$$

If $A_1 = Z$, we are through; otherwise the process may be repeated on A_1. After r steps, the resulting matrix has the form claimed in the theorem.

Theorem 9.5.   Every real symmetric matrix of rank r is congruent over $\Re$ to a diagonal matrix with 1 in the first p diagonal positions, -1 in the next $r - p$ positions, and zeros elsewhere.

P R O O F :   Let a real symmetric matrix A be reduced to the diagonal form of Theorem 9.4.   By interchanging rows i and j and then columns i and j we may permute any two diagonal elements.   Hence A is congruent to a diagonal matrix D in which the positive diagonal elements are $d_{11}, \ldots, d_{pp}$, the negative diagonal elements are $-d_{p+1,p+1}, \ldots, -d_{rr}$, and the other elements 0.   Then for $k = 1, \ldots, r$ multiply row k and column k by $(d_{kk})^{-\frac{1}{2}}$ to obtain the stated form.

In § 9.5 we shall examine the meaning of r and p and show that this form is canonical.   Note that Theorem 9.5 is not valid for matrices over the rationals, because the operation of root extraction cannot be performed in that field.   Thus we see how the base field plays a vital role.   A symmetric matrix over the complex field is congruent to a matrix in even simpler form, as indicated by the following theorem.

Theorem 9.6.   Every symmetric complex matrix of rank r is congruent over $\mathbb{C}$ to the matrix

$$\begin{pmatrix} I_r & Z \\ Z & Z \end{pmatrix}.$$

P R O O F :   Exercise.

Exercises

1. Verify that for any bilinear function f and any vector η

$$f(\theta, \eta) = 0.$$

2. (i) Write a matric representation of each of the bilinear forms on $\mathcal{V}_2$

$$x_1y_1 - x_2y_1 + 2x_2y_2,$$

and

$$4u_1v_1 + 4u_1v_2 + 2u_2v_1 + 4u_2v_2.$$

(ii) Are these matrices congruent?

(iii) What does your answer to (ii) imply about the two forms?

3. Prove that congruence over $\mathfrak{F}$ is an equivalence relation on $n \times n$ matrices.

4. Prove that B is congruent to A if and only if B can be obtained from A by identical sequences of elementary row and column operations.

5. Let A be a skew matrix.

(i) Show that $a_{ii} = 0$ if $1 + 1 \neq 0$ in $\mathfrak{F}$.

(ii) Prove that if B is congruent to A, then B is skew.

6. Perform row and column operations to reduce the following skew matrix to a congruent matrix in the canonical form stated in the text:

$$\begin{pmatrix} 0 & 3 & -2 & 1 & 0 \\ -3 & 0 & 1 & -4 & 1 \\ 2 & -1 & 0 & 0 & -2 \\ -1 & 4 & 0 & 0 & 1 \\ 0 & -1 & 2 & -1 & 0 \end{pmatrix}.$$

7. Show that any skew matrix is congruent to a matrix in the canonical diagonal block form described in the text.

8. Prove that if A and B are symmetric matrices of complex numbers, then A and B are congruent over $\mathcal{C}$ if and only if $\rho(A) = \rho(B)$.

9. Given $A = \begin{pmatrix} -10 & 5 & 2 \\ 5 & 0 & 3 \\ 2 & 3 & 6 \end{pmatrix}$.

(i) Find a matrix congruent to A over the rational field and in the form of Theorem 9.4.

(ii) Find a matrix congruent to A over $\mathcal{R}$ and in the form of Theorem 9.5.

(iii) Find a matrix congruent to A over $\mathcal{C}$ and in the form of Theorem 9.6.

(iv) Illustrate that Theorem 9.4 does not describe a canonical form for congruence over $\mathfrak{F}$.

10. Prove Theorem 9.6.

§9.2. *Inner Product*

Before continuing with a general investigation of the background of metric notions, let us return to a familiar example to see where we have been and where we are going.   In the real plane $\mathcal{E}_2$, the dot product of vectors is a bilinear function.   If $\xi = (x_1, x_2)$ and $\eta = (y_1, y_2)$, then

$$\xi \cdot \eta = f(\xi, \eta) = x_1 y_1 + x_2 y_2.$$

The length of the vector ξ is

$$\|\xi\| = \sqrt{x_1^2 + x_2^2} = [f(\xi, \xi)]^{\frac{1}{2}},$$

which has one important property which length should possess; namely, that the length of a vector is a positive real number, except for the zero vector which has zero length.

If we attempt to parallel this construction for the two-dimensional complex space, then the same dot product (with x_1, x_2, y_1, y_2 complex) is a bilinear form, and since root extraction is defined for all complex numbers, it is *possible* to define length as we have for the real case. But then $\|\xi\|$ is a complex number. Therefore, let us try again, starting with a different function from which to define length.

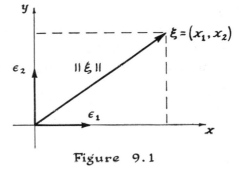

Figure 9.1

The key to this problem is the use of conjugates of complex numbers. (Readers who are not familiar with the arithmetic of complex numbers should study Exercise 1, § 9.2, before proceeding.)   The function we seek is

$$g(\xi, \eta) = x_1 \bar{y}_1 + x_2 \bar{y}_2,$$

where $\xi = (x_1, x_2)$ and $\eta = (y_1, y_2)$, each component complex.   It is important to observe that if the components are real, g reduces to the bilinear form g, defined above.   Now if length is defined by

$$\|\xi\| = [g(\xi, \xi)]^{\frac{1}{2}} = \sqrt{|x_1|^2 + |x_2|^2},$$

the length of every non-zero vector is a positive real number, as desired.

From this we see that not all bilinear functions lead to a reasonable concept of length.   The important distinction is the type of symmetry in the two vector variables possessed by the functions, for we observe by direct calculation that

$$f(\xi, \eta) = f(\eta, \xi),$$

while

$$g(\xi, \eta) = \overline{g(\eta, \xi)}.$$

Of course g is not a bilinear function.   Rather, it is linear in its first component and conjugate-linear in its second component, since

$$g(c_1\xi_1 + c_2\xi_2, \eta) = c_1 g(\xi_1, \eta) + c_2 g(\xi_2, \eta),$$

$$g(\xi, c_1\eta_1 + c_2\eta_2) = \bar{c}_1 g(\xi, \eta_1) + \bar{c}_2 g(\xi, \eta_2).$$

Such a function is sometimes called *conjugate-bilinear*.   Now we are ready to define the concept of an *inner product* which is based upon these considerations.

> **Definition 9.4.**   Let $\mathcal{V}$ be a vector space over $\mathcal{R}$ (or $\mathcal{C}$).   A real (or complex) *inner product* is a function p with domain $\mathcal{V} \times \mathcal{V}$ and range $\mathcal{R}$ (or $\mathcal{C}$) which satisfies
>
> (a) $p(c_1\xi_1 + c_2\xi_2, \eta) = c_1 p(\xi_1, \eta) + c_2 p(\xi_2, \eta),$
> (b) $p(\xi, \eta) = \overline{p(\eta, \xi)},$
> (c) $p(\xi, \xi) > 0$ if $\xi \neq \theta$, and $p(\theta, \theta) = 0.$

This definition is summarized by saying that an inner product is a scalar-valued function which is *conjugate-bilinear*, (a) and (b), and *positive definite*, (c).   For a real inner product, (b) reduces to the assertion of symmetry in ξ and η.   Thus a real inner product is a real valued function of two vector variables which is bilinear, symmetric, and positive definite.   In the complex case property (b) is called *conjugate symmetry* or *Hermitian symmetry*.   In either case, (b) implies that $p(\xi, \xi)$ is real.

> **Definition 9.5.**
> (a) A real vector space $\mathcal{V}$ for which a real inner product is defined is called a *Euclidean space*.
> (b) A complex vector space $\mathcal{V}$ for which a complex inner product is defined is called a *unitary space*.
> (c) Euclidean spaces and unitary spaces collectively are called *inner product spaces*.

EXAMPLES OF INNER PRODUCT SPACES

(a) Euclidean n-space $\mathcal{R}_n$ with the dot product

$$p(\xi, \eta) = x_1 y_1 + x_2 y_2 + \ldots + x_n y_n.$$

(b) The infinite-dimensional space of all real valued functions continuous on the interval $0 \leq t \leq 1$ with the inner product

$$p(f, g) = \int_0^1 f(t)g(t)dt.$$

(c) Unitary n-space $\mathfrak{C}_n$ with the inner product

$$p(\xi, \eta) = x_1\bar{y}_1 + x_2\bar{y}_2 + \ldots + x_n\bar{y}_n.$$

(d) The infinite-dimensional space of all complex valued functions continuous on the real interval $0 \leq t \leq 1$ with the inner product

$$p(f, g) = \int_0^1 f(t)\overline{g(t)}dt.$$

We conclude this section by deriving a general inequality which has many important applications in Euclidean and unitary spaces.

Theorem 9.7. (The Schwarz inequality.) In any inner product space $\mathfrak{V}$

$$|p(\xi, \eta)|^2 \leq p(\xi, \xi)p(\eta, \eta)$$

for all $\xi, \eta \in \mathfrak{V}$.

PROOF: For any α, $p(\alpha, \alpha)$ is real and non-negative. Let $\alpha = a\xi + b\eta$, where $a = -p(\eta, \xi)$ and $b = p(\xi, \xi)$; then $\bar{b} = b \geq 0$, and $\bar{a} = -p(\xi, \eta)$. Therefore, we have

$$\begin{aligned} 0 \leq p(a\xi + b\eta, a\xi + b\eta) &= ap(\xi, a\xi + b\eta) + bp(\eta, a\xi + b\eta) \\ &= a\bar{a}p(\xi, \xi) + a\bar{b}p(\xi, \eta) + b\bar{a}p(\eta, \xi) + b\bar{b}p(\eta, \eta) \\ &= a\bar{a}b - ab\bar{a} - b\bar{a}a + bbp(\eta, \eta) = b[-a\bar{a} + bp(\eta, \eta)] \\ &= b[p(\xi, \xi)p(\eta, \eta) - p(\xi, \eta)\overline{p(\xi, \eta)}]. \end{aligned}$$

If $b = 0$, we have $\xi = 0$, and the Schwarz inequality is trivially valid with both sides equal to zero. Otherwise, the last bracket above must be non-negative, which is the assertion of the Schwarz inequality.

Exercises

1. Operations for complex numbers are defined as follows, where a, b, c, and d are real:

Sum: $(a + ib) + (c + id) = (a + c) + i(b + d)$.
Product: $(a + ib)(c + id) = (ac - bd) + i(ad + bc)$.
Conjugate: $\overline{a + ib} = a - ib$.
Magnitude: $|a + ib| = \sqrt{a^2 + b^2}$.

Show that if x, y are complex numbers, then

    (i) $\overline{x + y} = \bar{x} + \bar{y}$,
    (ii) $\overline{xy} = \bar{x}\,\bar{y}$,
    (iii) $\bar{\bar{x}} = x$,

(iv) $x\bar{x} = |x|^2$,

(v) $x + \bar{x}$ is real,

(vi) $|x|$ is real and non-negative,

(vii) $|xy| = |x| \cdot |y|$,

(viii) $|x + y| \le |x| + |y|$.

2. Verify that examples (b) and (c) actually satisfy the definition of an inner product.

3. Show that $p(c\xi, d\eta) = c\bar{d}p(\xi, \eta)$.

4. Show that $p(\theta, \eta) = p(\xi, \theta) = 0$.

5. Prove that equality holds in the Schwarz inequality if and only if the set $\{\xi, \eta\}$ is linearly dependent.

6. Show that the following general theorems are direct consequences of the Schwarz inequality:

(i) If $x_1, \ldots, x_n$ and $y_1, \ldots, y_n$ are any real numbers, then

$$\left(\sum_{i=1}^{n} x_i y_i \right)^2 \le \left(\sum_{i=1}^{n} x_i^2 \right) \left(\sum_{i=1}^{n} y_i^2 \right).$$

(ii) (Cauchy inequality.) If $x_1, \ldots, x_n$ and $y_1, \ldots, y_n$ are any complex numbers, then

$$\left| \sum_{i=1}^{n} x_i \bar{y}_i \right|^2 \le \left(\sum_{i=1}^{n} |x_i|^2 \right) \left(\sum_{i=1}^{n} |y_i|^2 \right).$$

(iii) If f and g are real functions continuous on the interval $a \le x \le b$, then

$$\left(\int_a^b f(x)g(x)dx \right)^2 \le \int_a^b f^2(x)dx \cdot \int_a^b g^2(x)dx.$$

§9.3. *Length, Distance, and Orthogonality*

Let $\mathcal{U}$ be an inner product space which is either Euclidean or unitary. The inner product function p is used to define length, distance, and perpendicularity; we begin with length.

Definition 9.6.   The *length* $\|\xi\|$ of a vector ξ is defined by

$$\|\xi\| = [p(\xi, \xi)]^{\frac{1}{2}}.$$

Theorem 9.8.   Length has the following properties:

(a) $\|c\xi\| = |c| \cdot \|\xi\|$.

(b) $\|\xi\| > 0$ if $\xi \ne \theta$, and $\|\theta\| = 0$.

(c) $\|\xi + \eta\| \le \|\xi\| + \|\eta\|$.

P R O O F :   Property (a) follows from Exercise 3 of the preceding section,

and property (b) from part (c) of Definition 9.4.   To prove property (c)
we first note that the Schwarz inequality can be written

$$|p(\xi, \eta)| = |p(\eta, \xi)| \leq \|\xi\| \cdot \|\eta\|.$$

Since $p(\xi, \eta) = \overline{p(\eta, \xi)}$, $p(\xi, \eta) + p(\eta, \xi)$ is real, and

$$|p(\xi, \eta) + p(\eta, \xi)| \leq |p(\xi, \eta)| + |p(\eta, \xi)| \leq 2\|\xi\| \cdot \|\eta\|.$$

Thus

$$
\begin{aligned}
\|\xi + \eta\|^2 &= p(\xi + \eta, \xi + \eta) \\
&= p(\xi, \xi) + p(\xi, \eta) + p(\eta, \xi) + p(\eta, \eta) \\
&\leq p(\xi, \xi) + |p(\xi, \eta) + p(\eta, \xi)| + p(\eta, \eta) \\
&\leq \|\xi\|^2 + 2\|\xi\| \cdot \|\eta\| + \|\eta\|^2
\end{aligned}
$$

from which (c) follows immediately.

For the case of Euclidean n-space where p is the dot product, the length of
$\xi = (x_1, \ldots, x_n)$ is simply the familiar form

$$\|\xi\| = \sqrt{x_1^2 + x_2^2 + \ldots + x_n^2}.$$

Property (c) is interpreted geometrically as the observation that the length
of any side of a triangle does not exceed the sum of the lengths of the other
two sides.   Hence (c) is called the *triangle inequality.*

Since the points of n-space may be interpreted as n-tuples, or vectors, the
distance between vectors can be regarded as the distance between those points,
or, equivalently, the length of the arrow from one point to the other.

Definition 9.7.   The *distance* $d(\xi, \eta)$ between two vectors ξ and η is
defined by

$$d(\xi, \eta) = \|\xi - \eta\|.$$

Theorem 9.9.   Distance has the following properties:
(a) $d(\xi, \eta) = d(\eta, \xi)$,
(b) $d(\xi, \eta) > 0$ if $\xi \neq \eta$, and $d(\xi, \xi) = 0$,
(c) $d(\xi, \eta) \leq d(\xi, \zeta) + d(\zeta, \eta)$.
P R O O F :   Exercise.

Thus the distance which results from any inner product has the familiar
properties of distance as defined by coordinates in analytic geometry: it is
symmetric, is positive for distinct points, and satisfies the triangle inequality.
Any space for which a distance function is defined satisfying these three properties is called a *metric space.*

When we come to angle, we must distinguish between Euclidean space and
unitary space.   The Schwarz inequality can be written

$$\frac{|p(\xi, \eta)|}{\|\xi\| \cdot \|\eta\|} \leq 1.$$

If $p(\xi, \eta)$ is real, as in the Euclidean case, this means that

$$\frac{p(\xi, \eta)}{\|\xi\| \cdot \|\eta\|}$$

is a real number between -1 and $+1$. Hence it is the cosine of a uniquely determined angle Ψ in the range $0 \leq \Psi \leq \pi$. In the unitary case $p(\xi, \eta)$ is complex, and the corresponding interpretation is not valid. For our work, however, it is not important to have a measure of the angle between two vectors, but it is most convenient to have a definition of orthogonality (perpendicularity). In the real case the necessary definition for orthogonality is clear because the cosine of the angle between perpendicular non-zero vectors must be zero, and hence $p(\xi, \eta) = 0$. This is the definition we adopt for the complex case as well.

Definition 9.8. Two vectors ξ and η are *orthogonal* if and only if $p(\xi, \eta) = 0$.

Theorem 9.10. In any inner product space $\mathcal{V}$,

(a) ξ is orthogonal to every $\eta \in \mathcal{V}$ if and only if $\xi = \theta$,

(b) if ξ is orthogonal to every vector of a set S, then ξ is orthogonal to the subspace spanned by S,

(c) any set of mutually orthogonal vectors is linearly independent.

PROOF: Exercise.

This theorem hints that several important geometric properties which are familiar in $\mathcal{E}_2$ and $\mathcal{E}_3$ also hold in any space for which any inner product is defined. For example, (c) suggests that a basis of mutually orthogonal vectors (a rectangular coordinate system) always can be found for $\mathcal{V}$; in the next theorem we construct such a basis by the use of projections to split a vector ξ into orthogonal components, $\xi = \sigma + \eta$. This construction in its general form is known as the *Gram-Schmidt orthogonalization process*.

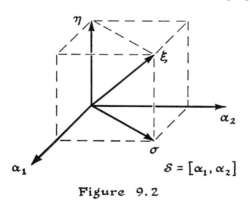

$$S = [\alpha_1, \alpha_2]$$

Figure 9.2

Theorem 9.11. In any finite-dimensional inner product space $\mathcal{V}$, there exists a basis consisting of mutually orthogonal vectors.

P R O O F :   If $\mathcal{V}$ is one-dimensional, any non-zero vector forms such a basis. We proceed by induction, assuming the theorem for any space of dimension k. Let $\mathcal{V}$ be of dimension $k + 1$, and let $\mathcal{S}$ be any subspace of dimension k. By the induction hypothesis there exists an orthogonal basis $\{\alpha_1, \ldots, \alpha_k\}$ for $\mathcal{S}$. For $\xi \notin \mathcal{S}$, let

$$\sigma = \sum_{i=1}^{k} \frac{p(\xi, \alpha_i)}{p(\alpha_i, \alpha_i)}\, \alpha_i = \sum_{i=1}^{k} c_i \alpha_i,$$

and let

$$\eta = \xi - \sigma.$$

Clearly, $\sigma \in \mathcal{S}$, and we now show that η is orthogonal to each α_i:

$$
\begin{aligned}
p(\eta, \alpha_i) &= p(\xi - \sigma, \alpha_i) \\
&= p(\xi, \alpha_i) - p\left(\sum_{j=1}^{k} c_j \alpha_j, \alpha_i\right) \\
&= p(\xi, \alpha_i) - \sum_{j=1}^{k} c_j p(\alpha_j, \alpha_i) \\
&= p(\xi, \alpha_i) - c_i p(\alpha_i, \alpha_i) \\
&= p(\xi, \alpha_i) - \frac{p(\xi, \alpha_i)}{p(\alpha_i, \alpha_i)} \cdot p(\alpha_i, \alpha_i) = 0.
\end{aligned}
$$

Hence the vectors $\{\alpha_1, \ldots, \alpha_k, \eta\}$ are mutually orthogonal and by Theorem 9.10 (c) form a basis for $\mathcal{V}_{k+1}$.

The vector σ in the preceding proof is called the *orthogonal projection* of ξ on $\mathcal{S}$; the coefficients c_i of σ relative to the α-basis for $\mathcal{S}$ can be written

$$c_i = \frac{p(\xi, \alpha_i)}{p(\alpha_i, \alpha_i)} = \frac{\|\xi\|}{\|\alpha_i\|} \cdot \frac{p(\xi, \alpha_i)}{\|\alpha_i\| \|\xi\|}.$$

In the Euclidean case if the basis vectors are so chosen that $\|\alpha_i\| = 1$, this reduces to

$$c_i = \|\xi\| \cos \Psi_i,$$

where Ψ_i is the angle between ξ and α_i. The numbers c_i are called *direction numbers* of ξ.

Theorem 9.12.   If $\mathcal{S}$ is any subspace of an inner product space $\mathcal{V}_n$, there exists a unique subspace $\mathcal{S}^o$ such that

(a) $\mathcal{V}_n = \mathcal{S} \oplus \mathcal{S}^o$,
(b) $p(\sigma, \sigma') = 0$ for every $\sigma \in \mathcal{S}$ and $\sigma' \in \mathcal{S}^o$.

P R O O F :   Exercise. ($\mathcal{S}^o$ is called the *orthogonal complement* of $\mathcal{S}$.)

Now we combine the notions of length and orthogonality to define a normal orthogonal basis, which is simply a basis of the form $\{\epsilon_1, \ldots, \epsilon_n\}$ for $\mathcal{E}_n$, and show that these metric concepts assume a very familiar form relative to such a basis.

Definition 9.9. In any inner product space a vector of unit length is called *normal*. A set of mutually orthogonal vectors, each of which is normal, is called a *normal orthogonal* (or *orthonormal*) set.

If α is any non-zero vector in an inner product space, then $\|\alpha\|^{-1}\alpha$ is normal. Hence a normal orthogonal basis is obtained by normalizing in this manner each vector of an orthogonal basis. The importance of a normal orthogonal basis is revealed by the next theorem which implies that in Euclidean space any inner product p assumes the form of the dot product relative to a normal orthogonal basis.

Theorem 9.13. Let p be any inner product for the space $\mathcal{U}_n$, let $\{\alpha_1, \ldots, \alpha_n\}$ be a normal orthogonal basis for $\mathcal{U}_n$, let $\xi = \sum_{i=1}^{n} x_i\alpha_i$, and let $\eta = \sum_{i=1}^{n} y_i\alpha_i$. Then

$$p(\xi, \eta) = x_1\bar{y}_1 + x_2\bar{y}_2 + \ldots + x_n\bar{y}_n.$$

P R O O F :

$$p(\xi, \eta) = p\left(\sum_{i=1}^{n} x_i\alpha_i, \sum_{j=1}^{n} y_j\alpha_j\right)$$

$$= \sum_{i=1}^{n} x_i p\left(\alpha_i, \sum_{i=1}^{n} y_j\alpha_j\right)$$

$$= \sum_{i=1}^{n} x_i\left(\sum_{j=1}^{n} \bar{y}_j p(\alpha_i, \alpha_j)\right)$$

$$= \sum_{i=1}^{n} x_i\bar{y}_i p(\alpha_i, \alpha_i)$$

$$= \sum_{i=1}^{n} x_i\bar{y}_i,$$

where the last equality holds since the α_i are normal, and the preceding equality holds since the α_i are orthogonal.

From this it is clear that in any n-dimensional Euclidean space, with the metric concepts defined by any inner product, if we choose a normal orthogonal basis, the following familiar formulas for length, distance, and angle are valid:

$$\|\xi\| = \sqrt{x_1^2 + x_2^2 + \ldots + x_n^2},$$

$$\|\xi - \eta\| = \sqrt{(x_1 - y_1)^2 + \ldots + (x_n - y_n)^2},$$

$$\cos \Psi(\xi, \eta) = \frac{x_1y_1 + \ldots + x_ny_n}{\sqrt{x_1^2 + \ldots + x_n^2}\sqrt{y_1^2 + \ldots + y_n^2}}.$$

This last formula is simply the law of cosines,

$$\|\xi - \eta\|^2 = \|\xi\|^2 + \|\eta\|^2 - 2\|\xi\| \cdot \|\eta\| \cos \Psi.$$

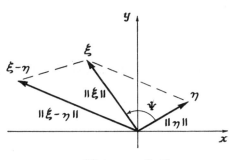

Figure 9.3

It is also worth noticing the relationship between matrix multiplication and a real inner product. If $A = (a_{ij})$, $B = (b_{ij})$, and $AB = (c_{ij})$, then

$$c_{ij} = \sum_{k=1}^{n} a_{ik} b_{kj}$$

$$= p(\alpha_i, \beta_j),$$

where p is the real dot product of the ith *row* vector of A with the jth *column* vector of B. This observation is valid for matrices over any field, but the dot product referred to has the form of the real dot product.

Exercises

1. Prove that the following theorems of geometry hold in any Euclidean space. Illustrate each in $\mathcal{E}_2$.

(i) The Pythagorean theorem and its converse:
ξ is orthogonal to η if and only if

$$\|\xi\|^2 + \|\eta\|^2 = \|\xi + \eta\|^2.$$

(ii) The law of cosines:

$$\|\xi - \eta\|^2 = \|\xi\|^2 + \|\eta\|^2 - 2\|\xi\| \cdot \|\eta\| \cdot \cos \Psi.$$

(iii) The diagonals of a rhombus are perpendicular:

if $\|\xi\| = \|\eta\|$, then $p(\xi + \eta, \xi - \eta) = 0$.

2. (i) Prove that in any inner product space

$$p(\xi + \eta, \xi + \eta) + p(\xi - \eta, \xi - \eta) = 2p(\xi, \xi) + 2p(\eta, \eta).$$

(ii) What familiar geometric theorem does (i) assert?

3. State and prove in the language of arbitrary Euclidean space the the-

orem that the midpoints of the sides of any quadrilateral are the vertices
of a parallelogram.

4. Let $\mathcal{U}$ be an inner product space with $\{\alpha_1, \ldots, \alpha_n\}$ as a normal orthogonal basis.

(i) Prove Bessel's inequality:

if $p(\xi, \alpha_i) = c_i$ for $i = 1, 2, \ldots, m \leq n$, then $\sum\limits_{i=1}^{m} |c_i|^2 \leq \|\xi\|^2$.

(ii) Prove Parseval's identity:

$$p(\xi, \eta) = \sum_{i=1}^{n} p(\xi, \alpha_i)p(\alpha_i, \eta).$$

(iii) Interpret each in $\mathcal{E}_3$ by a diagram.

5. Prove that in any Euclidean space $p(\alpha, \beta) = 0$ if and only if

$$\|\alpha + c\beta\| \geq \|\alpha\|$$

for every real number c.

6. Prove Theorem 9.10.

7. Prove that if $\mathcal{S}$ is any subspace of an inner product space $\mathcal{U}$, then every
$\xi \in \mathcal{U}$ has a unique decomposition

$$\xi = \sigma + \eta,$$

where $\sigma \in \mathcal{S}$ and η is orthogonal to $\mathcal{S}$.

8. Prove Theorem 9.12.

9. Let $\mathcal{S}$ and $\mathcal{T}$ be subspaces of an inner product space $\mathcal{U}$.   Prove that

(i) $(\mathcal{S}^\circ)^\circ = \mathcal{S}$.

(ii) $(\mathcal{S} + \mathcal{T})^\circ = \mathcal{S}^\circ \cap \mathcal{T}^\circ$.

(iii) $(\mathcal{S} \cap \mathcal{T})^\circ = \mathcal{S}^\circ + \mathcal{T}^\circ$.

10. Beginning with the orthogonal vectors

$$\alpha_1 = (2, 1, -5, 0)$$
$$\alpha_2 = (3, -1, 1, 0)$$

in $\mathcal{E}_4$, use the Gram-Schmidt orthogonalization process on the normalized
form of α_1 and α_2 to obtain a normal orthogonal basis for $\mathcal{E}_4$.

11. Prove that the mapping $\xi \longrightarrow \sigma$ as defined in the proof of Theorem 9.11
by the Gram-Schmidt orthogonalization process is a projection, as defined
in § 8.1.

§9.4. *Orthogonal Transformations*

In many important physical problems the transformations which arise are
ones which leave all distances fixed.   Such a transformation is called a *rigid*

motion, and any motion of a rigid body can be described by a transformation of this type. It is intuitively clear that the product of rigid motions is a rigid motion, that the identity transformation is a rigid motion, and that each rigid motion has an inverse which is a rigid motion. In other words, the set of all rigid motions of a space forms a group, and for Euclidean space the group is called the *Euclidean group.*

A simple example of a rigid motion is a translation, wherein each point in space is moved the same fixed distance in the same direction:

$$\xi\mathbf{T} = \xi + \alpha \text{ for fixed } \alpha \text{ and all } \xi.$$

But for $\alpha \neq \theta$, $\theta\mathbf{T} = \theta + \alpha = \alpha$, so a non-zero translation is not linear. However, any rigid motion can be decomposed into the product of a linear transformation and a translation. It is the linear component of rigid motion which we now propose to study.

Parallel theories of linear rigid motions can be developed for Euclidean spaces and unitary spaces; we shall concentrate on the former case, and the exercises will indicate the corresponding results for complex spaces.

Definition 9.10. An *orthogonal transformation* $\mathbf{T}$ on a Euclidean space $\mathcal{V}$ is a linear transformation which has the property

$$\|\xi\mathbf{T}\| = \|\xi\| \text{ for all } \xi \in \mathcal{V}.$$

In a unitary space the name *unitary transformation* is used for a linear transformation which satisfies the condition of Definition 9.10. Since orthogonal and unitary transformations preserve length, they also preserve distance. It is a consequence of the following theorem that orthogonal transformations preserve angle as well.

Theorem 9.14. A linear transformation $\mathbf{T}$ is orthogonal if and only if $p(\xi, \eta) = p(\xi\mathbf{T}, \eta\mathbf{T})$ for all $\xi, \eta \in \mathcal{V}$.

P R O O F : Since the corresponding theorem is valid for unitary spaces, we carry part of the proof in complex form. We have

$$p(\xi + \eta, \xi + \eta) = p(\xi, \xi) + p(\xi, \eta) + p(\eta, \xi) + p(\eta, \eta),$$
$$\|\xi + \eta\|^2 = \|\xi\|^2 + p(\xi, \eta) + \overline{p(\xi, \eta)} + \|\eta\|^2.$$

But $p(\xi, \eta) + \overline{p(\xi, \eta)}$ is twice the real part of $p(\xi, \eta)$, and it is expressed as an algebraic sum of squares of lengths which are preserved by $\mathbf{T}$. If $p(\xi, \eta)$ is real, this means $p(\xi, \eta)$ is preserved by $\mathbf{T}$. If $p(\xi, \eta)$ is complex, a similar calculation for $p(\xi + i\eta, \xi + i\eta)$ shows that the complex part of $p(\xi, \eta)$ is also preserved by $\mathbf{T}$. In the Euclidean case angle is defined in terms of p, so angle is preserved by $\mathbf{T}$. Conversely, if p is preserved by $\mathbf{T}$, length is also preserved, since $\|\xi\| = p(\xi, \xi)^{\frac{1}{2}}$.

Next we consider the effect of an orthogonal transformation on a normal orthogonal basis $\{\alpha_1, \ldots, \alpha_n\}$. Since $\mathbf{T}$ preserves inner product,

$$\|\alpha_i \mathbf{T}\| = 1, \qquad i = 1, \ldots, n$$

and

$$p(\alpha_i \mathbf{T}, \alpha_j \mathbf{T}) = \delta_{ij}.$$

Thus an orthogonal transformation maps a normal orthogonal basis into a normal orthogonal basis. The row vectors of the matrix A which represents $\mathbf{T}$ relative to this basis must therefore be of unit length and mutually orthogonal.

Definition 9.11. A real $n \times n$ matrix $A = (a_{ij})$ is said to be *orthogonal* if and only if

$$\sum_{k=1}^{n} a_{ik} a_{jk} = \delta_{ij}, \qquad i, j = 1, \ldots, n.$$

Theorem 9.15. A real $n \times n$ matrix A represents an orthogonal transformation $\mathbf{T}$ relative to a normal orthogonal basis if and only if A is orthogonal.

P R O O F : Our previous remarks show that an orthogonal transformation is represented by an orthogonal matrix relative to a normal orthogonal basis. Conversely, the rows of a matrix represent the image of the basis vectors under the corresponding transformation.

Theorem 9.16.   An orthogonal matrix is non-singular.

P R O O F : The row vectors are mutually orthogonal and hence linearly independent.

Theorem 9.17. A is an orthogonal matrix if and only if $A^{-1} = A'$.

P R O O F : Let A be orthogonal, and let $AA' = C = (c_{ij})$. Then $c_{ij} = \sum_{k=1}^{n} a_{ik} a'_{kj} = \sum_{k=1}^{n} a_{ik} a_{jk} = \delta_{ij}$. Hence $C = I$. Conversely, if $A' = A^{-1}$, $AA' = I$, so $\sum_{k=1}^{n} a_{ik} a_{jk} = \delta_{ij}$.

Of all the methods described for calculating the inverse of a matrix, this is by far the simplest, but unfortunately perhaps, not all matrices are orthogonal!

Theorem 9.18.   If A is orthogonal, det $A = \pm 1$.

P R O O F : Exercise.

Notice that for orthogonal transformations the two equivalence relations of similarity and congruence coincide:

Similarity: $B = PAP^{-1}$,
Congruence: $B = PAP'$,

where P is a non-singular matrix and hence represents a change of basis. If the transformation which maps one basis into the other is orthogonal, then A and B are simultaneously similar and congruent.   Such a transformation must be a linear rigid motion.

Exercises

1. (i) Find a matric representation for the linear transformation which rotates each vector of the real plane through a fixed angle Ψ.

(ii) Prove that this matrix A is orthogonal by verifying $AA' = I$.

2. Prove Theorem 9.18.

3. (i) Find a matric representation B for the rigid motion of $\mathcal{E}_3$ which reflects each vector across the line

$$\begin{cases} x_3 = 0 \\ x_1 = x_2. \end{cases}$$

(ii) Prove that B is orthogonal since it satisfies Definition 9.11.

(iii) Find B^{-1} and describe the linear transformation it represents.

4. Reason as follows to show that any linear rigid motion of the real plane is either a rotation, or a rotation followed by a reflection across an axis.

(i) Write four quadratic conditions on the elements a, b, c, d of a real 2×2 matrix A which are necessary and sufficient that A be orthogonal.

(ii) Show that the only such matrices are

$$\begin{pmatrix} a & b \\ -b & a \end{pmatrix} \text{ and } \begin{pmatrix} a & b \\ b & -a \end{pmatrix}, \text{ where } a^2 + b^2 = 1.$$

(iii) Show that the former is a rotation through the angle $\cos^{-1} a$, while the latter is a rotation followed by a reflection across an axis.

5. Prove that a linear transformation $\mathbf{T}$ is unitary if and only if

$$p(\xi\mathbf{T}, \eta\mathbf{T}) = p(\xi, \eta).$$

6. The complex analogue of an orthogonal matrix is called a *unitary matrix* and is defined by

$$\sum_{k=1}^{n} a_{ik}\bar{a}_{jk} = \delta_{ij}.$$

State and prove for a unitary space the analogues of the following theorems:

(i) Theorem 9.15,

(ii) Theorem 9.16,

(iii) Theorem 9.17,

(iv) Theorem 9.18.

7. Prove that the characteristic values of a unitary matrix satisfy $|\lambda| = 1$.

8. Does the following matrix represent a rigid motion in $\mathcal{E}_3$?

$$A = \tfrac{1}{6}\begin{pmatrix} 1 & -5 & \sqrt{10} \\ -5 & 1 & \sqrt{10} \\ \sqrt{10} & \sqrt{10} & 4 \end{pmatrix}.$$

9. Prove that if K is a real skew matrix and if $I + K$ is non-singular, then

$$(I - K)(I + K)^{-1}$$

is orthogonal.

10. Let α_i denote the ith row of a real $n \times n$ matrix A; let $AA' = C = (c_{ij})$. Prove the following:

(i) $c_{ij} = p(\alpha_i, \alpha_j)$, p an inner product;

(ii) if the α_i are mutually orthogonal, $\det C = [\|\alpha_1\| \cdot \|\alpha_2\| \ldots \|\alpha_n\|]^2$;

(iii) if $|a_{ij}| \leq k$ for $i, j = 1, 2, \ldots, n$ and some fixed number k, then $\|\alpha_i\| \leq k \sqrt{n}$;

(iv) if $|a_{ij}| \leq k$, and if the α_i are mutually orthogonal, then

$$|\det A| \leq \|\alpha_1\| \cdot \|\alpha_2\| \ldots \|\alpha_n\| \leq k^n n^{n/2}.$$

§9.5. *Quadratic Functions*

Now we turn our attention to quadratic functions from $\mathcal{V}$ to $\mathcal{F}$.   In doing so we concentrate our attention on the real case, again leaving the parallel complex case to be developed as exercises.   Let f be any bilinear function from $\mathcal{V} \times \mathcal{V}$ to $\mathcal{R}$.   By considering only the numbers $f(\xi, \xi)$ we obtain a function q which maps $\mathcal{V}$ into $\mathcal{R}$,

$$q(\xi) = f(\xi, \xi).$$

Relative to a basis $\{\alpha_1, \ldots, \alpha_n\}$ for $\mathcal{V}$ this function takes the form

$$q(\xi) = \sum_{i=1}^{n} \sum_{j=1}^{n} x_i x_j f(\alpha_i, \alpha_j) = XAX',$$

where $\xi = \sum_{i=1}^{n} x_i \alpha_i$, and $a_{ij} = f(\alpha_i, \alpha_j)$, as in § 9.1.

Since each term in the expression for $q(\xi)$ is quadratic in the components $x_1, \ldots, x_n$ of ξ, we call q a *real quadratic function*.   Correspondingly, any quadratic expression in $x_1, \ldots, x_n$ with real coefficients is called a *real quadratic form*.

Observe that the quadratic form

$$3x_1^2 + 4x_1 x_2 - x_2^2$$

can be expressed in matric form in many ways:

$$(x_1 \; x_2) \begin{pmatrix} 3 & 0 \\ 4 & -1 \end{pmatrix} \begin{pmatrix} x_1 \\ x_2 \end{pmatrix},$$

$$(x_1 \; x_2) \begin{pmatrix} 3 & 4 \\ 0 & -1 \end{pmatrix} \begin{pmatrix} x_1 \\ x_2 \end{pmatrix},$$

$$(x_1 \; x_2) \begin{pmatrix} 3 & 2 \\ 2 & -1 \end{pmatrix} \begin{pmatrix} x_1 \\ x_2 \end{pmatrix},$$

and so on. The variations occur from different decompositions of the co-efficient of $x_i x_j$ into the two numbers a_{ij} and a_{ji}. An easy resolution of the ambiguity appears if we decompose A as the sum of its symmetric and skew-symmetric parts:

$$A = S + K.$$

Then

$$XAX' = X(S + K)X' = XSX' + XKX';$$

but a simple calculation verifies that

$$XKX' = 0.$$

Hence only the symmetric component of A contributes to the value of $q(\xi)$, and we lose nothing by insisting that a real quadratic function be represented by a real symmetric quadratic form.

Definition 9.12.

(a) A *real symmetric quadratic form* in the n variables $x_1, \ldots, x_n$ is an expression of the type

$$\sum_{i=1}^{n} \sum_{j=1}^{n} a_{ij} x_i x_j,$$

where $a_{ij} = a_{ji} \in \Re$ for all i, j.

(b) The form is said to be *positive definite* if and only if for all $x_i \in \Re$, $i = 1, \ldots, n$

$$\sum_{i=1}^{n} \sum_{j=1}^{n} a_{ij} x_i x_j \geq 0,$$

with equality holding if and only if $x_1 = x_2 = \ldots = x_n = 0$.

It is clear that $p(\xi, \xi)$, the square of the distance function, in any Euclidean space defines a real, symmetric, positive definite quadratic form. In the re-mainder of this chapter we shall study such functions without necessarily as-suming that the form is positive definite. We now summarize the results already obtained.

Theorem 9.19. Let q be a quadratic function from $\mathcal{U}$ to $\mathcal{R}$. Relative to the basis $\{\alpha_1, \ldots, \alpha_n\}$ for $\mathcal{U}$, q is represented by a uniquely determined matrix A such that

(a) A is real and symmetric,

(b) if $\xi = \sum_{i=1}^{n} x_i\alpha_i$, then $q(\xi) = XAX'$.

Furthermore, q is represented relative to the basis $\{\beta_1, \ldots, \beta_n\}$ by the real symmetric matrix B if and only if A and B are congruent.

P R O O F : The last statement follows directly from Theorem 9.3, and the other statements were established by our previous remarks.

EXAMPLES OF REAL SYMMETRIC QUADRATIC FORMS

(a) The expression for the fundamental metric (element of arc length) in three-dimensional space is

$$ds^2 = dx^2 + dy^2 + dz^2 \text{ in rectangular coordinates,}$$
$$= dr^2 + r^2 d\theta^2 + dz^2 \text{ in cylindrical coordinates,}$$
$$= d\rho^2 + \rho^2 \sin^2\psi d\theta^2 + \rho^2 d\psi^2 \text{ in spherical coordinates.}$$

In the study of differential geometry the expression for the fundamental metric of a surface is of basic importance.

(b) In classical mechanics the kinetic energy of a particle of mass m and having n degrees of freedom is given by

$$KE = \frac{m}{2} \sum_{i=1}^{n} \left(\frac{dx_i}{dt}\right)^2,$$

where the x_i are the position coordinates of the particle. In more general systems the kinetic energy is represented by more complicated quadratic forms.

(c) The equation of a central quadric surface is

$$ax^2 + bxy + cy^2 + dxz + eyz + fz^2 = k,$$

the left hand member being a quadratic form. The numbers b, d, and e are zero only if the axes of the quadric surface coincide with the coordinate axes; in case these are not zero we are interested in finding an orthogonal change of coordinates which will simplify the form to a sum of squares.

Since a quadratic function from $\mathcal{U}$ to $\mathcal{R}$ is represented uniquely relative to a fixed basis by a real symmetric matrix A, it is natural that our investigation of quadratic functions and quadratic forms reduces to a study of real symmetric matrices. We shall see that characteristic values and vectors of such matrices have rather remarkable properties.

The *conjugate* $\overline{A}$ of a complex matrix $A = (a_{ij})$ is defined by

$$\overline{A} = (\bar{a}_{ij});$$

then a real matrix is characterized by $\overline{A} = A$. Other conjugate properties of complex matrices, which may be proved as an exercise, are

$$\overline{\overline{A}} = A,$$
$$\overline{AB} = \overline{A}\,\overline{B},$$
$$\overline{A'} = \overline{A}'.$$

Theorem 9.20.   Every characteristic value of a real symmetric matrix A is real.

P R O O F :   Let A be real and symmetric; $\overline{A} = A = A'$. If λ is a characteristic value of A associated with the row vector $X \neq Z$, then

$$XA = \lambda X,$$
$$XA\overline{X}' = \lambda X\overline{X}', \text{ where } X\overline{X}' \text{ is real.}$$

But also $XA\overline{X}'$ is real, since

$$\overline{XA\overline{X}'} = \overline{X}\overline{A}\overline{\overline{X}}' = (XA\overline{X}')' = XA\overline{X}'.$$

The last equality holds, since the scalar $XA\overline{X}'$ equals its transpose. Thus for $X \neq Z$, λ is the quotient of the real number $XA\overline{X}'$ by the real number $X\overline{X}'$.

Theorem 9.20 implies that the characteristic polynomial, and therefore the minimal polynomial, of a real symmetric matrix A can be factored as a product of real linear factors.

Theorem 9.21.   If λ_1 and λ_2 are distinct characteristic values of a real symmetric matrix A, and if X_1 and X_2 are associated row vectors, then $X_1 X_2' = 0$.

P R O O F :   Let $X_i A = \lambda_i X_i,$ $i = 1, 2.$

Then

$$(X_1 A)X_2' = \lambda_1 X_1 X_2',$$
$$X_1(AX_2') = X_1(X_2 A')' = X_1(\lambda_2 X_2)' = \lambda_2 X_1 X_2'.$$

Hence $(\lambda_1 - \lambda_2)X_1 X_2' = 0$. Since $\lambda_1 \neq \lambda_2$, we conclude that $X_1 X_2' = 0$.

Geometrically, this proves that in a Euclidean space the characteristic vectors of a real symmetric matrix are orthogonal whenever they are associated with distinct characteristic values, since $X_1 X_2' = p(\xi_1, \xi_2)$ relative to a normal orthogonal basis.

The next result is the matric form of the Principal Axes theorem which asserts that any quadratic form may be reduced to the sum of squares by an appropriate orthogonal transformation. In particular, the axes of any quadric surface are orthogonal, and a rigid motion of the axes of any rectangular coordinate system aligns the new coordinate axes with those of the quadric.

Theorem 9.22. (Principal Axes theorem.) Any real symmetric matrix is simultaneously similar to and congruent to a diagonal matrix D; that is, there exists an orthogonal matrix P such that

$$D = PAP^{-1}$$

is diagonal, with the characteristic values of A along the diagonal.

P R O O F : Let $\{\alpha_1, \ldots, \alpha_n\}$ be a normal orthogonal basis for the Euclidean space $\mathcal{V}$, and let $\mathbf{T}$ be the linear transformation represented by A in that basis. If ξ is any characteristic vector of $\mathbf{T}$, then $\|\xi\|^{-1}\xi$ is of unit length, characteristic, and associated with the same characteristic value as is ξ. Let $\beta_1 = \|\xi\|^{-1}\xi$, where ξ is characteristic, associated with λ_1. Extend to a normal orthogonal basis $\{\beta_1, \ldots, \beta_n\}$ for $\mathcal{V}$. Relative to the new basis, $\mathbf{T}$ is represented by the matrix

$$B = RAR^{-1} = RAR',$$

since R is orthogonal. Thus B is real and symmetric, of the form

$$B = \begin{pmatrix} \lambda_1 & Z \\ Z & B_1 \end{pmatrix},$$

where B_1 is a real symmetric square matrix of dimension $n - 1$. We repeat the argument, selecting γ_2 as a normal characteristic vector in the space $[\beta_2, \ldots, \beta_n]$, letting $\gamma_1 = \beta_1$. Since β_1 is orthogonal to $[\beta_2, \ldots, \beta_n]$, γ_1 and γ_2 form a normal orthogonal set which can be extended to a normal orthogonal basis $\{\gamma_1, \gamma_2, \ldots, \gamma_n\}$ for $\mathcal{V}$. Then $\mathbf{T}$ is represented by C, where

$$C = SBS^{-1} = SBS', \ S \text{ orthogonal},$$

$$C = \left(\begin{array}{cc|c} \lambda_1 & 0 & Z \\ 0 & \lambda_2 & \\ \hline & Z & C_1 \end{array} \right).$$

Since R and S are orthogonal, so is SR, and

$$C = S(RAR')S' = (SR)A(SR)'.$$

Hence A is simultaneously similar and congruent to C; the theorem follows after n steps.

In selecting the basis in the proof of the preceding theorem we could begin with vectors corresponding to positive characteristic values as long as such values remain; then we could select characteristic vectors associated with negative characteristic values as long as they last; and finally the remaining basis vectors are associated with the characteristic value zero. Hence D of Theorem 9.22 has positive characteristic values in the first p positions, negative characteristic values in the next $r - p$ positions, where $r = \rho(A)$, and zeros in the last $n - r$ positions. This refined form is clearly canonical for the similarity of real symmetric matrices, since similar matrices have the same characteristic values.

Theorem 9.23. Two real symmetric matrices are congruent if and only if each is congruent to a diagonal matrix with $+1$ in the first p diagonal positions, -1 in the next $r-p$ diagonal positions, and zeros elsewhere.

P R O O F : This theorem asserts that the form of Theorem 9.5 is canonical for congruence of real symmetric matrices. We have already shown that each real symmetric matrix is congruent to a diagonal matrix of $+1$'s, -1's, and 0's as described, and that congruent real symmetric matrices represent the same quadratic function q. Suppose q is represented relative to $\{\alpha_1, \ldots, \alpha_n\}$ by

$$q(\xi) = x_1^2 + \ldots + x_p^2 - x_{p+1}^2 - \ldots - x_r^2,$$

$$\xi = \sum_{i=1}^{n} x_i \alpha_i,$$

and relative to $\{\beta_1, \ldots, \beta_n\}$ by

$$q(\xi) = y_1^2 + \ldots + y_t^2 - y_{t+1}^2 - \ldots - y_s^2,$$

$$\xi = \sum_{i=1}^{n} y_i \beta_i.$$

Then q is represented by congruent matrices A and B, which must be of equal rank. Hence $r = s$, since $r = \rho(A)$ and $s = \rho(B)$. Now suppose $t > p$. Let $\mathcal{U} = [\alpha_{p+1}, \ldots, \alpha_r]$, and let $\mathcal{W} = [\beta_1, \ldots, \beta_t, \beta_{r+1}, \ldots, \beta_n]$. Then $\mathcal{U}$ is of dimension $r - p$ and $\mathcal{W}$ of dimension $t + n - r$. Since the sum of these dimensions is $n + t - p > n$, there exists a non-zero vector $\xi \in \mathcal{U} \cap \mathcal{W}$. Then $q(\xi) < 0$, since $\xi \in \mathcal{U}$, and $q(\xi) \geq 0$, since $\xi \in \mathcal{W}$, which is a contradiction. Hence $t \leq p$. By reversing the roles of p and t, the reverse inequality can be proved, so $t = p$.

Definition 9.13.

(a) The *rank* r of a real quadratic form is the number of non-zero coefficients in its canonical reduction to the sum and difference of squares.

(b) The *signature* s of a real quadratic form is the number $2p - r = p - (r - p)$, which is the number of positive squares

minus the number of negative squares in its canonical reduction to the
sum and difference of squares.

This definition could have been stated in terms of the characteristic values
of the symmetric matrix of the quadratic form, where the rank is the number
of non-zero characteristic values and the signature is the excess (perhaps
negative) of the number of positive characteristic values over the number of
negative characteristic values.

The meaning of Theorem 9.23 is that two real quadratic forms represent
the same quadratic function in two coordinate systems if and only if they
have the same rank and the same signature.   Hence the rank and signature
of a quadratic function can be defined as the rank and signature of any
quadratic form which represents that function.

Theorem 9.24.   A real quadratic form in n variables is positive definite
if and only if it has rank n and signature n.

P R O O F :   If $r = n = s$, the canonical form is

$$q(\xi) = x_1^2 + x_2^2 + \ldots + x_n^2,$$

which is clearly positive definite.   Conversely, the canonical form of
rank r, relative to some basis $\{\alpha_1, \ldots, \alpha_n\}$ is

$$q(\xi) = a_1 x_1^2 + a_2 x_2^2 + \ldots + a_r x_r^2, \qquad a_i = \pm 1.$$

But if $r < n$, $q(\alpha_n) = 0$, so the form is not positive definite.   If $r = n$
but $s < n$,

$$q(\xi) = x_1^2 + \ldots + x_p^2 - x_{p+1}^2 - \ldots - x_n^2,$$

where $p < n$.   Then $q(\alpha_n) < 0$.

Theorem 9.25.   A real symmetric $n \times n$ matrix A represents a positive definite quadratic form if and only if

$$A = PP'$$

for some non-singular $n \times n$ matrix P.

P R O O F :   The canonical form under congruence of a positive definite
quadratic form is represented by the identity matrix.   Hence A represents that form if and only if

$$A = PIP'$$

for some non-singular P.

Exercises

1. Verify that for any complex matrices A, B

   (i) $\overline{\overline{A}} = A$,

   (ii) $\overline{AB} = \overline{A}\,\overline{B}$,

   (iii) $\overline{A'} = \overline{A}'$.

2. Given the real quadratic form $ax_1^2 + 2bx_1x_2 + cx_2^2$.

   (i) Prove that the form is positive definite if and only if $a > 0$ and $b^2 - ac < 0$.

   (ii) Show that the central conic $ax^2 + 2bxy + cy^2 = 1$ is an ellipse or hyperbola according as the quadratic form on the left has $r = 2$ and $s = 2$, or $r = 2$ and $s = 0$.

3. Reduce the following real quadratic forms to the algebraic sum of squares. Give the rank and signature of each.

   (i) $x_1^2 - 2x_1x_3 + 2x_2^2 + 4x_2x_3 + 6x_3^2$.

   (ii) $16x_1x_2 - x_3^2$.

   (iii) $5x_1^2 + 2x_1x_2 - 2x_1x_3 - x_2^2 + 2x_2x_3 - x_3^2$.

4. Given the matrix $A = \begin{pmatrix} 3 & 2 & 4 \\ 2 & 0 & 2 \\ 4 & 2 & 3 \end{pmatrix}$.

   (i) Show that the characteristic vectors which correspond to distinct characteristic values are mutually orthogonal

   (ii) Find a set of three characteristic vectors which form a normal orthogonal basis.

   (iii) In general, does a normal orthogonal basis of characteristic vectors of a given real symmetric matrix always exist? Prove your answer.

5. Let A, B be two real symmetric matrices; for a given basis each determines a real quadratic form, q_A and q_B. Show that if q_A is positive definite, there exists a non-singular matrix P such that

$$PAP' = I$$

and

$$PBP' = D, \text{ where } D \text{ is diagonal.}$$

(Interpreted for quadratic forms, one of which is positive definite, this result shows that there exists a single change of coordinates which diagonalizes both forms, a fact which is of importance in the solution of vibration problems in dynamics and in other applications.)

6. The Taylor expansion of a function f of two variables at (a, b) is expressed in terms of the partial derivatives of f by

$$f(a + h, b + k) = f(a, b) + hf_x(a, b) + kf_y(a, b)$$
$$+ \tfrac{1}{2}[h^2 f_{xx}(a, b) + 2hk f_{xy}(a, b) + k^2 f_{yy}(a, b)] + \ldots ,$$

provided that $f_{xy} = \dfrac{\partial}{\partial y}\left(\dfrac{\partial f}{\partial x}\right) = \dfrac{\partial}{\partial x}\left(\dfrac{\partial f}{\partial y}\right) = f_{yx}$. If $f_x(a, b) = 0 = f_y(a, b)$, then (a, b) is a critical point for maximum or minimum. The term in brackets is a quadratic form in h and k; if the form has rank 2, it determines whether f has a maximum or minimum or neither at (a, b). Assuming $r = 2$, show that

    (i) $f(a, b)$ is a relative maximum if $s = -2$,
    (ii) $f(a, b)$ is a relative minimum if $s = 2$,
    (iii) $f(a, b)$ is neither maximum nor minimum otherwise.

7. For complex vector spaces, results very similar to those of § 9.5 are valid. We begin with a conjugate-bilinear function b, and define a complex valued function h on $\mathcal{V}$ by

$$h(\xi) = b(\xi, \xi).$$

Relative to a basis $\{\alpha_1, \ldots, \alpha_n\}$, h assumes the form

$$h(\xi) = \sum_{i=1}^{n} \sum_{j=1}^{n} x_i \bar{x}_j b(\alpha_i, \alpha_j), \text{ where } \xi = \sum_{i=1}^{n} x_i \alpha_i.$$

Since b is conjugate-bilinear, $b(\alpha_i, \alpha_j) = \overline{b(\alpha_j, \alpha_i)}$. The function h is called a *Hermitian function*, the matrix $H = (h_{ij})$, $h_{ij} = b(\alpha_i, \alpha_j)$ is called a *Hermitian matrix* and is characterized by $H = \bar{H}'$, and the complex quadratic form

$$\sum_{i=1}^{n} \sum_{j=1}^{n} c_{ij} x_i \bar{x}_j = XC\bar{X}'$$

is called a *Hermitian form*, provided $c_{ij} = \bar{c}_{ji}$. A complex matrix K is called *skew-Hermitian* if and only if

$$K = -\bar{K}'.$$

Two complex matrices A and B are said to be *conjunctive* if and only if $A = PB\bar{P}'$ for some non-singular matrix P.

   Prove the following results, which parallel those of § 9.5.

    (i) If A is complex, $A\bar{A}'$ and $\bar{A}'A$ are Hermitian.
    (ii) Each complex matrix is the sum of a Hermitian and a skew-Hermitian matrix, $A = H + K$.
    (iii) If $A = H + K$ as in (ii), $XA\bar{X}' = XH\bar{X}'$.
    (iv) If H is Hermitian, $XH\bar{X}'$ is real.
    (v) Every characteristic value of a Hermitian matrix is real.

(vi) In a unitary space two characteristic vectors of a Hermitian matrix are orthogonal if they are associated with distinct characteristic values.

(vii) If H is Hermitian, there exists a unitary matrix P such that

$$D = PHP^{-1} = PH\bar{P}'$$

is diagonal, the diagonal elements being the characteristic values of H.

(viii) Conjunctivity is an equivalence relation.

(ix) Two Hermitian matrices are conjunctive if and only if each is conjunctive to the diagonal matrix with $+1$ in the first p diagonal positions, -1 in the next $r - p$ diagonal positions, and zeros elsewhere.

(x) A Hermitian form in n variables is positive definite if and only if it has rank n and signature n, where the definitions of rank, signature, and positive definite are analogous to the real symmetric case.

8. Use the following chain of reasoning to prove Hadamard's inequality: If A is a real $n \times n$ matrix such that $|a_{ij}| \leq k$ for all i, j, then

$$|\det A| \leq k^n n^{n/2}.$$

(A special case of this result was derived in Exercise 10, § 9.4.)

(i) Let $B_0 = AA'$; then B_0 is real and symmetric.

(ii) If A is non-singular, B_0 is positive definite.

(iii) If B is any $n \times n$ real, symmetric, positive definite matrix, if $x_1, \ldots, x_n$ are any non-zero numbers, and if $c_{ij} = b_{ij} x_i x_j$, then C is symmetric and positive definite.

(iv) If C is any $n \times n$ real, symmetric, positive definite matrix, then

$$\det C \leq \left[\frac{\operatorname{tr} C}{n} \right]^n.$$

(v) Let C be defined as in (iii), using $B = B_0$ and $x_i = b_{ii}^{-1/2}$. Show that $\operatorname{tr} C = n$, and $\det B = \det C \cdot \Pi_{i-1}^n b_{ii}$.

(vi) Complete the proof of Hadamard's inequality.

CHAPTER 10

Functions of Matrices

§10.1. *Preliminary Remarks*

Up to this point most of the material we have considered is central to a general study of matrices. This is not to claim that we have investigated every central idea, nor that every previous result is basic for any given application of matrix theory. Certainly only the surface has been scratched on some important topics, and a considerable body of material remains to be investigated. But almost any introductory course in matrix theory will be concerned with the material of Chapters 2–9, perhaps with a different ordering of these topics and with variations of the degree of generality with which each is considered.

The question of what topics should be studied next would receive different answers according to the interests of the individual. For prospective mathematicians there are many important applications to geometry, analysis, probability theory, and algebra. The generalization to infinite-dimensional vector spaces is of special interest and importance. The physicist may be more interested in applications to Newtonian mechanics, quantum mechanics, and relativity, the chemist to crystal structure or spectroscopy. The engineer will find applications to elasticity, electrical networks, wave propagation, and aircraft flutter. The economist might prefer to learn how to apply matrices to linear programming and game theory in order to solve problems in transportation, logistics, communications, and assignments. The biologist would wish to relate matrix theory to genetics, the psychologist to theory of learning or to dominance relations, and the sociologist to group relations and social customs.

Such applications of matrix theory are of genuine interest, not only for their effectiveness in solving significant problems of social and scientific import, but also because applications stimulate the development of new knowledge about

192

matrices.   Thus there is a strong temptation to discuss some of these applications in this final chapter.   Several considerations militate against this.
First, the fields of application are sufficiently technical that a brief account of
the background material would be necessarily fragmentary and perhaps
superficial.   Second, the range of applications is so broad that the selection
of only a few topics would be either biased or capricious.

Therefore you are strongly encouraged to consult other sources for information on applications of matrix theory.   In particular, Chapters 6 and 7 of
Reference 22 contain an introductory exposition of several of these topics, and
References 3 and 21 contain extensive references to applications, listed according to subject matter.

In this last chapter we shall draw upon the content of normal undergraduate work in function theory, extending to matrices the concepts of sequences,
series, and functions.   The problem of convergence is especially important
in many of the iterative methods of machine computation with matrices.

§10.2. *Sequences and Series of Matrices*

It is assumed that you are already familiar with the basic facts about infinite sequences and series of complex numbers, or at least about real power
series.   In particular we shall refer to the following:

The definitions of convergence of infinite sequences and series of numbers.

The circle of convergence of a complex power series (interval of convergence
in the real case).

Taylor series expansions for such functions as

$$e^x = \sum_{n=0}^{\infty} \frac{x^n}{n!}, \text{ valid for all complex } x,$$

$$\sin x = \sum_{n=0}^{\infty} (-1)^n \frac{x^{2n+1}}{(2n+1)!}, \text{ valid for all complex } x,$$

$$\cos x = \sum_{n=0}^{\infty} (-1)^n \frac{x^{2n}}{(2n)!}, \text{ valid for all complex } x,$$

$$\log (1+x) = \sum_{n=1}^{\infty} (-1)^{n+1} \frac{x^n}{n}, \text{ valid for all complex } x \text{ such that } |x| < 1,$$

$$\frac{1}{1-x} = \sum_{n=0}^{\infty} x^n, \text{ valid for all complex } x \text{ such that } |x| < 1.$$

Definition 10.1.   A *sequence* $\{A^{(k)}\} = A^{(1)}, A^{(2)}, \dots, A^{(n)}, \dots$ of $m \times n$
matrices is a function whose domain is the natural numbers and whose
range is a set of $m \times n$ matrices.   Let $A^{(k)} = (a_{ij}^{(k)})$.   The sequence

$\{A^{(k)}\}$ is said to *converge* to the matrix $A = (a_{ij})$ if and only if for every $i = 1, 2, \ldots, m$ and every $j = 1, 2, \ldots, n$, the number sequence $\{a_{ij}^{(k)}\}$ converges to a_{ij}.

EXAMPLE

Let
$$A^{(k)} = \begin{pmatrix} 1 + \dfrac{1}{k} & \dfrac{-1}{k^2} \\ \dfrac{k-2}{k^2+2} & 1 - \dfrac{1}{k^3} \end{pmatrix}.$$

Then $\{A^{(k)}\}$ converges to I, since $\{a_{ij}^{(k)}\}$ converges to δ_{ij} for $i, j = 1, 2$.

Theorem 10.1. If $\{A^{(k)}\}$ converges to A, if P is a fixed $h \times m$ matrix, and if Q is a fixed $n \times t$ matrix, then $\{PA^{(k)}Q\}$ converges to PAQ.

P R O O F : Let $B^{(k)} = PA^{(k)}Q$. For fixed i, j,

$$b_{ij}^{(k)} = \sum_{r=1}^{m} \sum_{s=1}^{n} p_{ir} a_{rs}^{(k)} q_{sj}.$$

By hypothesis, $\{a_{rs}^{(k)}\}$ converges to a_{rs}, for every $r = 1, 2, \ldots, m$ and every $s = 1, 2, \ldots, n$. Hence $\{p_{ir} a_{rs}^{(k)} q_{sj}\}$ converges to $p_{ir} a_{rs} q_{sj}$, and

$$\sum_{r=1}^{m} \sum_{s=1}^{n} \{p_{ir} a_{rs}^{(k)} q_{sj}\} \text{ converges to } \sum_{r=1}^{m} \sum_{s=1}^{n} p_{ir} a_{rs} q_{sj},$$

since a linear combination of convergent number sequences converges to the same linear combination of their limits. Hence $\{PA^{(k)}Q\}$ converges to PAQ.

The significance of this theorem is that convergence is preserved under the various equivalence relations which we have considered for matrices, and particularly by similarity. Thus it is possible to define convergence of a sequence of linear transformations by means of convergence of the matrices which represent those linear transformations in any coordinate system.

Definition 10.2. An *infinite series*

$$\sum_{k=0}^{\infty} A^{(k)} = A^{(0)} + A^{(1)} + \ldots + A^{(p)} + \ldots$$

of $m \times n$ matrices is said to *converge* to the matrix A if and only if for every $i = 1, 2, \ldots, m$ and every $i = 1, 2, \ldots, n$, the series $\sum_{k=0}^{\infty} a_{ij}^{(k)}$ converges to a_{ij}.

Thus convergence of a series of matrices is defined by the convergence of the mn number series of the elements in the same position. We shall consider only *power series* of matrices, that is, series for which

$$A^{(k)} = a_k X^k,$$

where a_k is a scalar and X is a square matrix.   (Previously we used X only to denote row vectors.)

Definition 10.3.   Given a scalar power series, $\sum_{k=0}^{\infty} a_k x^k$, let f be the function defined by

$$f(x) \;=\; \sum_{k=0}^{\infty} a_k x^k$$

for all x for which the series converges.   The *matric-valued function f of the square matrix X* is defined by

$$f(X) \;=\; \sum_{k=0}^{\infty} a_k X^k, \qquad X^0 = I$$

for all matrices X for which the series converges.

We recognize, of course, that the Hamilton-Cayley theorem makes it possible to avoid calculating powers of X higher than $n-1$, since X^n is a linear combination of lower powers of X.   If all such higher powers are thus converted, the infinite series

$$f(X) \;=\; \sum_{k=0}^{\infty} a_k X^k$$

is changed into the form

$$f(X) \;=\; \sum_{k=0}^{n-1} s_k X^k,$$

where each s_k is an infinite series of scalars.   The convergence of $f(X)$ is then a question of the convergence of each of the s_k.   (In this connection see Exercise 4.)

It is clear that Definition 10.3 is an extension of the correspondence between scalar polynomials and matric polynomials with scalar coefficients. When we speak of the matric functions e^X, $(I - X)^{-1}$, $\cos X$, we mean

$$e^X \;=\; \sum_{k=0}^{\infty} \frac{X^k}{k!},$$

$$(I - X)^{-1} \;=\; \sum_{k=0}^{\infty} X^k,$$

$$\cos X \;=\; \sum_{k=0}^{\infty} (-1)^k \frac{X^{2k}}{(2k)!}.$$

Two questions arise immediately:

For what matrices X does a power series converge?

If a series converges for some X, to what matrix does it converge?

Our method of answering these questions will be to reduce X to Jordan form J with diagonal blocks of a simple form, to answer the questions for J, and then to extract corresponding answers for X. The following three theorems, which may be proved as exercises, pertain to this method. In these theorems f refers to a function defined by a power series, $\sum_{k=0}^{\infty} a_k X^k$.

Theorem 10.2. If $f(X)$ converges and if $Y = PXP^{-1}$, then $f(Y)$ converges to $Pf(X)P^{-1}$.

P R O O F : Exercise. Apply Theorem 10.1 and the definition of convergence of a series of matrices.

Theorem 10.3. If X is a diagonal block matrix,

$$X = \begin{pmatrix} X_1 & Z \\ Z & X_2 \end{pmatrix}, \; X_1 \text{ and } X_2 \text{ square matrices,}$$

then

(a) $f(X)$ converges if and only if $f(X_1)$ and $f(X_2)$ converge, and
(b) if $f(X)$ converges, then

$$f(X) = \begin{pmatrix} f(X_1) & Z \\ Z & f(X_2) \end{pmatrix}.$$

P R O O F : Exercise. Observe that this theorem can be generalized by induction to the case in which there are any finite number of diagonal blocks.

Theorem 10.4. If X is nilpotent, $f(X)$ converges.

P R O O F : Exercise.

Theorems 10.2 and 10.3 reduce the questions of convergence of a matric series to questions about the convergence of the series for a matrix in the form

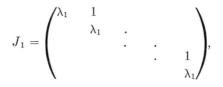

$$J_1 = \begin{pmatrix} \lambda_1 & 1 & & \\ & \lambda_1 & \cdot & \\ & & \cdot & \cdot & \\ & & & \cdot & 1 \\ & & & & \lambda_1 \end{pmatrix},$$

since any X is similar to a diagonal block matrix where each block is of this form. Thus our attention is focused on the convergence of the series

$$\sum_{k=0}^{\infty} a_k(\lambda I + N)^k,$$

where λ is a characteristic value of X and N is nilpotent.

Theorem 10.5. If $\sum_{k=0}^{\infty} a_k x^k$ converges for all x such that $|x| < r$, and if $|\lambda| < r$ for every characteristic value λ of X, then $\sum_{k=0}^{\infty} a_k X^k$ converges.

P R O O F :   Consider the diagonal block J_1 of the Jordan matrix similar to X such that λ appears in every diagonal position and 1 in every super-diagonal position.   Let

$$S_m(J_1) = \sum_{k=0}^{m} a_k(\lambda I + N)^k.$$

Since N is nilpotent of some index p, there are no more than p terms in the expansion of $(\lambda I + N)^k$ even for large k.   Let $m > p$.   Then

$$
\begin{aligned}
S_m(J_1) = \quad & a_0 I \\
+ \quad & a_1 \lambda I + & & a_1 N \\
+ \quad & a_2 \lambda^2 I + & & 2a_2 \lambda N + a_2 N^2 \\
& \vdots & & \vdots \\
+ \; & a_{m-1}\lambda^{m-1}I + C_1^{m-1}a_{m-1}\lambda^{m-2}N + \ldots + C_{p-1}^{m-1}a_{m-1}\lambda^{m-p}N^{p-1} \\
+ \; & a_m \lambda^m I + \quad C_1^m a_m \lambda^{m-1} N + \ldots + C_{p-1}^m a_m \lambda^{m-p+1}N^{p-1},
\end{aligned}
$$

where $C_s^m = \dfrac{m!}{s!(m-s)!}$ is the binomial coefficient.

Summing on like powers of N, we have

$$S_m(J_1) = \sum_{r=0}^{p-1}\left(\sum_{k=r}^{m} a_k C_r^k \lambda^{k-r} \right)N^r.$$

But

$$a_k C_r^k \lambda^{k-r} = \frac{a_k}{r!}\frac{k!}{(k-r)!}\lambda^{k-r} = \frac{a_k}{r!}\frac{d^r}{dx^r}(x^k) \bigg]_{x=\lambda},$$

so

$$\sum_{k=r}^{m} a_k C_r^k \lambda^{k-r} = \frac{1}{r!}\sum_{k=r}^{m} a_k \frac{d^r}{dx^r}(x^k) \bigg]_{x=\lambda} = \frac{1}{r!}S_m^{(r)}(\lambda),$$

where $S_m^{(r)}(\lambda)$ is the rth derivative of $S_m(x)$, evaluated at $x = \lambda$.   Therefore, $S_m(J_1)$ has the upper triangular form,

$$
S_m(J_1) =
\begin{pmatrix}
S_m(\lambda) & S_m^{(1)}(\lambda) & \tfrac{1}{2}S_m^{(2)}(\lambda) \cdots & \dfrac{1}{(p-1)!}S_m^{(p-1)}(\lambda) \\[2ex]
 & S_m(\lambda) & S_m^{(1)}(\lambda) \cdots & \dfrac{1}{(p-2)!}S_m^{(p-2)}(\lambda) \\[2ex]
 & & S_m(\lambda) \cdots & \dfrac{1}{(p-3)!}S_m^{(p-3)}(\lambda) \\[2ex]
 & & & \vdots \\[1ex]
 & & & S_m(\lambda)
\end{pmatrix}
$$

By hypothesis, $\sum_{k=0}^{\infty} a_k\lambda^k$ converges, since $|\lambda| < r$.   Thus the sequence $\{\sum_{k=0}^{m} a_k\lambda^k\} = \{S_m(\lambda)\}$ converges.   But from the theory of infinite series it is known that the series obtained by differentiating $\sum_{k=0}^{\infty} a_k x^k$ term by term will converge for $|x| < r$. Hence the sequence $\{S_m(J_1)\}$ converges, which means that the series $\sum_{k=0}^{\infty} a_k J_1^k$ converges, so the proof is complete.

This theorem shows that such functions as e^X, $\sin X$, and $\cos X$ exist for all X, since the corresponding scalar series converge for all x. However, we cannot assume that the matric function possesses all the properties of the corresponding scalar function; for example,

$$e^X e^Y \neq e^{X+Y},$$

although equality does hold if X and Y commute.

Another important consequence of Theorem 10.5 is the special role played by the characteristic value of largest absolute value. If f is defined by an infinite series whose radius of convergence is r, and if λ_0 is the characteristic value of largest magnitude of a matrix X, then $f(X)$ converges if $|\lambda_0| < r$ and diverges if $|\lambda_0| > r$. If $|\lambda_0| = r$, $f(X)$ may or may not converge. In the next section we show how λ_0 can be estimated under suitable conditions. A simple relation between the characteristic values of X and those of $f(X)$ is given in the next theorem.

Theorem 10.6. If $f(X)$ converges and if λ is a characteristic value of X, then $f(\lambda)$ is a characteristic value of $f(X)$.

P R O O F : If $J = PXP^{-1}$ is the Jordan form of X, then X and J have the same characteristic values, and $f(J) = Pf(X)P^{-1}$. But the proof of Theorem 10.5 shows that $f(J)$ is an upper triangular matrix with $f(\lambda_1)$, $f(\lambda_2), \ldots, f(\lambda_n)$ as the diagonal elements. Hence these are the characteristic values of $f(J)$ and of the similar matrix $f(X)$.

Theorem 10.7. For every matrix X, $\det e^X = e^{\operatorname{tr} X}$ and therefore e^X is non-singular. Furthermore, $(e^X)^{-1} = e^{-X}$.

P R O O F : Exercise.

Exercises

1. Prove each of the following theorems:
    (i) Theorem 10.2,
    (ii) Theorem 10.3,
    (iii) Theorem 10.4,
    (iv) Theorem 10.7.

2. Evaluate e^A, given

(i) $A = \begin{pmatrix} -1 & 0 \\ 0 & 1 \end{pmatrix}$,

(ii) $A = \begin{pmatrix} -1 & 3 \\ 1 & 1 \end{pmatrix}$,

(iii) $A = \begin{pmatrix} 2 & 0 & 0 \\ 0 & -1 & 3 \\ 0 & 1 & 1 \end{pmatrix}$,

(iv) $A = \begin{pmatrix} 0 & 1 & 1 \\ 0 & 0 & 1 \\ 0 & 0 & 0 \end{pmatrix}$.

3. Prove that a series $\sum_{k=0}^{\infty} A^{(k)}$ of matrices converges if and only if the sequence $\{S^{(n)}\}$ of matrices converges, where $S^{(n)} = A^{(0)} + A^{(1)} + \ldots + A^{(n)}$.

4. Let $f(x) = \sum_{k=0}^{\infty} a_k x^k$, let A be a matrix with distinct characteristic values $\lambda_1, \lambda_2, \ldots, \lambda_n$ for which $f(A)$ converges. It can be proved that

$$f(A) = D^{-1}[D_0 I + D_1 A + \ldots + D_{n-1} A^{n-1}],$$

where D is the Vandermonde determinant

$$D = \begin{vmatrix} 1 & 1 & \ldots 1 \\ \lambda_1 & \lambda_2 & \ldots \lambda_n \\ \lambda_1^2 & \lambda_2^2 & \ldots \lambda_n^2 \\ . & . & . \\ . & . & . \\ . & . & . \\ \lambda_1^{n-1} & \lambda_2^{n-1} & \ldots \lambda_n^{n-1} \end{vmatrix},$$

and D_k is the determinant which coincides with D except that the $(k+1)$ row vector is $(f(\lambda_1), f(\lambda_2), \ldots, f(\lambda_n))$. (This formula is reminiscent of Cramer's rule.)

(i) Apply the method described above to calculate $f(A)$, where

$$A = \begin{pmatrix} 3 & 2 & 2 \\ 1 & 4 & 1 \\ -2 & -4 & -1 \end{pmatrix}.$$

(ii) Check your result in (i) by using it to compute A^2.

(iii) For A as given in (i) find necessary and sufficient conditions on f that $f(A)$ be a scalar matrix.

(iv) Calculate e^A.

§10.3. *Iterative Methods of Computation*

Since calculations with large matrices demand the use of high speed computing machines, and since machine computations are necessarily approximations due to internal limitations of the machine, considerable attention has been given in recent years to the art of computation by successive approximation.   The idea is simple: To calculate some quantity q related to a matrix A, we begin with an approximation q_0 of q, and then use properties of A to obtain an approximation q_1, which we hope is an improvement over q_0.   The process is repeated to obtain successive approximations $q_2, q_3, \ldots$ until no further change is noticed; that is, until $q_k = q_{k+1}$.   This represents convergence, or at least approximate convergence, of the sequence $\{q_i\}$.   We then can verify whether or not q_k is the desired approximation for q.   Clearly, questions of convergence arise in any iterative process.

As illustrations of this general notion we present two iterative methods of calculating A^{-1} and one method of finding the largest characteristic value of A.

Inverse of A (first method).   Let $B = I - A$.   Then $A = I - B$ and $A^{-1} = (I - B)^{-1} = \sum_{k=0}^{\infty} B^k = I + B + B^2 + \ldots$.   For convergence it is necessary and sufficient that all characteristic values of A satisfy $|\lambda| < 1$, so this method is not generally applicable.

Inverse of A (second method).   Another iterative method for finding A^{-1} is to begin with an educated guess, B_0, and then to define B_k inductively by

$$B_k = B_{k-1}(2I - AB_{k-1}), \qquad k = 1, 2, \ldots .$$

There is no assurance that the sequence $\{B_k\}$ will converge, but suppose it does converge to B.   Then $\{B_{k-1}\}$ also converges to B, and we have

$$B = B(2I - AB),$$

which implies that $B = A^{-1}$ if B is non-singular.

Largest characteristic value of A.   The method described here assumes that A is similar to a diagonal matrix.   Then by Theorem 7.7 (e) there exist scalars $a_1, \ldots, a_r$ and matrices $E_1, \ldots, E_r$ such that

$$A = \sum_{i=1}^{r} a_i E_i.$$

By Exercise 5, § 7.4, the a_i are characteristic values of A.   The E_i represent supplementary, orthogonal projections as described in § 8.1.   Hence

$$A^k = \sum_{i=1}^{r} a_i^k E_i.$$

Now suppose a_1 is such that $|a_1| > |a_i|$ for $i = 2, \ldots, r$.   Then

$$A^k = a_1^k \left[E_1 + \left(\frac{a_2}{a_1} \right)^k E_2 + \ldots + \left(\frac{a_r}{a_1} \right)^k E_r \right];$$

for sufficiently large k, $\left| \dfrac{a_i}{a_1} \right|^k$ is arbitrarily small, $i = 2, \ldots, r$.   Therefore, for large k, $a_1^k E_1$ is a good approximation to A^k;

$$A^{k+1} \doteq a_1^{k+1} E_1 = a_1 (a_1^k E_1) \doteq a_1 A^k.$$

For any vector X_0 such that $X_0 A^k \neq Z$, we conclude that

$$(X_0 A^k) A = X_0 A^{k+1} \doteq X_0 (a_1 A^k) = a_1 (X_0 A^k);$$

hence $X_0 A^k$ is an approximation to a characteristic vector of A associated with the characteristic value a_1 of largest magnitude.   In summary the procedure is as follows: Given A, choose X_0 so that $X_0 A \neq Z$; then calculate $X_0 A^2$, $X_0 A^3$, ... until for some m, $X_0 A^m$ is approximately a non-zero scalar multiple of $X_0 A^{m-1} \neq Z$.   That scalar is then an approximation to the characteristic value of A of largest magnitude, and $X_0 A^{m-1}$ is a corresponding characteristic vector.

Exercises

1. Given the matrix $A = \begin{pmatrix} \frac{1}{2} & 1 & 0 \\ 0 & \frac{2}{3} & 0 \\ -\frac{1}{2} & -1 & \frac{2}{3} \end{pmatrix}$.

    (i) Use the first method to approximate A^{-1} by calculating
    $$C = I + B + B^2 + B^3.$$

    (ii) Check the accuracy by computing AC.

    (iii) Will the process converge in this case?

2. Guided by the results of the previous problem, we round off C to obtain

$$B_0 = \begin{pmatrix} 2 & -\frac{7}{3} & 0 \\ 0 & \frac{3}{2} & 0 \\ \frac{7}{6} & 1 & \frac{3}{2} \end{pmatrix}.$$

    (i) Use the second method to calculate B_1 and B_2.

    (ii) Compute AB_2.

3. Given the matrix $A = \begin{pmatrix} 2 & -2 & 3 \\ 1 & 1 & 1 \\ 1 & 3 & -1 \end{pmatrix}$.

    (i) Approximate the largest characteristic value of A by starting with

$$X_0 = (1, 1, 1)$$

but not continuing beyond $X_0 A^5$.

(ii) Repeat with your own choice of X_0, perhaps suggested by your computations in (i).

§10.4. *Matrices of Functions*

We now consider an $m \times n$ matrix whose entries are not scalars, but scalar-valued functions. To be specific, let

$$X(t) = (x_{ij}(t)), \ i = 1, 2, \ldots, m; j = 1, 2, \ldots, n,$$

where $x_{ij}(t)$ is a real-valued function defined for all t in an interval $a \leq t \leq b$. Now X is a function whose domain includes $a \leq t \leq b$, and whose value at t is an $m \times n$ matrix of real-valued functions. In this section we shall indicate how a calculus of matrices of functions can be defined.

The idea is extremely simple, since continuity, derivative, and integral are defined component by component.

Definition 10.4. Let X be an $m \times n$ matrix of real-valued functions x_{ij} which are defined for all t in some set of real numbers.

(a) X is *continuous* at t_0 if and only if x_{ij} is continuous at t_0 for
$i = 1, 2, \ldots, m; j = 1, 2, \ldots, n$.

(b) The *derivative* $\mathcal{D}X$ of X is defined by

$$\mathcal{D}X(t_0) = \left(\frac{d}{dt} x_{ij}(t_0) \right),$$

if and only if $\frac{d}{dt} x_{ij}(t_0)$ exists for $i = 1, 2, \ldots, m; j = 1, 2, \ldots, n$.

(c) The *definite integral* $\int_a^b X$ is defined by

$$\int_a^b X = \left(\int_a^b x_{ij}(t) dt \right),$$

if and only if $\int_a^b x_{ij}(t) dt$ exists for $i = 1, 2, \ldots, m; j = 1, 2, \ldots, n$.

We shall develop only enough calculus of matrices to enable us to apply our results to the solution of a differential equation.

Theorem 10.8. If X is $n \times n$, if Y is $n \times p$, and if $\mathcal{D}X$ and $\mathcal{D}Y$ exist, then

(a) $\mathcal{D}(XY) = (\mathcal{D}X)Y + X(\mathcal{D}Y)$,

(b) $\mathcal{D}(X^p) = \sum_{i=1}^{p} X^{p-i}(\mathcal{D}X)X^{i-1}$, p a positive integer,

(c) $\mathfrak{D}(X^{-1}) = -X^{-1}(\mathfrak{D}X)X^{-1}$, if X is non-singular.

P R O O F : Exercise.

Observe that these rules are generalizations of the corresponding results for scalar functions, which reduce to the usual differentiation formulas if all of the matrices involved commute with each other. In general, however, even X and $\mathfrak{D}X$ do not commute, so we must be careful to preserve the order of the matrices in these formulas.

Theorem 10.9. If A is an $n \times n$ matrix of scalars, then

$$\mathfrak{D}(e^{At}) = Ae^{At} = e^{At}A.$$

P R O O F : By definition, we have

$$e^{At} = \sum_{k=0}^{\infty} \frac{(At)^k}{k!} = I + \frac{At}{1} + \frac{A^2t^2}{2!} + \dots.$$

Thus

$$\mathfrak{D}(e^{At}) = \sum_{k=0}^{\infty} \frac{kA^kt^{k-1}}{k!} = \sum_{k=1}^{\infty} \frac{A(At)^{k-1}}{(k-1)!} = \sum_{j=0}^{\infty} \frac{A(At)^j}{j!}$$

$$= Ae^{At} = e^{At}A.$$

This result is reminiscent of the corresponding property of the exponential function,

$$\frac{d}{dt} e^{at} = ae^{at}$$

which plays such an important role in the solution of certain differential equations. In the next theorem we consider the analogous problem for matrices.

Theorem 10.10. Consider the matric differential equation

$$\mathfrak{D}X(t) = X(t)A,$$

where $X(t)$ is an $m \times n$ matrix of differentiable functions and A is an $n \times n$ matrix of scalars. Then
(a) for any fixed value t_0 of t, the matrix

$$X(t) = X(t_0)e^{(t-t_0)A}$$

is a solution of the differential equation,
(b) any solution is of the form specified in (a) for some value of t_0,
(c) the rank of a given solution $X(t)$ is the same for all values of t.
P R O O F : Conclusion (a) follows directly from Theorem 10.9. To prove (b) let $X(t)$ be any solution, and let

$$Y(t) = X(t)e^{-At}.$$

Then
$$\mathfrak{D}Y(t) = [\mathfrak{D}X(t)]e^{-At} + X(t)\mathfrak{D}e^{-At}$$
$$= [\mathfrak{D}X(t)]e^{-At} - X(t)Ae^{-At}$$
$$= [\mathfrak{D}X(t) - X(t)A]e^{-At}$$
$$= Z,$$

since $\mathfrak{D}X(t) = X(t)A$ by hypothesis. Then Y is a constant $m \times n$ matrix C. For any value t_0 of t,

$$Y(t_0) = C = X(t_0)e^{-At_0},$$

so

$$X(t) = Ce^{At} = X(t_0)(e^{-At_0})e^{At}$$
$$= X(t_0)e^{(t-t_0)A},$$

where the last equality is valid since At_0 and At commute. Furthermore, by Theorem 10.7, $e^{(t-t_0)A}$ is non-singular, so the rank of $X(t)$ is the same as the rank of $X(t_0)$, which proves (c).

In the next section we shall apply Theorem 10.10 in the special case in which X is a row vector.

Exercises

1. Prove that $\mathfrak{D}X$ as given in Definition 10.4 satisfies

$$\mathfrak{D}X(t_0) = \lim_{h \to 0} \frac{1}{h} [X(t_0 + h) - X(t_0)]$$

if limit is understood to operate on each component.

2. Prove Theorem 10.8.

3. Does an analogue of the fundamental theorem of calculus hold for matrix calculus? Explain.

4. Does an analogue of the mean value theorem of the derivative hold for matrix calculus? Explain.

5. Derive an expression for the derivative of det $X(t)$.

6. Derive an expression for the derivative of tr $X(t)$, and prove that

$$\frac{d}{dt} [\text{tr } X(t)] = \text{tr}[\mathfrak{D}X(t)].$$

§10.5. *An Application to Differential Equations*

We now consider the problem of determining all solutions of a linear, homogeneous, n^{th} order differential equation with constant coefficients,

$$(10.1) \qquad \frac{d^n}{dt^n} x + a_1 \frac{d^{n-1}}{dt^{n-1}} x + \ldots + a_{n-1} \frac{d}{dt} x + a_n x = 0.$$

Most of the essential facts concerning the solutions of this equation can be verified easily by direct calculations. Our first observations are that any scalar multiple of a solution is also a solution, and that the sum of any two solutions is a solution. Therefore, the set of all solutions of *(10.1)* forms a vector space, called the *solution space*. Furthermore, the dimension of the solution space is n, a fact which follows from a theorem concerning the uniqueness of solutions of *(10.1)*. Therefore, the problem of finding all solutions of *(10.1)* reduces to the problem of finding a basis for the solution space, a set of n linearly independent solutions.

If we let $x = e^{rt}$, then x is a solution if and only if r satisfies the polynomial equation

$$(10.2) \qquad r^n + a_1 r^{n-1} + \ldots + a_{n-1} r + a_n = 0.$$

At this point we separate the discussion into two cases. First, if the roots $r_1, r_2, \ldots, r_n$ of *(10.2)* are distinct, then the solution set $\{e^{r_1 t}, e^{r_2 t}, \ldots, e^{r_n t}\}$ is linearly independent, so any solution has the form

$$x = \sum_{i=1}^{n} c_i e^{r_i t},$$

where the c_i are suitable scalars. As the alternative to the case in which *(10.2)* has n distinct roots, suppose that the distinct roots are $r_1, r_2, \ldots, r_k$, and that r_i is a root of multiplicity m_i, for $i = 1, 2, \ldots, k$. Then for each i each of the functions

$$\{e^{r_i t}, t e^{r_i t}, \ldots, t^{m_i - 1} e^{r_i t}\}$$

is a solution, and this set of solutions is linearly independent. The collection of all solutions obtained in this way by letting i vary from 1 to k forms a basis for the solution space. Thus we have full information concerning the solutions of *(10.1)*.

Although verification of the preceding statements is not difficult, this approach is not completely satisfying because the success of the method seems to depend upon a mystic process of guessing that functions such as $t^2 e^{r_i t}$ are solutions. In this section we shall restate and resolve the problem in matric notation, observing that the solutions arise in a natural way from the Jordan form of a matrix determined by *(10.1)*.

First we make a change of variables in order to replace the single equation *(10.1)* of order n by a set of n equations of order 1. Let $y_1 = x$, $y_2 = \frac{d}{dt} y_1$, $\ldots, y_n = \frac{d}{dt} y_{n-1}$. Then we obtain the n equations

$$
(10.3) \quad
\begin{cases}
\dfrac{d}{dt}\,y_1 = y_2 \\[2mm]
\dfrac{d}{dt}\,y_2 = y_3 \\[1mm]
\quad \vdots \\[1mm]
\dfrac{d}{dt}\,y_{n-1} = y_n \\[2mm]
\dfrac{d}{dt}\,y_n = -a_n y_1 - a_{n-1} y_2 - \ldots - a_1 y_n.
\end{cases}
$$

Let

$$ Y = (y_1, y_2, \ldots, y_n), $$

and let

$$
A =
\begin{pmatrix}
0 & 0 & 0 \ldots 0 & -a_n \\
1 & 0 & 0 \ldots 0 & -a_{n-1} \\
0 & 1 & 0 \ldots 0 & -a_{n-2} \\
\cdot & \cdot & \cdot \quad\; \cdot & \cdot \\
\cdot & \cdot & \cdot \quad\; \cdot & \cdot \\
0 & 0 & 0 \ldots 1 & -a_1
\end{pmatrix}.
$$

Then (10.3) or, equivalently, (10.1) is written simply $\mathfrak{D}Y = YA$, and by Theorem 10.10 any solution is of the form

$$ Y(t) = Y(t_0)e^{(t-t_0)A}. $$

Now for some non-singular matrix P, $J = P^{-1}AP$, where J is a Jordan matrix. Let $W = YP$; then

$$
\begin{aligned}
W(t) = Y(t)P &= [Y(t_0)P]P^{-1}e^{(t-t_0)A}P \\
&= W(t_0)e^{(t-t_0)J} \\
&= W(t_0)e^{(t-t_0)[\mathrm{diag}(\lambda_1, \ldots, \lambda_n)+N]}.
\end{aligned}
$$

The characteristic values λ_i of A are the solutions of (10.2) because the characteristic equation of A is

$$ \lambda^n + a_1\lambda^{n-1} + \ldots + a_{n-1}\lambda + a_n = 0. $$

(See Exercise 7, § 7.3, and apply the result to A'.) We now consider the form of $W(t)$ for two special cases.

Case I. $\lambda_1, \lambda_2, \ldots, \lambda_n$ all distinct. Then $N = Z$, and we have

$$
\begin{aligned}
W(t) &= W(t_0)e^{(t-t_0)\mathrm{diag}(\lambda_1, \ldots, \lambda_n)} \\
&= W(t_0)\mathrm{diag}(e^{\lambda_1(t-t_0)}, \ldots, e^{\lambda_n(t-t_0)}) \\
&= (w_1(t_0)e^{\lambda_1(t-t_0)}, \ldots, w_n(t_0)e^{\lambda_n(t-t_0)}),
\end{aligned}
$$

where the kth component of the vector $W(t_0)$ is denoted $w_k(t_0)$. Thus any solution vector is a linear combination of the vectors determined by the distinct characteristic values,

$$(0, \ldots, 0, e^{\lambda_k(t-t_0)}, 0, \ldots, 0).$$

Case II. $\lambda_1 = \lambda_2 = \ldots = \lambda_n$. Then N has zeros and ones on the superdiagonal, and

$$W(t) = W(t_0)e^{(t-t_0)[\lambda I + N]}$$

$$= W(t_0)[e^{\lambda(t-t_0)I}][e^{(t-t_0)N}]$$

$$= W(t_0)e^{\lambda(t-t_0)}[I + (t-t_0)N + \ldots + \frac{(t-t_0)^{n-1}}{(n-1)!} N^{n-1}].$$

Thus an arbitrary solution vector has for its kth component an expression of the form

$$p_k(t)e^{\lambda(t-t_0)},$$

where $p_k(t)$ is a polynomial in t of degree less than k. Those polynomials are generated by the various powers of the non-vanishing nilpotent part of the Jordan form of the matrix A. Thus a basis for the solution space can be chosen to be the vectors

$$\{e^{\lambda t}, te^{\lambda t}, \ldots, t^{n-1}e^{\lambda t}\}.$$

The general case in which there are r distinct characteristic values λ_i, each of multiplicity m_i, is a combination of the two cases described, any solution vector being a linear combination of the vectors

$$p_j(t)e^{\lambda_j t},$$

where $p_j(t)$ is a polynomial of degree less than m_j, $j = 1, 2, \ldots, r$. Hence a basis for the solution space is

$$\{e^{\lambda_1 t}, te^{\lambda_1 t}, \ldots, t^{m_1-1}e^{\lambda_1 t}, e^{\lambda_2 t}, te^{\lambda_2 t}, \ldots, t^{m_2-1}e^{\lambda_2 t}, \ldots, e^{\lambda_r t}, te^{\lambda_r t}, \ldots, t^{m_r-1}e^{\lambda_r t}\}.$$

Exercises

1. Work through the method of the text to solve the differential equation

$$\frac{d^3}{dt^3}x - \frac{d^2}{dt^2}x - \frac{d}{dt}x + x = 0,$$

showing that any solution vector can be written in the form

$$(ae^t, (at + b)e^t, ce^{-t}).$$

Observe the manner in which the second component arises from the nilpotent part of the Jordan form of the matrix determined by the equation.

APPENDIX A

Algebraic Concepts

The objective of this appendix is to formulate fundamental algebraic concepts in terms of the notion of sets, thus supplementing the discussion of abstract systems in Chapter 1. The treatment is brief and somewhat formal. Exercises, arranged in the order of the text discussion, are provided to augment the reader's understanding of this material.

§A.1. *Cartesian Product of Sets*

At the end of § 1.2 the cartesian product $A \times B$ of any two sets, A and B, was defined to be the set of all ordered pairs of the form (a, b), where $a \in A$ and $b \subset B$. This definition is easily generalized to any finite number of sets.

Definition A.1. Let $S_1, S_2, \ldots, S_n$ be any sets. The *cartesian product* $S_1 \times S_2 \times \ldots \times S_n$ is the set of all ordered n-tuples,

$$S_1 \times S_2 \times \ldots \times S_n = \{(s_1, s_2, \ldots, s_n) \mid s_i \in S_i \text{ for } i = 1, \ldots, n\}.$$

Thus for each i, the ith component of any element of $S_1 \times S_2 \times \ldots \times S_n$ is an element of S_i, and $S_1 \times S_2 \times \ldots \times S_n$ consists of all n-tuples which can be formed in this manner.

§A.2. *Binary Relations*

Definition A.2. A *binary relation* $\mathbf{R}$ from a set A into a set B is a subset of $A \times B$. If $(a, b) \in \mathbf{R}$, we say that *a is related to b*, and write

$$a \, \mathbf{R} \, b.$$

The *domain* of **R** is the set of all elements of A which are related by **R** to at least one element of B;

$$\text{dom } \mathbf{R} = \{a \in A \mid a \mathbf{R} y \text{ for some } y \in B\}.$$

The *range* of **R** is the set of all elements of B to which at least one element of A is related by **R**;

$$\text{range } \mathbf{R} = \{b \in B \mid x \mathbf{R} b \text{ for some } x \in A\}.$$

A binary relation from A into A is called a *relation in A*.

It is sometimes convenient to think of a relation in geometric terms as an *association*, or many-valued correspondence, from A into B. Each element in dom **R** is associated by **R** with one or more elements in range **R**. For example, let $A = \{a_1, a_2, a_3\}$, $B = \{b_1, b_2, b_3, b_4\}$; let **R** be the subset of $A \times B$ which consists of the pairs (a_1, b_1), (a_1, b_2), (a_2, b_1), (a_2, b_4), and (a_3, b_4). Then dom $\mathbf{R} = A$ and range $\mathbf{R} = \{b_1, b_2, b_4\} \subset B$. **R** can be represented geometrically by the following diagram.

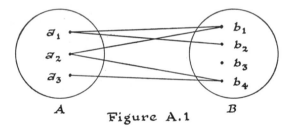

A Figure A.1 B

§A.3. *Functions*

Definition A.3.   A *function* **F** from a set A to a set B is a binary relation from A into B which satisfies the additional properties,
(a) dom $\mathbf{F} \neq \Phi$,
(b) if $a \mathbf{F} b_1$ and $a \mathbf{F} b_2$, then $b_1 = b_2$.
The *domain* and *range* of **F** are its domain and range as defined for relations.

The essential condition which distinguishes a function from an arbitrary relation is the requirement that each $a \in$ dom **F** be associated with one and only one $b \in$ range **F**. Because b is uniquely determined by a and **F**, the relation notation $a \mathbf{F} b$ can be replaced for functions by the notation described in § 1.3,

$$b = a\mathbf{F}.$$

Thus

$$\text{dom } \mathbf{F} = \{a \in A \mid y = a\mathbf{F} \text{ for some } y \in B\},$$
$$\text{range } \mathbf{F} = \{b \in B \mid b = x\mathbf{F} \text{ for some } x \in A\}.$$

If range $\mathbf{F} = B$, we say that $\mathbf{F}$ is a function from A *onto* B.

Described geometrically, each $a \in \text{dom } \mathbf{F}$ is associated with one and only one image $a\mathbf{F} \in \text{range } \mathbf{F}$. To distinguish the unique association of a function from the multiple association of an arbitrary relation, we say that a function is a *mapping*. Each *image* $a\mathbf{F}$ of the mapping $\mathbf{F}$ is uniquely determined by its antecedent a. However, it is possible that different antecedents, $a \neq x$, determine the same image, $a\mathbf{F} = x\mathbf{F}$. In general, mappings are *many-to-one*, which means that many distinct points of the domain are mapped into the same image point of the range.

Definition A.4. A mapping $\mathbf{F}$ is said to be *one-to-one* if and only if the following condition holds for all $a, x \in \text{dom } \mathbf{F}$:

$$\text{if } a\mathbf{F} = x\mathbf{F}, \text{ then } a = x.$$

§A.4. *Binary Operations*

Definition A.5. A *binary operation* on a set A is a function from $A \times A$ into A. An operation on A is said to be *closed* if and only if the domain of the operation is the full set $A \times A$. More generally, an *n-ary operation* on A is a function whose domain is the set $A \times A \times \ldots \times A$ (n times) of ordered n-tuples of elements of A and whose range is a subset of A.

It is customary to use special symbols, rather than function notation, for binary operations. Thus $a_1 * a_2$ denotes the image in A of the ordered pair $(a_1, a_2) \in A \times A$ under the mapping which defines the operation $*$.

§A.5. *Summary of Abstract Systems*

In § 1.4 an abstract system

$$\mathcal{S} = \{E; R; O\}$$

was described as a set E of elements, a set R of binary relations in E, and a set O of closed operations on E, together with a set of postulates which endow the elements, relations, and operations with their distinctive properties. Each binary relation is a subset of $E \times E$; each n-ary operation is a function from $E \times E \times \ldots \times E$ (n times) into E. Since a function is a type of relation, each n-ary operation can be described as a subset of $E \times E \times \ldots \times E$ ($n + 1$ times). In this way the components of an abstract system are represented as subsets of sets formed from the set of elements of the system.

§A.6. *Homomorphisms and Isomorphisms*

We begin by defining homomorphism in the simple case of two systems, $\mathcal{S} = \{E; *\}$ and $\mathcal{S}' = \{E'; \star\}$, each having one operation.

Definition A.6. A mapping $\mathbf{H}$ of E into E' is called a *homomorphism* of $\mathcal{S}$ into $\mathcal{S}'$ if and only if for all $a, b \in E$

$$(a * b)\mathbf{H} = a\mathbf{H} \star b\mathbf{H}.$$

The domain of $\mathbf{H}$ is E; whenever the range of $\mathbf{H}$ is the full set E', $\mathbf{H}$ is called a homomorphism of $\mathcal{S}$ *onto* $\mathcal{S}'$. A homomorphism $\mathbf{H}$ of $\mathcal{S}$ onto $\mathcal{S}'$ is called an *isomorphism* if and only if $\mathbf{H}$ is a one-to-one mapping of E onto E'.

Thus a homomorphism is a many-to-one mapping of the elements of one system into those of another, having the special property that the operation is preserved by the mapping. By this we mean that the image in E' of the $*$-product of any two elements of E equals the $\star$-product in E' of the images in E' of those two elements of E. Similarly, an isomorphism of $\mathcal{S}$ onto $\mathcal{S}'$ is a

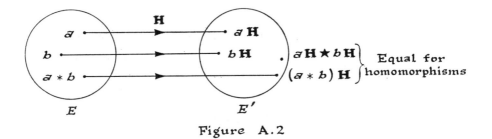

Figure A.2

one-to-one mapping of E onto E' which preserves the operation.

Now consider the more general case of homomorphism of two systems $\mathcal{S}$ and $\mathcal{S}'$, each of which has m relations and n operations. As before, a homomorphism is a mapping of E into E' which preserves the corresponding relations and operations. However, it is not immediately clear what is meant by "corresponding." Suppose we make a one-to-one pairing of the rela-

The following diagram might help to fix in mind the essential points of this theorem.

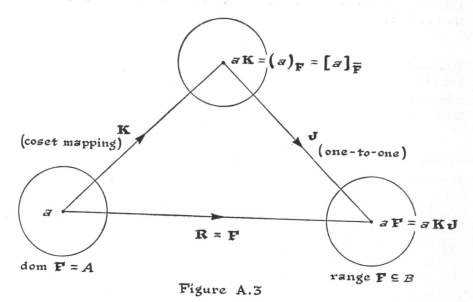

Figure A.3

This analysis of the role of cosets in the theory of mappings takes on special significance when it is applied to homomorphisms of abstract systems. Let $\mathbf{H}$ be a homomorphism of $\mathcal{S} = \{E; *\}$ onto $\mathcal{S}' = \{E'; \star\}$. From the theorem just proved, we know that the $\mathbf{H}$-cosets are equivalence classes which form a partition of E. Let $\overline{E}$ be the collection of the $\mathbf{H}$-cosets of E. The mapping $\mathbf{H}$ can be represented as the successive mappings $\mathbf{KJ}$, where $\mathbf{K}$ maps each $x \in E$ into its $\mathbf{H}$-coset, $[x]_{\mathbf{H}}$, and where $\mathbf{J}$ is the one-to-one mapping of $\overline{E}$ onto E' which assigns to $[x]_{\mathbf{H}}$ the image $x\mathbf{H}$:

$$x \xrightarrow{\ \mathbf{K}\ } [x]_{\mathbf{H}} \xrightarrow{\ \mathbf{J}\ } x\mathbf{H}.$$

But much more can be said; because of the operation which is defined on E, it is possible to define an operation $\bullet$ on $\overline{E}$ by the rule

$$[x]_{\mathbf{H}} \bullet [y]_{\mathbf{H}} = [x * y]_{\mathbf{H}}.$$

It is necessary again to prove that the definition is not ambiguous; that is, to prove that the "product" of two cosets is independent of the choice of representative elements. Suppose $a \in [x]_{\mathbf{H}}$ and $b \in [y]_{\mathbf{H}}$. Then $a\mathbf{H} = x\mathbf{H}$ and $b\mathbf{H} = y\mathbf{H}$. Since $\mathbf{H}$ is a homomorphism,

$$(a * b)\mathbf{H} = a\mathbf{H} \star b\mathbf{H} = x\mathbf{H} \star y\mathbf{H} = (x * y)\mathbf{H}.$$

Hence, $a * b \in [x * y]_{\mathbf{H}}$, and finally $[a * b]_{\mathbf{H}} = [x * y]_{\mathbf{H}}$ because the $\mathbf{H}$-cosets

lations of $\mathcal{S}$ with the relations of $\mathcal{S}'$, and a one-to-one pairing of the operations of $\mathcal{S}$ with the operations of $\mathcal{S}'$; say, $r_i \leftrightarrow r_i'$, $i = 1, \ldots, m$, and $o_j \leftrightarrow o_j'$ $j = 1, \ldots, n$.

Definition A.7.   A *homomorphism* of $\mathcal{S}$ into $\mathcal{S}'$ is a mapping $\mathbf{H}$ of E into E' such that

(a) if $a\, r_i\, b$ in E, then $a\mathbf{H}\, r_i'\, b\mathbf{H}$ in E', $i = 1, \ldots, m$,

(b) $(a\, o_j\, b)\mathbf{H} = a\mathbf{H}\, o_j'\, b\mathbf{H}$ for all $a, b \in E$, $j = 1, \ldots, n$.

If $E' = $ range $\mathbf{H}$, then $\mathbf{H}$ is called a homomorphism of $\mathcal{S}$ *onto* $\mathcal{S}'$. A homomorphism $\mathbf{H}$ of $\mathcal{S}$ onto $\mathcal{S}'$ is called an *isomorphism* if and only if $\mathbf{H}$ is a one-to-one mapping of E onto E'.

Although the notation of (b), above, implicitly assumes that all operations are binary, it is not difficult to formulate a corresponding statement for a homomorphism of systems which have n-ary operations.

§A.7. *Equivalence Relations and Partitions*

Definition A.8.   An *equivalence relation* on a set A is a binary relation $\mathbf{R}$ in A which is reflexive, symmetric, and transitive.

(a) *Reflexive:* $a\, \mathbf{R}\, a$ for every $a \in A$.

(b) *Symmetric:* If $a\, \mathbf{R}\, b$, then $b\, \mathbf{R}\, a$.

(c) *Transitive:* If $a\, \mathbf{R}\, b$ and $b\, \mathbf{R}\, c$, then $a\, \mathbf{R}\, c$.

It follows from (a) that dom $\mathbf{R} = A = $ range $\mathbf{R}$.

We now consider the effect imposed by an equivalence relation $\mathbf{R}$ on a non-void set A. For each $a \in A$ let $[a]_{\mathbf{R}}$ denote the set of all elements which are related to a by $\mathbf{R}$:

$$[a]_{\mathbf{R}} = \{x \in A \mid x\, \mathbf{R}\, a\}.$$

The set $[a]_{\mathbf{R}}$ is called the *equivalence class determined by* a. Since $\mathbf{R}$ is reflexive, $a\, \mathbf{R}\, a$, so $a \in [a]_{\mathbf{R}}$. This implies that the set union of all the equivalence classes equals A. If $b \in [a]_{\mathbf{R}}$, then $b\, \mathbf{R}\, a$, and $a\, \mathbf{R}\, b$ since $\mathbf{R}$ is symmetric. Hence if $b \in [a]_{\mathbf{R}}$, then $a \in [b]_{\mathbf{R}}$. Suppose also that $y \in [b]_{\mathbf{R}}$. Then $y\, \mathbf{R}\, b$ and $b\, \mathbf{R}\, a$, so transitivity implies $y\, \mathbf{R}\, a$; hence $y \in [a]_{\mathbf{R}}$, and $[b]_{\mathbf{R}} \subseteq [a]_{\mathbf{R}}$. By reversing the roles of a and b we obtain $[a]_{\mathbf{R}} \subseteq [b]_{\mathbf{R}}$, so $[b]_{\mathbf{R}} = [a]_{\mathbf{R}}$ whenever $b \in [a]_{\mathbf{R}}$. This implies that two equivalence classes are either equal or have no elements in common.

Therefore, an equivalence relation $\mathbf{R}$ on a set A decomposes A into disjoint subsets, called equivalence classes. Such a decomposition of a set is called a *partition*.

Definition A.9.   A *partition* of a set A is a collection $\mathcal{P}$ of subsets of A, called classes of the partition, such that

(a) if $x \in A$, then $x \in C$ for some $C \in \mathcal{P}$, and

(b) if $C, D \in \mathcal{P}$, then either $C = D$ or $C \cap D = \Phi$.

Now suppose we reverse the situation and start with any partition $\mathcal{P}$ of A. A relation $\mathbf{R}$ can be defined on A by writing $a \mathbf{R} b$ if and only if a and b are in the same class of $\mathcal{P}$. It can be proved as an exercise that $\mathbf{R}$ is an equivalence relation on A for which the equivalence classes are the classes of $\mathcal{P}$. Therefore, each equivalence relation on A determines a partition of A, and, conversely, each partition determines an equivalence relation.

§A.8. *Cosets*

We conclude this discussion of general algebraic concepts with one further notion of widespread applicability in the study of algebraic systems. In doing so we shall discover an intimate connection between mappings, equivalence relations, homomorphisms, and isomorphisms.

Let $\mathbf{R}$ be a relation from A into B, and suppose $A = \operatorname{dom} \mathbf{R}$. We first show how $\mathbf{R}$ can be used to define a relation $\overline{\mathbf{R}}$ in A. Each $a \in A$ is related to one or more $b \in B$. Another element $x \in A$ might also be related to one or more of those same elements of B. With this fact in mind we make the following definition.

Definition A.10.   The $\mathbf{R}$-*coset* of $a \in A$ is the set

$$(a)_{\mathbf{R}} = \{x \in A \mid x \mathbf{R} b \text{ and } a \mathbf{R} b \text{ for some } b \in B\}.$$

We immediately deduce from the definition that

$$a \in (a)_{\mathbf{R}}$$

and

$$x \in (a)_{\mathbf{R}} \text{ if and only if } a \in (x)_{\mathbf{R}}.$$

A relation $\overline{\mathbf{R}}$, which we call the *relation induced in A by the $\mathbf{R}$-cosets*, is defined by writing

$$x \, \overline{\mathbf{R}} \, a, \text{ if and only if } x \in (a)_{\mathbf{R}}.$$

It follows that $\operatorname{dom} \overline{\mathbf{R}} = A = \operatorname{range} \overline{\mathbf{R}}$, and that $\overline{\mathbf{R}}$ is both reflexive and symmetric. In the example illustrated in Figure A.1, we observe that $(a_1)_{\mathbf{R}} = \{a_1, a_2\}$, $(a_2)_{\mathbf{R}} = \{a_1, a_2, a_3\}$, and $(a_3)_{\mathbf{R}} = \{a_2, a_3\}$. This shows that $\overline{\mathbf{R}}$ is not always transitive.

However, suppose that the original relation $\mathbf{R}$ is actually a mapping $\mathbf{F}$, so that each $a \in A$ has a unique image $a\mathbf{F} \in B$. Then the $\mathbf{F}$-coset of a is

$$(a)_{\mathbf{F}} = \{x \in A \mid x\mathbf{F} = a\mathbf{F}\}.$$

Therefore, the relation $\overline{\mathbf{F}}$ induced in A by the $\mathbf{F}$-cosets is characterized by the statement

$$x \, \overline{\mathbf{F}} \, a \text{ if and only if } x\mathbf{F} = a\mathbf{F}.$$

We now prove that this reflexive and symmetric relation is also transitive. Let $y \, \overline{\mathbf{F}} \, x$ and $x \, \overline{\mathbf{F}} \, a$; then $y\mathbf{F} = x\mathbf{F} = a\mathbf{F}$, so $y \, \overline{\mathbf{F}} \, a$. Hence $\overline{\mathbf{F}}$ is an equivalence relation. Furthermore, the $\overline{\mathbf{F}}$-equivalence class which contains a is simply the $\mathbf{F}$-coset of a, for

$$[a]_{\overline{\mathbf{F}}} = \{x \in A \mid x \, \overline{\mathbf{F}} \, a\} = \{x \in A \mid x\mathbf{F} = a\mathbf{F}\} = (a)_{\mathbf{F}}.$$

These results are summarized and an additional fact asserted in the following theorem.

Theorem A.1.   Let $\mathbf{R}$ be a relation from A into B for which $A = \operatorname{dom} \mathbf{R}$, and let $\overline{\mathbf{R}}$ be the relation induced on A by the $\mathbf{R}$-cosets of A. Then $\overline{\mathbf{R}}$ is reflexive and symmetric. If $\mathbf{R}$ is a mapping $\mathbf{F}$, then $\overline{\mathbf{F}}$ is an equivalence relation whose equivalence classes are the $\mathbf{F}$-cosets. Let $\overline{A}$ be the collection of these equivalence classes; there exist a mapping $\mathbf{K}$ from A onto $\overline{A}$ and a one-to-one mapping $\mathbf{J}$ of $\overline{A}$ onto range $\mathbf{F} \subseteq B$ such that

$$\mathbf{F} = \mathbf{KJ}.$$

PROOF: To verify the last sentence of the theorem we define the mapping $\mathbf{K}$ from A onto $\overline{A}$ as follows:

$$\mathbf{K}: \qquad a \longrightarrow [a]_{\overline{\mathbf{F}}}.$$

$\mathbf{K}$ maps each $a \in \operatorname{dom} \mathbf{F}$ into the equivalence class ($\mathbf{F}$-coset) of all elements x for which $x\mathbf{F} = a\mathbf{F}$. The mapping $\mathbf{J}$ of $\overline{A}$ onto range $\mathbf{F}$ is defined by

$$\mathbf{J}: \qquad [a]_{\overline{\mathbf{F}}} \longrightarrow a\mathbf{F}.$$

It is necessary now to consider an important technical point: the description just given as a definition of the mapping $\mathbf{J}$ is open to criticism, since the $\mathbf{J}$-image of the equivalence class $[a]_{\overline{\mathbf{F}}}$ was specified as $a\mathbf{F}$, the $\mathbf{F}$-image of one of the members of $[a]_{\overline{\mathbf{F}}}$. At first glance it appears that this definition might be ambiguous, because different members of $[a]_{\overline{\mathbf{F}}}$ might have different $\mathbf{F}$-images in B. But $x \in [a]_{\overline{\mathbf{F}}}$ if and only if $x\mathbf{F} = a\mathbf{F}$, which shows that all members of $[a]_{\overline{\mathbf{F}}}$ do have the same $\mathbf{F}$-image. Hence, $\mathbf{J}$ is properly defined, after all.

To prove that $\mathbf{J}$ is one-to-one, suppose $[a]_{\overline{\mathbf{F}}}\mathbf{J} = [b]_{\overline{\mathbf{F}}}\mathbf{J}$. Then $a\mathbf{F} = b\mathbf{F}$, so $b \in [a]_{\overline{\mathbf{F}}}$. But two equivalence classes which are not disjoint must be equal, so $[a]_{\overline{\mathbf{F}}} = [b]_{\overline{\mathbf{F}}}$. Finally, $a\mathbf{K} = [a]_{\overline{\mathbf{F}}}$, and $a\mathbf{KJ} = [a]_{\overline{\mathbf{F}}}\mathbf{J} = a\mathbf{F}$, so $\mathbf{KJ} = \mathbf{F}$.

form a partition of E. Therefore, the operation $\bullet$ is properly defined on $\overline{E}$, and $\overline{S} = \{\overline{E}; \bullet\}$ is an abstract system.

Now consider the mapping $\mathbf{K}$ of E onto $\overline{E}$. We have

$$(x * y)\mathbf{K} = [x * y]_\mathrm{H} = [x]_\mathrm{H} \bullet [y]_\mathrm{H} = x\mathbf{K} \bullet y\mathbf{K}.$$

Hence $\mathbf{K}$ is a homomorphism of S onto $\overline{S}$. Likewise, the one-to-one mapping $\mathbf{J}$ of $\overline{E}$ onto E' preserves the corresponding operation:

$$([x]_\mathrm{H} \bullet [y]_\mathrm{H})\mathbf{J} = [x * y]_\mathrm{H}\mathbf{J} = (x * y)\mathbf{H} = x\mathbf{H} \star y\mathbf{H} = [x]_\mathrm{H}\mathbf{J} \star [y]_\mathrm{H}\mathbf{J}.$$

Therefore $\mathbf{J}$ is an isomorphism of the systems $\overline{S}$ and S'.

> **Fundamental Isomorphism Theorem.** Let $\mathbf{H}$ be a homomorphism of the system $S = \{E; *\}$ onto the system $S' = \{E'; \star\}$. Then a product $\bullet$ can be defined on the set $\overline{E}$ of $\mathbf{H}$-cosets such that
>
> (a) there exists a mapping $\mathbf{K}$ which is a homomorphism of the system S onto the system $\overline{S} = \{\overline{E}; \bullet\}$,
>
> (b) there exists a mapping $\mathbf{J}$ which is an isomorphism of the system $\overline{S}$ onto the system S',
>
> (c) $\mathbf{H} = \mathbf{KJ}$.

Finally, we remark that no specific properties of any of the systems were assumed, and therefore the preceding theorem is extremely general. In various applications the system $\overline{S}$ of cosets is called the *factor-system, quotient-system,* or *difference-system* of S.

Exercises

1. If S_i is a set of m_i elements, for $i = 1, 2, \ldots, n$, how many elements are in the set $S_1 \times S_2 \times \ldots \times S_n$?

2. How many different binary relations can be defined in a set of n elements?

3. Describe the number pairs which comprise each of the following relations.

    (i) The order relation $<$ for real numbers.

    (ii) The order relation $\geq$ for real numbers.

    (iii) The relation "a divides b evenly" for integers.

    (iv) The relation "a divides b evenly" for positive integers.

4. Since the void set Φ and $A \times A$ are subsets of $A \times A$, each represents a relation in A. Describe each of these two relations.

5. By recalling the definition of a function in terms of sets, state what it means for two functions to be equal.

6. Consider the function F of two real variables defined by
$$F(x, y) = x\sqrt{1 - y}\,\sin(x + y).$$
Show how this function is described by Definition A.3.   Specify the domain and range of F.

7. Let R be the set of all real numbers.   Give a specific example of a function F from R to R for each of the following conditions.

(i) dom $F \subset R$, range $F \subset R$.

(ii) dom $F = R$, range $F \subset R$, F one-to-one.

(iii) dom $F \subset R$, range $F = R$, F not one-to-one.

(iv) dom $F = R$, range $F = R$, F not one-to-one.

(v) dom $F = R$, range $F = R$, F one-to-one.

8. Explain how a closed binary operation on a set S can be considered as a subset of $S \times S \times S$, having special properties.   List all properties needed to make your description precise.

9. How many closed binary operations can be defined on a set having n elements?

10. Let R be the set of real numbers, described geometrically by a coordinate axis.   State what you mean by a graph of each of the following, listing any special restrictions you need to make your description accurate.

(i) A binary relation on R.

(ii) A function from R to R.

(iii) A closed binary operation on R.

11. Consider the system $\{E; \odot\}$ where E is the set of three symbols, $\{-, \S, /\}$ and where $\odot$ is defined in the table below by the rule that $x \odot y$ is the symbol in the row which is labeled x at the left and in the column which is labeled y at the top.

$\odot$	$-$	$\S$	$/$
$-$	$-$	$\S$	$/$
$\S$	$\S$	$/$	$-$
$/$	$/$	$-$	$\S$

Show that this system is a commutative group as defined in § 1.5.

12. Discuss whatever similarities and distinctions you can detect between the systems of Exercise 11 and the group of Exercise 1 (i), § 1.5.

13. Determine whether each of the following mappings is a homomorphism, an isomorphism, or neither.

(i) The mapping $m \longrightarrow 2m$ of the additive group of integers into the additive group of even integers.

(ii) The mapping $a \longrightarrow 1/a$ of the multiplicative group of non-zero real numbers into the additive group of real numbers.

(iii) The mapping $a \longrightarrow 1/a^2$ of the multiplicative group of non-zero real numbers into the multiplicative group of positive real numbers.

14. Referring to Exercise 9, § 1.5, show by the mapping

$$(a, b) \longrightarrow a + ib$$

that $\{C; +, \bullet\}$ is isomorphic to the field of complex numbers.

15. Show that the additive group of real numbers is mapped homomorphically onto the multiplicative group of all complex numbers which lie on the unit circle by the mapping

$$x \longrightarrow \cos x + i \sin x.$$

16. Let $\mathcal{G} = \{G; *\}$ be any group, and let $\mathcal{I}$ be the additive group of the integers. For any fixed $g \in G$ show that the mapping

$$n \to g * g * g * \ldots * g \ (n \text{ times})$$

is a homomorphism of $\mathcal{I}$ into $\mathcal{G}$. Is this mapping a homomorphism of $\mathcal{I}$ onto $\mathcal{G}$?

17. Let **H** be a homomorphism of $\mathcal{S} = \{E; *\}$ onto $\mathcal{S}' = \{E'; \star\}$.

(i) Prove that if $\mathcal{S}$ has an identity element i, then $\mathcal{S}'$ must have an identity element i', and that $i' = i\mathbf{H}$.

(ii) Prove that if $a \in E$ has an inverse b, then $a\mathbf{H}$ has an inverse which must be $b\mathbf{H}$.

18. Is the additive group of all real numbers isomorphic to the multiplicative group of all positive real numbers? Explain.

19. Refer to Exercise 3, § 1.5, where the mappings $\mathbf{R}_g$ are defined for any group $\mathcal{G} = \{G; *\}$. The product $\mathbf{R}_{g_1} \odot \mathbf{R}_{g_2}$ of two such mappings is defined as the mapping which results when $\mathbf{R}_{g_1}$ is followed by $\mathbf{R}_{g_2}$. Let $R_G = \{\mathbf{R}_g | g \in G\}$.

(i) Show that $\{R_G; \odot\}$ is a group.

(ii) Show that the mapping $g \longrightarrow \mathbf{R}_g$ is an isomorphism of $\{G; *\}$ onto $\{R_G; \odot\}$, thus proving *Cayley's Theorem*: Every group is isomorphic to a transformation group.

20. Given a symmetric and transitive relation **R** in a set A. Is **R** reflexive? Distinguish between the cases dom $\mathbf{R} = A$ and dom $\mathbf{R} \subset A$.

21. Let I be the set of all positive integers. For any fixed $n \in I$ we define on I the relation *congruence modulo n* by writing

$$a \equiv b(\bmod n)$$

if and only if $a - b$ is divisible by n.

(i) Prove that this is an equivalence relation on I.

(ii) Prove that if $a \equiv b(\bmod n)$ and if $c \equiv d(\bmod n)$, then

$$a + c \equiv b + d(\bmod n) \quad \text{and} \quad ac \equiv bd(\bmod n).$$

(iii) Show by an example that if $c \not\equiv 0(\bmod n)$ and if $ac \equiv bc(\bmod n)$, it does not necessarily follow that $a \equiv b(\bmod n)$.

22. Consider the points of a plane P as described in a rectangular coordinate system by pairs of real numbers, and let m be a fixed real number. Define on P the relation **M** as follows:

$$(x_1, y_1)\mathbf{M}(x_2, y_2) \text{ if and only if } y_1 - y_2 = m(x_1 - x_2).$$

(i) Prove that **M** is an equivalence relation.

(ii) Describe geometrically the equivalence classes of **M**.

23. Given a partition $\mathcal{P}$ of a set A. Show, as indicated in the text, that a corresponding equivalence relation **R** can be defined on A such that the equivalence classes of **R** are the classes of the partition $\mathcal{P}$.

24. Let $E(n)$ denote the number of different partitions which can be defined on a set of n identical objects.

(i) Evaluate $E(n)$ for $n = 1, 2, 3, 4$.

(ii) Relate $E(n)$ to the number of different ways the integer n may be written as the sum of positive integers in non-increasing order; e.g.,

$$5 = 3 + 2 = 3 + 1 + 1 = 4 + 1 \text{ and so on.}$$

25. Describe the **R**-cosets of each of the following relations.

(i) The order relation $<$ for real numbers.

(ii) The relation "a divides b" for positive integers.

(iii) The relation "L_1 is perpendicular to L_2" for lines of the plane.

26. Let S be the set of all humans living at a given instant, and let **F** be the age function, $s\mathbf{F}$ being the age in years of s on his most recent birthday. Describe the **F**-cosets.

27. Refer to the relation **R** of congruence modulo n, as defined for integers in Exercise 21.

(i) Describe the **R**-cosets.

(ii) Let I_n denote the collection of these cosets, which we denote by $(0)_n, (1)_n, \ldots, (n - 1)_n$. We define on I_n two operations:

$$(a)_n \oplus (b)_n = (a + b)_n,$$

$$(a)_n \odot (b)_n = (ab)_n.$$

Verify that these operations are unambiguously defined.

(iii) Show that the system $\mathcal{J}_n = \{I_n; \oplus\}$ is a commutative group.

(iv) Show that the system $\mathcal{J}_n = \{I_n; \oplus, \odot\}$ is a field if and only if n is prime.

(v) Show that the mapping **H** of the integers onto $\mathcal{J}_n$ is a homomorphism, where **H** is defined by

$$x\mathbf{H} = [a]_n \text{ if and only if } x \equiv a(\mathrm{mod}\ n),\ a = 0, \ldots, n - 1.$$

28. Let $\mathcal{S} = \{E; *\}$ be a group whose identity is denoted i, and let **H** be a homomorphism of $\mathcal{S}$ onto $\mathcal{S}' = \{E'; \star\}$. From Exercise 17 we know that $i\mathbf{H}$ is the identity of $\mathcal{S}'$. The **H**-coset $(i)_{\mathbf{H}}$ is called the *kernel* of **H**. Prove that **H** is an isomorphism if and only if the kernel of **H** has i as its only element.

APPENDIX B

Combinatorial Equivalence

Within the past decade a great deal of attention has been given to developing better methods of solving large systems of linear equations and inequalities, a problem which was technically inaccessible before the advent of high speed computers. Among such methods, the simplex method devised by G. B. Dantzig is remarkably effective and has become a basic tool of the rapidly developing theory of linear programming. In a recent analysis of the simplex method, A. W. Tucker has introduced the concept of *combinatorial equivalence* of matrices, which is essentially different from other equivalence relations studied in Chapters 6 and 9.

Combinatorial equivalence of matrices is based on the pivot operation which was described in § 5.5. We recall that pivot operations can be used to solve a system of m equations in n unknowns,

$$y_1 = a_{11}x_1 + a_{12}x_2 + \ldots + a_{1n}x_n$$
$$y_2 = a_{21}x_1 + a_{22}x_2 + \ldots + a_{2n}x_n$$
$$\cdot \qquad \cdot \qquad \cdot \qquad \qquad \cdot$$
$$\cdot \qquad \cdot \qquad \cdot \qquad \qquad \cdot$$
$$\cdot \qquad \cdot \qquad \cdot \qquad \qquad \cdot$$
$$y_m = a_{m1}x_1 + a_{m2}x_2 + \ldots + a_{mn}x_n,$$

which can be written in matrix form as

$$Y = AX,$$

or in block form as

$$(-I|A)\left(\frac{Y}{X}\right) = Z,$$

where I is $m \times m$, A is $m \times n$, Y is $m \times 1$, X is $n \times 1$, and Z is the $m \times 1$ zero matrix.

If we solve the ith equation for x_j and substitute the resulting expression for x_j in the remaining equations, we obtain an equivalent system in the form

$$y_1 = a_{ij}^{-1} [\quad b_{11}x_1 + \ldots + a_{1j}y_i + \ldots + b_{1n}x_n]$$

$$x_j = a_{ij}^{-1} [-a_{i1}x_1 - \ldots + \quad 1\, y_i - \ldots - a_{in}x_n]$$

$$y_m = a_{ij}^{-1} [\quad b_{m1}x_1 + \ldots + a_{mj}y_i + \ldots + b_{mn}x_n].$$

In matrix form the new system becomes

$$V = BU,$$

where V and U coincide with X and Y except that y_i and x_j have been interchanged, and where the element in the (r, s) position of B is

$$
\begin{aligned}
&a_{ij}^{-1} [a_{rs}a_{ij} - a_{rj}a_{is}], &&\text{if } r \neq i \text{ and } s \neq j, \\
&a_{ij}^{-1} [a_{rj}], &&\text{if } r \neq i \text{ and } s = j, \\
&a_{ij}^{-1} [-a_{is}], &&\text{if } r = i \text{ and } s \neq j, \\
&a_{ij}^{-1} [1], &&\text{if } r = i \text{ and } s = j.
\end{aligned}
$$

This equation can be written in block form as

$$(-I|B) \left(\frac{V}{U}\right) = Z.$$

If this pivot operation is repeated, each time interchanging a different x with an appropriate y, until either all the x's appear on the left or else all the y's appear on the right, the solution of the system is obtained. Each stage of the process produces a system of equations whose coefficient matrix is obtained from the previous matrix by a pivot operation. This fact is the motivation for the following definition.

Definition B.1. Let A and B be two $m \times n$ matrices. B is said to be *combinatorially equivalent* to A if and only if B can be obtained from A by a finite sequence of pivot operations on non-zero elements.

We shall denote by A_{ij}^* the matrix which results from a pivot operation on A with a_{ij} as pivot. Clearly, it is necessary that $a_{ij} \neq 0$. We recall from § 6.2 that the symbol P_{ij} denotes the elementary matrix obtained by permuting rows i and j of I. It is important to observe that a permutation of two rows (or two columns) of a matrix can be performed by a succession of pivot operations.

Theorem B.1.

$$[(A_{ij}^*)_{kj}^*]_{ij}^* = P_{ik}A, \text{ if } k \neq i;$$

$$[(A_{ij}^*)_{ik}^*]_{ij}^* = AP_{kj}, \text{ if } k \neq j.$$

P R O O F : See Exercise 2 (iv) and (v).

Since a succession of three pivot operations is unnecessarily complicated as a method of performing a simple interchange of two rows or two columns, we should observe that a matrix B is combinatorially equivalent to A if and only if B can be obtained from A by a finite succession of row permutations, column permutations, and pivot operations. In the problem of solving a system of linear equations, row and column permutations merely amount to permutations within each set of variables.

Theorem B.2. Combinatorial equivalence is an equivalence relation on the set of all $m \times n$ matrices.

P R O O F : Clearly the relation of combinatorial equivalence is reflexive and transitive. But by Exercise 2 (i)

$$(A_{ij}^*)_{ij}^* = A,$$

which implies that the relation is symmetric as well.

Thus, just as elementary row operations led to the concept of row equivalence, pivot operations induce combinatorial equivalence. However, whereas all of the equivalence relations previously studied for matrices determine equivalence classes containing infinitely many matrices, we shall see later that only a finite number of matrices are combinatorially equivalent to any given matrix.

In the next theorem we establish a matric characterization of combinatorial equivalence which is more convenient to apply than the formal definition and which leads directly to other characterizations.

Theorem B.3. B is combinatorially equivalent to A if and only if there exist an $(m + n) \times (m + n)$ permutation matrix P and an $m \times m$ non-singular matrix Q such that

$$Q(-I|A)P = (-I|B).$$

P R O O F : By a permutation matrix P we mean a product of elementary permutation matrices P_{ij}. Beginning with the matrix $(-I|A)$, let i and j be fixed such that $a_{ij} \neq 0$. Perform the following operations in succession: for each $k \neq i$ multiply row k by a_{ij}; for each $k \neq i$ add $-a_{kj}$ times row i to row k; permute column i and column $j + m$; multiply each row by a_{ij}^{-1}. Finally, multiply row i by -1. It can be verified that the result is $(-I|A_{ij}^*)$. Since all these row operations are elementary and since the only column operation is a permutation, we have

$$Q_0(-I|A)P_{i,j+m} = (-I|A_{ij}^*)$$

for some non-singular Q_0. Thus any pivot operation on A can be performed by premultiplying $(-I|A)$ by some non-singular matrix and postmultiplying by some elementary permutation matrix. A finite succession of pivots on A can be performed by premultiplying $(-I|A)$ by a suitable non-singular matrix and postmultiplying by a suitable permutation matrix. Thus if B is combinatorially equivalent to A, then for suitable Q, P,

$$Q(-I|A)P = (-I|B).$$

Conversely, suppose this last equation holds for some non-singular matrix Q and some permutation matrix P. Write P as a product of elementary permutation matrices, P_{rs}. Since

$$P_{rs} = P_{sr},$$

each such matrix is in exactly one of the following three forms:

1. if $r \leq m < s$, $P_{rs} = P_{i,j+m}$,
2. if $r,s \leq m$, $\quad P_{rs} = P_{ij}$,
3. if $m < r,s$, $\quad P_{rs} = P_{i+m, j+m}$,

where $i, j \leq m$. Concentrating on the first such elementary permutation matrix, P_{rs}, we write

$$Q(-I|A)P = Q(-I|A)P_{rs}\hat{P},$$

and we consider separately the three possibilities listed above.

1. If P_{rs} is of the form $P_{i,j+m}$, we use the first part of this proof, letting Q_0 be the non-singular matrix which performs the row operations needed for a pivot on some $a_{ij} \neq 0$;

$$Q(-I|A)P = QQ_0^{-1}[Q_0(-I|A)P_{i,j+m}]\hat{P}$$
$$= QQ_0^{-1}[(-I|A_{ij}^*)]\hat{P}.$$

2. If P_{rs} is of the form P_{ij}, where $i, j \leq m$, we write

$$Q(-I|A)P = QP_{ij}^{-1}[P_{ij}(-I|A)P_{ij}]\hat{P}$$
$$= QP_{ij}^{-1}[(-I|P_{ij}A)]\hat{P}.$$

We recall that $P_{ij}A$ is combinatorially equivalent to A, since P_{ij} as a premultiplier merely permutes rows i and j.

3. If P_{rs} is of the form $P_{i+m,j+m}$, we write

$$Q(-I|A)P = Q[(-I|A)P_{i+m,j+m}]\hat{P}$$
$$= Q[(-I|AP_{ij})]\hat{P}.$$

Again, AP_{ij} is combinatorially equivalent to A.

Hence in each case the result is

$$Q(-I|A)P = \hat{Q}(-I|C)\hat{P},$$

where $\hat{Q}$ is non-singular, $\hat{P}$ is a product of one fewer P_{ij} than is P, and C is combinatorially equivalent to A. After exhausting the factors of $\hat{P}$ in this way, we have

$$(-I|B) = Q(-I|A)P = R(-I|D) = (-RI|RD),$$

where D is combinatorially equivalent to A. But then $I = RI$ and $B = RD$. Hence $B = D$, so B is combinatorially equivalent to A. This completes the proof of Theorem B.3.

It is helpful to compare Theorem B.3 with Theorem 6.12.

Theorem B.4. B is combinatorially equivalent to A if and only if some permutation of the columns of $(-I|A)$ produces the matrix $(-G|H)$, where G is $m \times m$ and non-singular and $GB = H$.

P R O O F :   Suppose $Q(-I|A)P = (-I|B)$, and let $(-I|A)P = (-G|H)$. Then $(-QG|QH) = (-I|B)$, so $I = QG$ and $B = QH = G^{-1}H$. Conversely, if G, H exist as stated, then $(-I|A)P = (-G|H) = (-G|GB)$ for some permutation matrix P. Then $G^{-1}(-I|A)P = (-I|B)$.

There are $(m + n)!$ possible permutations of the columns of $(-I|A)$, not all of which necessarily produce a non-singular G in the first m columns. But for each P, $(-I|A)P$ is row equivalent to a uniquely determined matrix in reduced echelon form. Thus Q is uniquely determined by A and P such that $Q(-I|A)P$ is in reduced echelon form. This may or may not have the form $(-I|B)$ for some B.

Theorem B.5.   There are at most $(m + n)!$ matrices which are combinatorially equivalent to A; this maximal number is achieved if and only if every set of m columns of $(-I|A)$ is linearly independent.

P R O O F :   Our previous remarks show that each of the $(m + n)!$ permutations of the columns of $(-I|A)$ determines at most one matrix which is combinatorially equivalent to A. If every set of m columns of $(-I|A)$ is linearly independent, then each permutation determines a non-singular matrix G as in Theorem B.4. Then A is combinatorially equivalent to $G^{-1}H$. If there exists a set of m linearly dependent columns of $(-I|A)$, let P be the permutation which places these columns in the first m columns of $(-I|A)P$. Since linear dependence of columns is preserved by row operations, the reduced echelon form of $(-I|A)P$ has linearly dependent columns in the first m positions and hence is not of the form $(-I|B)$.

Theorem B.6. B is combinatorially equivalent to A if and only if the systems of linear equations

$$AX = Y,$$
$$BU = V$$

are equivalent, where the set of variables $\{v_1, \ldots, v_m, u_1, \ldots, u_n\}$ is some permutation of the variables $\{y_1, \ldots, y_m, x_1, \ldots, x_n\}$.

PROOF: If B is combinatorially equivalent to A, then $(-I|A)P$ is row equivalent to $(-I|B)$. Hence the systems

$$(-I|A)P\left(\frac{Y}{X}\right) = Z$$

and

$$(-I|B)\left(\frac{V}{U}\right) = Z$$

are equivalent. Conversely, if these systems are equivalent for some permutation P of the variables,

$$P\left(\frac{Y}{X}\right) = \left(\frac{V}{U}\right),$$

their matrices are row equivalent, so $Q(-I|A)P = (-I|B)$.

Theorem B.7. If A is non singular, A and A^{-1} are combinatorially equivalent.

PROOF: $AX = Y$ and $X = A^{-1}Y$ are equivalent systems.

This implies, of course, that A^{-1} can be computed by a sequence of pivot operations. Since the number of such operations need not exceed the dimension n of A, and since each pivot can be performed by $n^2 - n$ multiplications and n divisions, A^{-1} can be computed by n^3 or fewer multiplications and divisions.

Theorem B.8. B is combinatorially equivalent to A if and only if $-B'$ is combinatorially equivalent to $-A'$.

PROOF: As an exercise you may verify that

$$-(A_{ij}^*)' = (-A')_{ji}^*.$$

Thus any pivot operation on A produces a matrix whose negative transpose is combinatorially equivalent to $-A'$. The remainder of the proof follows easily from this fact.

Finally we remark that the statement of Theorem B.8 would not be valid if either the negative signs or the transpose signs were omitted. This essential combination of negative and transpose expresses a form of duality which is important in the theory of games and linear programming.

Exercises

1. Use Theorem B.3 to prove that combinatorial equivalence is an equivalence relation.

2. Let A_{ij}^* denote the matrix derived from A by a pivot operation on the (i, j) element of A. Prove the following statements:

    (i) $(A_{ij}^*)_{ij}^* = A$.

    (ii) $(A_{ij}^*)_{kj}^* = P_{ik} A_{kj}^*$,   if $k \neq i$.

    (iii) $(A_{ij}^*)_{ik}^* = A_{ik}^* P_{jk}$,   if $k \neq j$.

    (iv) $((A_{ij}^*)_{kj}^*)_{ij}^* = P_{ik} A$, if $k \neq i$.

    (v) $((A_{ij}^*)_{ik}^*)_{ij}^* = A P_{kj}$, if $k \neq j$.

3. (i) Write out all matrices which are combinatorially equivalent to

$$A = \begin{pmatrix} 2 & 5 \\ 0 & 3 \end{pmatrix}.$$

By Theorem B.5 there are at most 24 (actually 20) such matrices, which can be computed by four pivot operations together with row and column permutations.

    (ii) Verify that A^{-1} is in the list.

4. Calculate the inverse of each matrix of Exercise 1, § 6.3, by means of pivot operations.

5. Verify in detail the statements in the proof of Theorem B.8.

References

The references given here are intended as a guide for undergraduate students, with no pretense of completeness. In the hope that readers will make a habit of consulting the literature freely, these references are classified somewhat arbitrarily into three categories: introductory *textbooks* on matrices and vector spaces, which roughly parallel the content of this book; supplementary *treatises* on matrices and abstract algebra; books which discuss *applications* of matrices. References to important journal articles can be found in some of these volumes and by consulting *Mathematical Reviews*.

Textbooks

1. Birkhoff, G. and MacLane, S., *A Survey of Modern Algebra*, Revised edition. New York: Macmillan Co., 1953.
2. Halmos, P. R., *Finite Dimensional Vector Spaces*, Second edition. Princeton: D. Van Nostrand Co., Inc., 1958.
3. Hohn, Franz E., *Elementary Matrix Algebra*. New York: Macmillan Co., 1958.
4. MacDuffee, C. C., *Vectors and Matrices*. Mathematical Association of America, 1943.
5. Murdoch, D. C., *Linear Algebra for the Undergraduate*. New York: John Wiley and Sons, Inc., 1957.
6. Perlis, S., *The Theory of Matrices*. Cambridge, Mass.: Addison-Wesley Press, Inc., 1952.
7. Stoll, R. R., *Linear Algebra and Matrix Theory*. New York: McGraw-Hill Book Company, Inc., 1952.
8. Thrall, R. M. and Tornheim, L., *Vector Spaces and Matrices*. New York: John Wiley and Sons, Inc., 1957.

Treatises

9. Aitken, A. C., *Determinants and Matrices*. New York: Interscience Publishers, 1954.
10. Artin, E., *Galois Theory*, Second edition. University of Notre Dame, 1944.
11. Bodewig, E., *Matrix Calculus*. Amsterdam: North Holland Publishing Company, 1956.

12. Frazer, R. A., Duncan, W. J., and Collar, A. R., *Elementary Matrices*. Cambridge: Cambridge University Press, 1938.

13. Halmos, P. R., *Introduction to Hilbert Space*, New York: Chelsea Publishing Company, 1951.

14. Jacobson, N., *Lectures in Abstract Algebra*, volume II. New York: D. Van Nostrand Company, 1953.

15. MacDuffee, C. C., *The Theory of Matrices*. New York: Chelsea Publishing Company, 1946.

16. Schreier, O. and Sperner, E., *Vorlesungen über Matrizen*. Leipzig: Teubner, 1932.

17. Turnbull, H. W. and Aiken, A. C., *An Introduction to the Theory of Canonical Matrices*. Glasgow: Blackie and Son, Ltd., 1932.

18. Wedderburn, J. H. M., *Lectures on Matrices*. New York: American Mathematical Society, 1934.

Applications

19. Beckenbach, E. F. (editor), *Modern Mathematics for the Engineer*. New York: McGraw-Hill Book Company, Inc., 1956.

20. Feller, W., *An Introduction to Probability Theory and its Applications*. New York: John Wiley and Sons, Inc., 1957.

21. Higman, Bryan, *Applied Group-Theoretic and Matrix Methods*. London: Oxford University Press, 1955.

22. Kemeny, J. G., Snell, J. L., and Thompson, G. L., *Finite Mathematics*. Englewood Cliffs: Prentice-Hall, Inc., 1957.

23. König, D., *Theorie der Endlichen und Unendlichen Graphen*. Leipzig: Academische verlagsgesellschaft, 1936.

24. Margenau, H. and Murphy, G. M., *The Mathematics of Physics and Chemistry*, Second edition. Princeton: D. Van Nostrand Company, Inc., 1956.

Suggestions and Answers for Selected Exercises

CHAPTER 1

§ **1.1.** 1. (i) Let $\mathcal{K}$ represent the club, and let x and y represent any two distinct members of $\mathcal{K}$, as guaranteed by (a). By (c) there is a committee C to which x and y belong. By (d) there is a member z of $\mathcal{K}$ who does not serve on C. Now finish the proof by using (c) again.

(ii) Let C be any committee and let x be any member of C. Use (d) and (e) to obtain a student y not on C, and a committee C_1 which has no members in common with C. By (c) x and y serve on a uniquely determined committee C_2, and by (d) some student z does not serve on C_2. Then y and z determine a committee C_3. Now consider the possibilities of C and C_3 having a member in common; to complete the proof you will have to construct a C_4 also.

§ **1.2.** 1. (i) There are 16 distinct subsets.
(ii) 2^m.
5. (i) The set of all points with integral coordinates.
6. (ii) m^2.
7. Use Exercises 1 (ii) and 6 (ii).
9. (v) Yes.
10. (ii) $n(A \cup B \cup C) = n(A) + n(B) + n(C) - n(A \cap B)$
$$- n(A \cap C) - n(B \cap C) + n(A \cap B \cap C).$$

§ **1.3.** 1. (i) dom $\mathbf{FG} \subseteq$ dom $\mathbf{F} \subseteq S$; range $\mathbf{FG}$ = range $\mathbf{G} \subseteq U$.

§ **1.4.** 1. (i) Show that if both e and i are identities relative to $*$, then $e = i$.
(ii) Let $\bar{x}$ and x' be inverses of x, and consider $\bar{x} * (x * x')$.
4. (i) Yes.
(ii) Yes.
(iii) No.

§ **1.5.** 4. First show that $\bar{x}$ is also a left inverse of x; then show that e is also a left identity.

6. Consider $90°$ rotations about two axes, performed in each of the two possible orders.

7.   (i) Consider $a \odot (o \oplus i)$.

(ii) Consider $[(-a) \odot b] \oplus (a \odot b)$, and use (i).

(iii) Consider $b^{-1} \odot [-(b) \odot (-b)^{-1}]$, and use (ii).

8. Show that the operations are closed and that the field postulates are satisfied.

CHAPTER 2

§ 2.1.   2. Only (v) and (x) form groups.

§ 2.2.   2. The space of all real n-tuples is isomorphic to the space of all real polynomials of degree not exceeding $n - 1$.

4. No.   Why not?

5. Yes; yes; no; yes; no.

§ 2.3.   1. Yes; no; yes; no; yes; yes; yes; no; yes; yes.

2. (iii) Not a group.

3. $\mathcal{S} \cap \mathfrak{I} = [(-3, 1, 5)]$.

4. Let $\xi = \sigma + \tau = \sigma' + \tau'$.   Then $\theta = \sigma - \sigma' + \tau - \tau'$, where $\sigma - \sigma' \in \mathcal{S}$, since $\mathcal{S}$ is a subspace.   This equation implies that $\sigma - \sigma' \in \mathfrak{I}$.   Hence $\sigma - \sigma' = \theta$, and similarly for $\tau - \tau'$.   Conversely, if $\eta \in \mathcal{S} \cap \mathfrak{I}$, write $\eta = \theta + \eta = \eta + \theta$, which expresses η in two ways as a sum of a vector in $\mathcal{S}$ and a vector in $\mathfrak{I}$.

7. Let $\xi \in (\mathfrak{R} + \mathcal{S}) \cap \mathfrak{I}$ and write $\xi = \rho + \sigma$, where $\rho \in \mathfrak{R}$, and $\sigma \in \mathcal{S}$.   Prove that $\xi \in (\mathfrak{R} \cap \mathfrak{I}) + (\mathcal{S} \cap \mathfrak{I})$, and finally use the result of Exercise 6.

§ 2.4.   2. The number of vectors in a maximal linearly independent subset for each part is

(i) three;

(ii) four;

(iii) two.

§ 2.5.   5. $\epsilon_1 = \alpha_1 - \alpha_2,\ \epsilon_2 = \alpha_2 - \alpha_3,\ \epsilon_3 = \alpha_3 - \alpha_4,\ \epsilon_4 = \alpha_4$.

§ 2.6.   2. (a) n.

(b) 0.

(c) 1.

(d) $n + 1$.

(e) Infinite.

4. (i) Choose a basis $\{\alpha_1, \ldots, \alpha_k\}$ for $\mathcal{S}$; extend to a basis $\{\alpha_1, \ldots, \alpha_n\}$ for $\mathcal{V}$, and let $\mathfrak{I} = [\alpha_{k+1}, \ldots, \alpha_n]$.

5. Use Theorem 2.13 and Exercise 6, § 2.3.

§ 2.7.   1. Map $a_0 x^n + a_1 x^{n-1} + \ldots + a_n$ onto the $(n + 1)$-tuple

$$(a_0, a_1, \ldots, a_n).$$

CHAPTER 3

§ 3.1. 4. Write $\theta = \alpha + (-\alpha)$.

8. Only (ii) and (iv) are linear.

10. (ii) No.

(iii) Show that **MD** − **DM** maps any polynomial into itself.

(iv) Consider **D(MD** − **DM)M**.

§ 3.2. 1. (i) Let $\xi = \sum\limits_{i=1}^{m} a_i \alpha_i$ and $\eta = \sum\limits_{j=1}^{m} b_j \alpha_j$; calculate $\xi\eta$.

2. (i) Calculate $(a_1 1 + a_2 i + a_3 j + a_4 k)(b_1 1 + b_2 i + b_3 j + b_4 k)$.

(ii) Try $(a_1 1 - a_2 i - a_3 j - a_4 k)$ as an inverse of $(a_1 1 + a_2 i + a_3 j + a_4 k)$.

§ 3.3. 1. If $\xi \in \mathcal{R}_{TS}$, then $\xi = \eta TS$ for some $\eta \in \mathcal{V}$. Hence $\xi = \alpha S$, where $\alpha = \eta T \in \mathcal{W}$. Hence $\xi \in \mathcal{R}_S$.

3. (i) Show that $\mathcal{R}_{T+S} \subseteq \mathcal{R}_T + \mathcal{R}_S$ and then use Theorem 2.13.

(iii) Choose a basis $\{\alpha_1, \ldots, \alpha_k\}$ for $\mathfrak{N}_T$; extend to a basis $\{\alpha_1, \ldots, \alpha_m\}$ for $\mathfrak{N}_{TS}$, and show that $\{\alpha_{k+1}T, \ldots, \alpha_m T\}$ is a basis for the space $\mathfrak{N}_{TS}T$. Finally, observe that $\mathfrak{N}_{TS}T \subseteq \mathfrak{N}_S$, and complete the proof.

6. If $\rho(T) = 1$, each $\xi \in \mathcal{V}$ is mapped into a scalar multiple of some fixed vector $\alpha \cdot \xi T = k_\xi \alpha$, where k_ξ depends upon ξ. Choose $c = k_\mu$.

§ 3.4. 3. $ad \neq bc$.

§ 3.5. 1. (iii) $(a, b)T = (-a - b, -a + b)$.

(iv) $\beta_1 T = -2\beta_1 + 2\beta_2$

$\beta_2 T = -1\beta_1 + 2\beta_2$.

2. (ii) $\alpha_1 S = \alpha_1 + 2\alpha_2$

$\alpha_2 S = -\alpha_1 + \alpha_2$.

(iii) $\epsilon_1 S^{-1} = (\epsilon_1 - 2\epsilon_2)/3$

$\epsilon_2 S^{-1} = (\epsilon_1 + \epsilon_2)/3$.

3. (iii) $(a, b)TS = (-2b, -3a - b)$

$(a, b)ST = (-3a, a + 2b)$.

5. (ii) Show that a basis for $\mathcal{R}_T$ together with a basis for $\mathfrak{N}_T$ form the desired basis for $\mathcal{V}$.

CHAPTER 4

§ 4.1. 3. (i) $A = \begin{pmatrix} 1 & 0 \\ 0 & 0 \end{pmatrix}$, $B = \begin{pmatrix} 0 & 0 \\ 0 & 1 \end{pmatrix}$, $C = \begin{pmatrix} 0 & 1 \\ 1 & 0 \end{pmatrix}$.

4. (i) E_{ij} has 1 in the (i, j) position and 0 elsewhere.

§ 4.2. 3. (ii) The (i, j) elements of AD and DA are $a_{ij}d_{jj}$ and $d_{ii}a_{ij}$, respectively. These will be equal for all choices of the d's if and only if $a_{ij} = 0$ when $i \neq j$.

4. The major problem is to show that the inverse of a non-singular triangular matrix is triangular. Assume that $AT = I$, and show that if $a_{rs} \neq 0$ for $r > s$, then one of the diagonal elements of T must be zero. You may use Exercise 3, § 4.4, to conclude that T must then be singular.

8–12. Use Theorem 4.1.

13. (ii) $A = \begin{pmatrix} 1 & -2 & 0 \\ 1 & 1 & 1 \\ 0 & 1 & -1 \end{pmatrix}$.

(iii) $B = \frac{1}{4}\begin{pmatrix} 2 & 2 & 2 \\ -1 & 1 & 1 \\ -1 & 1 & -3 \end{pmatrix}$.

§ 4.3. 2. (i) A reflection across the x axis.

(iii) A reflection across the line $y = x$, followed by a projection onto the y axis.

3. (i) Let $A = \begin{pmatrix} a & b \\ c & d \end{pmatrix}$ be idempotent. Show that

$$(a - d)(a + d - 1) = 0,$$

and consider separately the two cases which arise from this equation.

(ii) As in (i), show that if A is nilpotent, then $(a - d)(a + d) = 0$, and consider separately the two cases which arise from this equation.

7. (i) Fix $\alpha \in \mathcal{V}$. As $\mathbf{f}$ varies over $\mathcal{V}^*$, the mapping $\mathbf{f} \longrightarrow \alpha\mathbf{f}$ defines a linear functional on $\mathcal{V}^*$. Hence each $\alpha \in \mathcal{V}$ determines a unique element of $\mathcal{V}^{**}$. This correspondence is an isomorphism.

§ 4.4. 3. Determine necessary and sufficient conditions that the row vectors form a linearly independent set.

4. To prove the assertion concerning dimension, choose a basis for $\mathcal{V}_n$ having ξ as its first vector. Then consider the effect on ξ of the linear transformations $\mathbf{T}_{ij}$ as defined in the proof of Theorem 3.1.

5. Use Exercise 3, § 3.3.

8. A Markov matrix can be singular.

9. Yes.

11. (iii) $I, X, Y, iZ, -I, -X, -Y, -iZ$.

12. (ii) Show that $L(v_1)L(v_2) = L(v')$, where

$$v' = \frac{(v_1 + v_2)c^2}{v_1 v_2 + c^2}.$$

§ 4.5. 3. (i) The space spanned by $\{\alpha_1, \ldots, \alpha_k\}$ is **T**-invariant, as defined in Exercise 7, § 3.3.

CHAPTER 5

§ 5.1. 1. Interpret the system *(5.3)* as defining a linear transformation **T** from $\mathcal{U}_n$ to $\mathcal{W}_m$. Then $\rho(A') = \rho(\mathbf{T})$.

    3. $x_1 = -1 - 3x_4 + x_5$
        $x_2 = -1 - 3x_4$
        $x_3 = 1 + x_4 - 2x_5$
        x_4 and x_5 arbitrary.

    4. $x_1 = -1$, $x_2 = -2$, $x_3 = 4$.   Solution is unique.

    5. No solution exists.

§ 5.2. 3. (i) If $\det\begin{pmatrix} a & b \\ c & d \end{pmatrix} = 0$, then $\det\begin{pmatrix} a & e \\ c & f \end{pmatrix} = 0$ and

$$\det\begin{pmatrix} e & b \\ f & d \end{pmatrix} = 0.$$

§ 5.3. 2. If $i \neq k$, $\sum\limits_{j=1}^{n} a_{ij}|A_{kj}|$ is the expression for expanding a determinant for which row i and row k are identical.

    4. Consider the various ways in which a non-zero product of n terms can be formed, one from each row and each column.

    6. (ii) det V is a polynomial of degree $n - 1$ in each x_i, which has the value zero if $x_i = x_j$ for $i \neq j$. Hence $(x_j - x_i)$ is a factor for each $j > i$, and det $V = k \prod\limits_{1 \leq i < j \leq n} (x_j - x_i)$, where k is a constant, perhaps depending upon n. Prove that $k = 1$.

§ 5.4. 1. $x_1 = 2$, $x_2 = -2$, $x_3 = -1$.

    4. Use Theorem 5.12.

    5. $x = 1, 2, 3$.

    6. Use Exercise 6, § 5.3.

§ 5.5. 2. Multiply row i of B by a_{ij} and expand by Theorem 5.5(b) to obtain 2^{n-1} determinants, all but one of which are zero.

    3. (i) det $A = -29$
       (ii) det $B = -11$
      (iii) det $C = -\frac{2}{7}$.

    4. Expand det B as the sum of 2^{n-1} determinants, all but n of which are zero; then apply Theorem 5.9.

    5. (i) Use Exercise 4, pivoting on d.

CHAPTER 6

§ 6.1. 2. (iii) A canonical form for $m \times n$ matrices of rank k is

$$\begin{pmatrix} I_k & Z \\ Z & Z \end{pmatrix}.$$

§ 6.2. 3. Consider the number of linearly independent rows of each type of matrix.

6. $M_i(c^{-1})A_{ij}M_i(c)$.

7. $\det A_{ij} = 1 = -\det P_{ij}$; $\det M_i(c) = \mathbf{c}$.

§ 6.3. 1. (i) $\frac{1}{8}\begin{pmatrix} -2 & 6 & 4 \\ 1 & -3 & 2 \\ 1 & 5 & 2 \end{pmatrix}$.

(ii) $\frac{1}{2}\begin{pmatrix} 1 & 1 & 1 & 0 \\ 0 & 1 & 0 & 1 \\ 1 & 1 & -1 & 0 \\ 0 & 1 & 0 & -1 \end{pmatrix}$.

2. Convert each to reduced echelon form and compare.

6. (i) The reduced echelon matrix E which is row equivalent to A has rank m. Hence there are m columns which have zero in all positions except one; these non-zero elements all equal 1 and appear in m distinct rows.

§ 6.4. 1. See the answer for Exercise 1, § 6.3.

4. All three matrices are of rank 2.

5. First observe that PAP' is symmetric if A is symmetric. If $a_{ij} \neq 0$, then $A_{ij}A(A_{ij})'$ has the element $2a_{ij}$ in the (j, j) position. A permutation of rows 1 and j and a like permutation of columns places $2a_{ij}$ in the $(1, 1)$ position. Multiplication of row 1 and column 1 by $(2a_{ij})^{-1/2}$ produces 1 in the $(1, 1)$ position. Row operations and corresponding column operations then produce zeros in the remaining positions of the first column and the first row.

6. (i) Yes.

(ii) Not necessarily.

(iii) Not necessarily, if both A and B are singular. Yes, if either A or B is non-singular.

§ 6.5. 4. $D = 3(e - 1)\begin{pmatrix} ez_1 + ez_2 + ez_3 & 0 & 0 \\ 0 & ez_1 + z_2 + e^2z_3 & 0 \\ 0 & 0 & ez_1 + e^2z_2 + z_3 \end{pmatrix}$.

5. $\begin{pmatrix} -2 & 0 & -1 \\ 4 & -3 & -1 \end{pmatrix}$.

6. Use the results of Exercise 5, § 3.5.

CHAPTER 7

§ 7.1. 1. (i) $\lambda_1 = -3$, $X_1 = (2a, -3a)$

$\lambda_2 = 2$, $X_2 = (a, a)$.

(ii) $\lambda_1 = -1 = \lambda_2$; two linearly independent characteristic vectors can be chosen.

$$\lambda_3 = 8, \qquad X_3 = (2a, a, 2a).$$

(iii) $\lambda_1 = 1 = \lambda_2 = \lambda_3, \qquad X_1 = (a, 0, -2a, 0)$

$$\lambda_4 = 3, \qquad X_4 = (a, 0, 0, 0).$$

9. M and M' have the same characteristic values. If $XM' = \lambda X$, let $m = \max |x_i|$, and show that $|\lambda x_i| \leq m$ for all i.

§ 7.2. 1. (i) $\lambda_1 = -2, \lambda_2 = 1, \lambda_3 = 3$. A suitable diagonalizing matrix is

$$P = \begin{pmatrix} 0 & 1 & -1 \\ 3 & -5 & 2 \\ 5 & 1 & 4 \end{pmatrix}.$$

(ii) $\lambda_1 = 3 = \lambda_2, \lambda_3 = 12$. A suitable diagonalizing matrix is

$$P = \begin{pmatrix} 1 & -1 & 0 \\ 1 & 0 & 1 \\ 4 & 4 & -1 \end{pmatrix}.$$

(iii) $\lambda_1 = 1 = \lambda_2, \lambda_3 = 2$. Since the characteristic vectors associated with the repeated characteristic value span only the one-dimensional space $[(5, 2, -5)]$, no diagonalizing matrix exists.

2. (i) and (ii) are similar to diagonal matrices; (iii) is not.

3. Use Exercise 8, § 7.1.

4. Use Exercise 7, § 7.1.

5. (i) Consider $\det(A - \lambda I)$, substituting each suggested value.

(ii) Use column operations on $\det(A - \lambda I)$.

6. (ii) Using D as defined in (i), let $C = Q^{-1}BP^{-1}$ and apply the results of (i).

7. (ii) An example which proves the assertion is given by

$$A = \begin{pmatrix} 0 & 1 & 0 \\ 0 & 0 & 1 \\ 0 & 0 & 0 \end{pmatrix}, \qquad B = \begin{pmatrix} 0 & 1 & 0 \\ 0 & 0 & 0 \\ 0 & 0 & 0 \end{pmatrix}.$$

§ 7.3. 6. (i) Let $A = \begin{pmatrix} a & b \\ c & d \end{pmatrix}$ and consider separately the cases $a + d = 0$ and $a + d \neq 0$.

(ii) If A is real and 3×3, the characteristic polynomial of A is of third degree with real coefficients; hence it has at least one real zero. Thus A^2 has at least one non-negative characteristic value. This implies that $A^2 \neq -I$.

§ 7.4. 1. (i) The minimal polynomial has distinct zeros.

(ii) The characteristic vectors do not span $\mathcal{U}_3$.

(iii) The characteristic vectors do not span $\mathcal{U}_3$.

(iv) The characteristic polynomial has distinct zeros.

2. A is similar to a diagonal matrix, which can be shown to be B.

5. Compute $E_j A$, and deduce that $A - a_j I$ is singular. Any nonzero vector of the form YE_j is characteristic.

CHAPTER 8

§ 8.1. 1.   (i) $\mathfrak{M} = [(1, 1)]$, $\mathfrak{N} = [(-1, 1)]$, $\mathcal{E}_2 = \mathfrak{M} \oplus \mathfrak{N}$.

(ii) $A = \begin{pmatrix} 0 & 1 \\ 1 & 0 \end{pmatrix}$.

(iii) $B = \begin{pmatrix} 1 & 0 \\ 0 & -1 \end{pmatrix}$.

(iv) $P = \begin{pmatrix} 1 & 1 \\ 1 & -1 \end{pmatrix}$.

6. (vi) $\mathbf{E}_i$ is represented by a matrix which consists of zeros except for a square block I of size equal to the dimension of $\mathfrak{R}_{\mathbf{E}_i}$, beginning in the $(k + 1, k + 1)$ position, where $k = \dim \mathfrak{R}_{\mathbf{E}_1} + \ldots + \dim \mathfrak{R}_{\mathbf{E}_{i-1}}$.
(vii) Examine the matrix of (vi) which represents $\mathbf{E}_i$.

§ 8.2. 2.   (i) $\rho(A) = 2$; $\mathfrak{N}_A = [(0, 0, 1)]$; A is nilpotent of index 3.
(ii) $\{\xi_1, \xi_1 \mathbf{T}, \xi_1 \mathbf{T}^2\}$ is a basis.
(iii) Relative to the basis of (ii), $\mathbf{T}$ is represented by the matrix

$$\begin{pmatrix} 0 & 1 & 0 \\ 0 & 0 & 1 \\ 0 & 0 & 0 \end{pmatrix}.$$

Hence $k = 1$ and $p_1 = 2$.
3.   (i) By direct calculation, $AN = NA$ if and only if $a_{i,j-1} = a_{i+1,j}$ for $i < n$ and $j > 1$, $a_{nj} = 0$ if $j < n$, and $a_{i1} = 0$ if $i > 1$.
(ii) The only characteristic value of A is a_{11}, and the characteristic vectors can be shown to be those of the form $(0, 0, \ldots, 0, x_n)$.
(iii) Under the hypotheses, direct computation shows that the characteristic vectors are those of the form $(0, \ldots, 0, x_{n-k+1}, \ldots, x_n)$.
4. The characteristic polynomial of a nilpotent matrix must be $(-1)^n \lambda^n$; hence the conditions are $c_{n1} = c_{n2} = \ldots = c_{nn} = 0$.

§ 8.3. 2. Find the Jordan form of A by determining whether A is similar to a diagonal matrix.
3. If A is not similar to a diagonal matrix, the two characteristic values of A must coincide, and the characteristic vectors must span a one-dimensional space. Necessary and sufficient conditions are $(a - d)^2 + 4bc = 0$ and $b^2 + c^2 > 0$.

4.   (i) $\begin{pmatrix} 1 & 1 & 0 \\ 0 & 1 & 0 \\ 0 & 0 & 2 \end{pmatrix}$.

(ii) $\begin{pmatrix} -1 & 1 & 0 \\ 0 & -1 & 1 \\ 0 & 0 & -1 \end{pmatrix}$.

(iii) $\begin{pmatrix} 1 & 1 & 0 \\ 0 & 1 & 0 \\ 0 & 0 & -1 \end{pmatrix}$.

6. By direct computation we can show that if $AJ = I$, where J is in Jordan form, then $a_{ij} = 0$ if $j \neq i, i+1$. A specific example can be used to show that J^{-1} need not have only zeros and ones on its super-diagonal.

7. (iv) Segre characteristic: $\{(4, 2)(4)(1, 1)\}$.

(v) Characteristic polynomial: $(\lambda - 2)^6(\lambda)^4(\lambda - 1)^2$.

(vi) Minimal polynomial: $(\lambda - 2)^4(\lambda)^4(\lambda - 1)$.

(vii) Elementary divisors: $(\lambda - 2)^4$, $(\lambda - 2)^2$, λ^4, $(\lambda - 1)$.

§ 8.4. 1. $A^3 = \begin{pmatrix} 2 & -6 & 2 & -4 \\ 0 & 2 & 0 & 2 \\ 2 & -2 & -2 & 0 \\ 0 & 2 & 0 & -2 \end{pmatrix}$, $\quad A^{-1} = \tfrac{1}{2}\begin{pmatrix} 1 & 1 & 1 & 0 \\ 0 & 1 & 0 & 1 \\ 1 & 1 & -1 & 0 \\ 0 & 1 & 0 & -1 \end{pmatrix}$.

2. Consider the Jordan form of A.

5. (i) Yes.

(ii) No.

6. (i) Recall that a projection is idempotent, and hence its characteristic values are zero or one.

CHAPTER 9

§ 9.1. 2. (i) $\begin{pmatrix} 1 & 0 \\ -1 & 2 \end{pmatrix}$ and $\begin{pmatrix} 4 & 4 \\ 2 & 4 \end{pmatrix}$.

(ii) Yes.

6. The canonical form has two diagonal blocks of the form $\begin{pmatrix} 0 & -1 \\ 1 & 0 \end{pmatrix}$, and all other elements are zero.

7. Begin by moving a non-zero element a_{ij} into the $(1, 2)$ position by means of congruence operations. Then multiply row 1 and column 1 by $-a_{ij}^{-1}$. This produces a canonical block in the upper left. Reduce to zero the remaining elements of the first two rows and columns.

8. Use Theorem 9.6.

9. (i) One correct answer is $\tfrac{1}{2}\begin{pmatrix} 5 & 0 & 0 \\ 0 & -20 & 0 \\ 0 & 0 & 0 \end{pmatrix}$.

(ii) $\begin{pmatrix} 1 & 0 & 0 \\ 0 & -1 & 0 \\ 0 & 0 & 0 \end{pmatrix}$.

(iii) $\begin{pmatrix} 1 & 0 & 0 \\ 0 & 1 & 0 \\ 0 & 0 & 0 \end{pmatrix}$.

§ 9.2. 5. If $\xi = k\eta$, direct calculations show that the Schwarz inequality reduces to equality. Conversely, if $|p(\xi, \eta)|^2 = p(\xi, \xi)p(\eta, \eta)$, let

$$k = \frac{ip(\xi, \eta)}{p(\eta, \eta)}$$

and show that $p(\xi + k\eta, \xi + k\eta) = 0$.

§ 9.3. 1. (i) Expand $p(\xi + \eta, \xi + \eta)$.
    (ii) Expand $p(\xi - \eta, \xi - \eta)$.
    (iii) Expand $p(\xi + \eta, \xi - \eta)$.
  5. Observe that $\|\alpha + c\beta\|^2 = \|\alpha\|^2 + c^2\|\beta\|^2 + 2cp(\alpha, \beta)$.
  7. Choose a normal orthogonal basis for $\mathcal{S}$; extend to a normal orthogonal basis for $\mathcal{V}$.
  9. (ii) $(\mathcal{S} + \mathcal{3})^{\circ}$ is orthogonal to $\mathcal{S}$ and hence is a subspace of $\mathcal{S}^{\circ}$. Likewise, $(\mathcal{S} + \mathcal{3})^{\circ}$ is a subspace of $\mathcal{3}^{\circ}$, and hence a subspace of $\mathcal{S}^{\circ} \cap \mathcal{3}^{\circ}$. The reverse relation can be established without difficulty.
  11. Compute $\xi \mathbf{T}^2$ and compare with $\xi \mathbf{T}$.

§ 9.4. 1. (i) $\begin{pmatrix} \cos \Psi & \sin \Psi \\ -\sin \Psi & \cos \Psi \end{pmatrix}$.

  3. (i) $B = \begin{pmatrix} 0 & 1 & 0 \\ 1 & 0 & 0 \\ 0 & 0 & -1 \end{pmatrix}$.

  4. (i) $a^2 + b^2 = 1,\ c^2 + d^2 = 1,\ ac + bd = 0 = ab + cd$.
  5. Adapt the proof of Theorem 9.14.
  7. If A is unitary, $\|X\| = \|XA\|$. If X is a characteristic vector, $XA = \lambda X$.
  9. Consider $[(I - K)(I + K)^{-1}][(I - K)(I + K)^{-1}]'$, and observe that $I + K$ and $I - K$ commute.

§ 9.5. 2. (i) Complete the square.
  3. (i) $r = 3,\ s = 3$.
    (ii) $r = 3,\ s = -1$.
    (iii) $r = 2,\ s = 0$.
  4. (i) The characteristic values are $\lambda_1 = -1 = \lambda_2,\ \lambda_3 = 8$.
    (ii) A particular choice of orthogonal characteristic vectors is $X_1 = (1, 0, -1)$, $X_2 = (-1, 4, -1)$, $X_3 = (2, 1, 2)$. These can be normalized to give a normal orthogonal basis.
    (iii) Yes.
  5. Since A is positive definite, a non-singular Q exists such that $QAQ' = I$. Then for any orthogonal R, $RQAQ'R' = I$. But QBQ' is real and symmetric, so R exists such that $RQBQ'R'$ is diagonal. Let $P = RQ$.
  7. (vii) Let $\mathbf{T}$ be represented by H relative to some normal orthogonal basis. Let ξ_1 be a characteristic vector of $\mathbf{T}$, and let $\beta_1 = \|\xi_1\|^{-1}\xi_1$. Extend to a normal orthogonal basis $\{\beta_1, \ldots, \beta_n\}$, relative to which $\mathbf{T}$ is represented by

$$B = \begin{pmatrix} \lambda_1 & 0 \ldots 0 \\ 0 & \\ \vdots & H_1 \\ \vdots & \\ 0 & \end{pmatrix} = PHP^{-1}, \text{ where } P \text{ is unitary.}$$

(ix) Adapt the proof of Theorem 9.23.

8. (ii) If A is non-singular, $\rho(B_0) = n$. $XB_0X' \geq 0$, for all X. The canonical matrix which is congruent to B_0 must be I. Why?

(iii) Observe that $C = DB_0D'$, where $D = \mathrm{diag}(x_1, \ldots, x_n)$. Hence B_0 and C represent the same quadratic function.

(iv) $\det C = \Pi\lambda_i$, where the λ_i are real and positive. But the geometric mean of any n positive real numbers never exceeds their arithmetic mean.

(v) Show that $c_{ii} = 1$ for all i.

CHAPTER 10

§ 10.2. 2. (i) $e^A = \begin{pmatrix} e^{-1} & 0 \\ 0 & e \end{pmatrix}$.

(ii) Diagonalize A to obtain $PAP^{-1} = J = \begin{pmatrix} 2 & 0 \\ 0 & -2 \end{pmatrix}$,

$$e^A = Pe^JP^{-1} = \tfrac{1}{4}\begin{pmatrix} e^2 + 3e^{-2} & 3e^2 - 3e^{-2} \\ e^2 - e^{-2} & 3e^2 + e^{-2} \end{pmatrix}.$$

(iii) Use the result of (ii), together with Theorem 10.3.

(iv) $e^A = \tfrac{1}{2}\begin{pmatrix} 2 & 2 & 3 \\ 0 & 2 & 2 \\ 0 & 0 & 2 \end{pmatrix}$. Observe that A is nilpotent.

4. (i) Characteristic values: $\lambda_1 = 1$, $\lambda_2 = 2$, $\lambda_3 = 3$.

$$f(A) = \begin{pmatrix} -a + 2b & -2a + 2b & -2a + 2b \\ -b + c & -b + 2c & -b + c \\ a & -c & 2a & -2c & 2a & -c \end{pmatrix},$$

where $a = f(1)$, $b = f(2)$, $c = f(3)$.

(iii) Necessary and sufficient conditions are $f(1) = f(2) = f(3)$.

(iv) $e^A = \begin{pmatrix} -e + 2e^2 + 0 & -2e + 2e^2 + 0 & -2e + 2e^2 + 0 \\ 0 - e^2 + e^3 & 0 - e^2 + 2e^3 & 0 - e^2 + e^3 \\ e + 0 - e^3 & 2e + 0 - 2e^3 & 2e + 0 - e^3 \end{pmatrix}$.

§ 10.3. 1. (i) $C = \begin{pmatrix} \frac{15}{8} & -\frac{85}{36} & 0 \\ 0 & \frac{40}{27} & 0 \\ \frac{85}{72} & \frac{11}{12} & \frac{40}{27} \end{pmatrix}$.   2. (i) $B_2 = \tfrac{1}{2}\begin{pmatrix} 4 & -6 & 0 \\ 0 & 3 & 0 \\ 3 & 0 & 3 \end{pmatrix}$.

3. (i) This approximation indicates that the largest characteristic value is close to 3.

§ 10.4. 5. $\dfrac{d}{dt} \det X(t) = \det (\dot{X}_1, X_2, \ldots, X_n) + \det (X_1, \dot{X}_2, \ldots, X_n) + \ldots + \det (X_1, X_2, \ldots, \dot{X}_n)$, where X_i denotes column i of $X(t)$.

§ 10.5. 1. $\dot{Y} = YA$, where $A = \begin{pmatrix} 0 & 0 & -1 \\ 1 & 0 & 1 \\ 0 & 1 & 1 \end{pmatrix}$.

The characteristic values of A are $1, 1, -1$, and A is similar to

$$J = \begin{pmatrix} 1 & 1 & 0 \\ 0 & 1 & 0 \\ 0 & 0 & -1 \end{pmatrix}; \quad e^{(t-t_0)J} = \begin{pmatrix} e^{t-t_0} & (t-t_0)e^{t-t_0} & 0 \\ 0 & e^{t-t_0} & 0 \\ 0 & 0 & e^{-t+t_0} \end{pmatrix}.$$

APPENDIX A

1. $m_1 m_2 \ldots m_n$ elements.
2. $2^{(n^2)}$ binary relations.
5. $\mathbf{F} = \mathbf{G}$ means dom $\mathbf{F}$ = dom $\mathbf{G}$ and $x\mathbf{F} = x\mathbf{G}$ for all $x \in$ dom $\mathbf{F}$.
9. $n^{(n^2)}$ binary operations.
12. The systems are isomorphic.
13. (i) An isomorphism.
     (ii) Neither.
     (iii) A homomorphism onto.
18. Yes.
20. $\mathbf{R}$ is reflexive if dom $\mathbf{R} = A$, but not otherwise.
22. Each equivalence class is a line of slope m, and any such line is an equivalence class.
24. $E(4) = 5$.
25. (i) (a) is the set of all real numbers.
     (ii) (a) is the set of all positive integers.
     (iii) (L) is the set of all lines parallel to L.
27. (i) $(a)_n = \{x \in I | x = kn + a \text{ for some } k \in I\}$.
     (iv) To show that each $(a)_n$, $a \neq 0$, has an inverse if n is prime, consider $(1)_n(k)_n$, $(2)_n(k)_n$, $\ldots$, $(n-1)_n(k)_n$ for any fixed $k = 1, \ldots, n-1$. These $n-1$ cosets can be proved to be distinct from one another and from $(0)_n$. Hence one of them must be $(1)_n$, which means that $(k)_n$ has a multiplicative inverse.

APPENDIX B

2. (iv) Show that $(P_{rs}B)^*_{st} = P_{rs}(B^*_{rt})$ and use (ii) and (i), recognizing that $P_{rs} = P_{sr}$.
     (v) Show that $(BP_{rs})^*_{tr} = (B^*_{ts})P_{rs}$ and use (iii) and (i).

3. (ii) $A^{-1} = \frac{1}{6}\begin{pmatrix} 3 & -5 \\ 0 & 2 \end{pmatrix}$.

INDEX